D1163245

INTRODUCTION TO
MATHEMATICAL STATISTICS

A series of advanced mathematics texts under the editorship of

CARL B. ALLENDOERFER

Theory and Solution of Ordinary Differential Equations by Donald Greenspan

Retracing Elementary Mathematics by Leon Henkin, W. Norman Smith, Verne J. Varineau, and Michael J. Walsh

Introduction to Mathematical Statistics by Robert V. Hogg and Allen T. Craig

Methods in Analysis by Jack Indritz

Statistical Theory by B. W. Lindgren

Elements of Abstract Algebra by John T. Moore

INTRODUCTION TO MATHEMATICAL STATISTICS

Robert V. Hogg

& Allen T. Craig

University of Iowa

NEW YORK · THE MACMILLAN COMPANY

COLOMBIERE TEXTBOOKS

9/64

© THE MACMILLAN COMPANY 1959

All rights reserved—no part of this book may be reproduced in any form without permission in writing from the publisher, except by a reviewer who wishes to quote brief passages in connection with a review written for inclusion in magazine or newspaper.

Second Printing 1962

Library of Congress catalog card number: 60-5006

The Macmillan Company, New York
Brett-Macmillan Ltd., Galt, Ontario

Printed in the United States of America

Preliminary edition copyright 1958 by The Macmillan Company

PREFACE

It is intended that this book be used in a two-semester course for advanced undergraduate students in mathematics and for certain first year graduate students. However, a reasonably satisfactory one-semester course can be based on Chapters One, Two, Three, and Seven, and Sections 9.1, 9.2, 9.3, 9.4, 5.1, 11.1, 11.2, and 11.4. No previous study of statistics is assumed, but some course work in mathematics beyond the traditional first course in calculus is often desirable. We have used a preliminary edition of the book in our classes at the University of Iowa, and it is our experience that the content of this additional mathematical training need not be prescribed. Thus a course in elementary analysis or a course in modern algebra seems to provide equally satisfactorily the desired mathematical maturity.

Our aim is to provide a book, at this mathematical level, that places the emphasis upon fundamental concepts. The fundamental notion of a distribution of probability is treated in some detail in Chapters One and Two. In Chapter Three, we take up stochastic independence and random sampling. The concepts of sufficiency and completeness are introduced in Chapter Five and are used to serve as a basis for a theory of point estimation. The interrelations of sufficiency, completeness, and stochastic independence are treated in Chapter Six. These interrelations often afford easy proofs of some theorems whose proofs are either omitted, in books at this level, or, if given, are quite tedious. The basic ideas of limiting distributions, distribution free statistics, and likelihood ratios are examined in the later chapters.

In emphasizing fundamental concepts, it becomes necessary, to keep the book within reasonable physical bounds, to treat lightly or to omit a number of important topics. But with the statistical background provided by this book, a student can, at the same mathematical level, easily pursue the study of such topics as sequential analysis, design of experiments, nonparametric inference, and multivariate analysis.

Throughout the book we invite the student to accept and to use theorems taken from various branches of mathematics. This not only enables the student to work more independently in probability and statistics but in some instances it also motivates him to pursue the study of mathematics.

We are indebted to Catherine Thompson and Maxine Merrington, and to Professor E. S. Pearson, editor of *Biometrika*, for permission to include Tables II and IV, which are abridgments and adaptations of tables published in *Biometrika*. We are also indebted to Professor Sir Ronald A. Fisher, Cambridge, to Dr. Frank Yates, Rothamsted, and to Messers. Oliver and Boyd, Ltd., Edinburgh, for permission to include Table III, which is an abridgment and adaptation of Table III from their book *Statistical Tables for Biological, Agricultural, and Medical Research*.

Although we give at the end of the text a short list of references to the literature, we have not attempted to include a bibliography. Certainly we have been influenced by many books and papers, but to include a bibliography of reasonable length would imply that we can account in detail for these influences.

Iowa City, Iowa   ROBERT V. HOGG
                                                    ALLEN T. CRAIG

TABLE OF CONTENTS

TRANSFORMATION OF VARIABLES cont.

CHAPTER FIVE

POINT ESTIMATION

CHAPTER SIX

SUFFICIENCY AND STOCHASTIC INDEPENDENCE

CHAPTER SEVEN

LIMITING DISTRIBUTIONS

CHAPTER EIGHT

SOME DISTRIBUTION-FREE PROBLEMS

CHAPTER ONE

DISTRIBUTIONS OF RANDOM VARIABLES

The primary purpose of having a mathematical theory of statistics is to provide a mathematical model for a certain type of experiment whose outcome cannot be predicted with certainty.   Once a model for such an experiment has been provided, and the theory worked out in detail, the statistician may, within this mathematical framework, make inferences about the experiment under consideration.   The construction of such a model requires a theory of probability, the concept of a random variable, and the concept of a probability distribution of a random variable.   One of the more logically satisfying theories of probability is that based on the concepts of sets and functions of sets.   These concepts are introduced in Sections 1.1 and 1.2.

1.1. Algebra of Sets.   The concept of a *set* or a *collection* of objects is usually left undefined.   However, a particular set can be described so that there is no misunderstanding as to what collection of objects is under consideration.   For example, the set of the first ten positive integers is sufficiently well described to make clear that the numbers $\frac{3}{4}$ and 14 are not in the set, while the number 3 is in the set.   If an object belongs to a set, it is said to be an *element* of the set.   For example, if A denotes the set of real numbers x for which $0 \leq x \leq 1$, then $\frac{3}{4}$ is an element of the set A.   The fact that $\frac{3}{4}$ is an element of the set A is indicated by writing $\frac{3}{4} \epsilon A$.   More generally, $a \epsilon A$ means that a is an element of the set A.

The sets that concern us will usually be *sets of numbers*.   However, the language of sets of *points* proves somewhat more convenient than that of sets of numbers.   Accordingly, we briefly indicate how we use this terminology.   In analytic geometry considerable emphasis is placed on the fact that to each point on a line (on which an origin and a unit point have been selected), there corresponds one and only one number, say, x; and that to each number x, there corresponds one and only one point on the line.   This one-to-one correspondence between the numbers and points on a line enables us to speak, without misunderstanding, of the "point x" instead of the "number x." Further, with a plane rectangular cordinate system and with x and y numbers, to each symbol (x, y) there corresponds one and only one point in the plane; and to each point in the plane there corresponds but one such symbol. Here again we may speak of the "point (x, y)," meaning the "ordered number pair x and y." This convenient language can be used when we have a rectangular coordinate system in a space of three or more dimensions. Thus, the "point $(x_1, x_2, \cdots, x_n)$" means the numbers $x_1, x_2, \cdots, x_n$ in the order stated. Accordingly, in describing our sets, we frequently speak of a set of points (a set whose elements are points), being careful, of course, to describe the set so as to avoid any ambiguity. The notation $A = \{x; 0 \leq x \leq 1\}$ is read "A is the one-dimensional set of points x for which $0 \leq x \leq 1$." Similarly, $A = \{(x, y); 0 \leq x \leq 1, 0 \leq y \leq 1\}$ can be read "A is the two-dimensional set of points (x, y) which are interior to, or on the boundary of, a square with opposite vertices at $(0, 0)$ and $(1, 1)$." We now give some definitions (together with illustrative examples) which lead to an elementary algebra of sets adequate for our purposes.

Definition 1. If each element of a set A_1 is also an element of set A_2, the set A_1 is called a *subset* of the set A_2. This is indicated by writing $A_1 \subset A_2$. If $A_1 \subset A_2$ and also $A_2 \subset A_1$, the two sets have the same elements, and this is indicated by writing $A_1 = A_2$.

EXAMPLE 1. Let $A_1 = \{x; 0 \leq x \leq 1\}$ and $A_2 = \{x; -1 \leq x \leq 2\}$. Here the one-dimensional set A_1 is seen to be a subset of the one-dimensional set A_2; that is, $A_1 \subset A_2$. Subsequently, when the dimensionality of the set is clear, we shall not make specific reference to it.

EXAMPLE 2. Let $A_1 = \{(x, y); 0 \leq x = y \leq 1\}$ and $A_2 = \{(x, y); 0 \leq x \leq 1, 0 \leq y \leq 1\}$. Since the elements of A_1 are the points on one diagonal of the square, then $A_1 \subset A_2$.

Definition 2. If a set A has no elements, A is called the *null* set. This is indicated by writing $A = 0$.

Definition 3. The set that consists of all elements which belong to A_1 or A_2 or both A_1 and A_2 is called the *union* of A_1 and A_2. The union of A_1 and A_2 is indicated by writing $A_1 \cup A_2$.

EXAMPLE 3. Let $A_1 = \{x; x = 0, 1, \cdots, 10\}$ and $A_2 = \{x; x = 8, 9, 10, 11, \text{ or } 11 < x \leq 12\}$. Then $A_1 \cup A_2 = \{x; x = 0, 1, \cdots, 8, 9, 10, 11, \text{ or } 11 < x \leq 12\} = \{x; x = 0, 1, \cdots, 8, 9, 10, \text{ or } 11 \leq x \leq 12\}$.

EXAMPLE 4. Let A_1 and A_2 be defined as in Example 1. Then $A_1 \cup A_2 = A_2$.

EXAMPLE 5. Let $A_2 = 0$. Then $A_1 \cup A_2 = A_1$ for every set A_1.

EXAMPLE 6. For every set A, $A \cup A = A$.

Definition 4. The set that consists of all elements which belong to both A_1 and A_2 is called the *intersection* of A_1 and A_2. The intersection of A_1 and A_2 is indicated by writing $A_1 \cap A_2$.

EXAMPLE 7.   Let $A_1 = \{(x, y); (x, y) = (0, 0), (0, 1), (1, 1)\}$ and $A_2 = \{(x, y);$ $(x, y) = (1, 1), (1, 2), (2, 1)\}$.   Then $A_1 \cap A_2 = \{(x, y); (x, y) = (1, 1)\}$.

EXAMPLE 8.   Let $A_1 = \{(x, y); 0 \leq x + y \leq 1\}$ and $A_2 = \{(x, y); 1 < x + y\}$. Then A_1 and A_2 have no points in common and $A_1 \cap A_2 = 0$.

EXAMPLE 9.   For every set A, $A \cap A = A$ and $A \cap 0 = 0$.

Definition 5.   In certain discussions or considerations the totality of all elements that pertain to the discussion can be described.   This set of all elements under consideration is given a special name.   It is called the *space* and is denoted by $\mathcal{A}$.

EXAMPLE 10.   Let the number of heads, in tossing a coin four times, be denoted by x.   Of necessity, the number of heads will be one of the numbers 0, 1, 2, 3, 4. Here, then, the space is the set $\mathcal{A} = \{x; x = 0, 1, 2, 3, 4\}$.

EXAMPLE 11.   Consider all nondegenerate rectangles of base x and height y. To be meaningful, both x and y must be positive.   Thus the space is the set $\mathcal{A} = \{(x, y); x > 0, y > 0\}$.

Definition 6.   Let $\mathcal{A}$ denote a space and let A be a subset of the set $\mathcal{A}$. The set which consists of all elements of $\mathcal{A}$ which are not elements of A is called the *complement* of A (actually, with respect to $\mathcal{A}$).   The complement of A is denoted by A^*.   In particular, $\mathcal{A}^* = 0$.

EXAMPLE 12.   Let $\mathcal{A}$ be defined as in Example 10, and let the set $A = \{x;$ $x = 0, 1\}$.   The complement of A (with respect to $\mathcal{A}$) is $A^* = \{x; x = 2, 3, 4\}$.

EXAMPLE 13.   Given $A \subset \mathcal{A}$.   Then $A \cup A^* = \mathcal{A}$, $A \cap A^* = 0$, $A \cup \mathcal{A}$ $= \mathcal{A}$, $A \cap \mathcal{A} = A$, and $(A^*)^* = A$.

Exercises

1.1.   Find the union $A_1 \cup A_2$ and the intersection $A_1 \cap A_2$ of the two sets A_1 and A_2, where

(a) $A_1 = \{x; x = 0, 1, 2\}$, $A_2 = \{x; x = 2, 3, 4\}$;

(b) $A_1 = \{x; 0 < x < 2\}$, $A_2 = \{x; 1 \leq x < 3\}$;

(c) $A_1 = \{(x, y); 0 < x < 2, 0 < y < 2\}$,
      $A_2 = \{(x, y); 1 < x < 3, 1 < y < 3\}$.

1.2.   Find the complement A^* of the set A with respect to the space $\mathcal{A}$ if

(a) $\mathcal{A} = \{x; 0 < x < 1\}$, $A = \{x; \frac{5}{8} \leq x < 1\}$;

(b) $\mathcal{A} = \{(x, y, z); x^2 + y^2 + z^2 \leq 1\}$, $A = \{(x, y, z); x^2 + y^2 + z^2 = 1\}$;

(c) $\mathcal{A} = \{(x, y); |x| + |y| \leq 2\}$, $A = \{(x, y); x^2 + y^2 < 2\}$.

1.3.   Let the space $\mathcal{A} = \{x; -2 < x < 2\}$, the set $A_1 = \{x; -2 < x < 0\}$, and the set $A_2 = \{x; -1 < x < 1\}$.   Find

(a) $(A_1 \cup A_2)^*$ (b) $A_1^* \cap A_2^*$

(c) $(A_1 \cap A_2)^*$ (d) $A_1^* \cup A_2^*$

(e)   Compare the results of (a) and (b) and of (c) and (d).

(f)   Are the relations $(A_1 \cup A_2)^* = A_1^* \cap A_2^*$ and $(A_1 \cap A_2)^*$
      $= A_1^* \cup A_2^*$ valid for all sets A_1 and A_2?

1.4.   Let A_1 and A_2 denote two sets.   If $a\epsilon A_1$, then $a\epsilon(A_1 \cup A_2)$, since a is an element of at least one of the two sets A_1 and A_2.   Thus $A_1 \subset (A_1 \cup A_2)$.   Show that $(A_1 \cap A_2) \subset A_1$.

1.5. Let $A_1 = \{(x, y); 0 \leq x \leq 3, 2 \leq y \leq 5\}$, $A_2 = \{(x, y); 2 \leq x \leq 5, 2 \leq y \leq 5\}$, and $A_3 = \{(x, y); 1 \leq x \leq 4, 0 \leq y \leq 3\}$. Find

(a) $A_1 \cap (A_2 \cup A_3)$ (b) $(A_1 \cap A_2) \cup (A_1 \cap A_3)$
(c) $A_1 \cup (A_2 \cap A_3)$ (d) $(A_1 \cup A_2) \cap (A_1 \cup A_3)$
(e) Compare the results of (a) and (b) and of (c) and (d).
(f) Are the relations $A_1 \cap (A_2 \cup A_3) = (A_1 \cap A_2) \cup (A_1 \cap A_3)$ and $A_1 \cup (A_2 \cap A_3) = (A_1 \cup A_2) \cap (A_1 \cup A_3)$ valid for every three sets, A_1, A_2 and A_3?

1.2. Set Functions.   In the calculus, functions like

$$f(x) = 2x, \quad -\infty < x < \infty,$$

or

$$g(x, y) = e^{-x-y}, \quad 0 < x < \infty, \quad 0 < y < \infty,$$
$$= 0 \text{ elsewhere,}$$

or possibly

$$h(x_1, x_2, \cdots, x_n) = 3x_1 x_2 \cdots x_n, \quad 0 \leq x_i \leq 1, \quad i = 1, 2, \cdots, n,$$
$$= 0 \text{ elsewhere,}$$

were of common occurrence. The value of $f(x)$ at the "point $x = 1$" is $f(1) = 2$; the value of $g(x, y)$ at the "point $(-1, 3)$" is $g(-1, 3) = 0$; the value of $h(x_1, x_2, \cdots, x_n)$ at the "point $(1, 1, \cdots, 1)$" is 3. Functions like these are called functions of a point or, more simply, *point functions* because they are evaluated (if they have a value) at a point in a space of indicated dimension.

There is no reason why, if they prove useful, we should not have functions that can be evaluated, not necessarily at a point but for an entire set of points. Such functions are naturally called functions of a set or, more simply, *set functions*. We shall give some examples of set functions and shall evaluate them for certain simple sets.

EXAMPLE 1. Let A be a set in one-dimensional space and let $Q(A)$ be equal to the number of points in A which correspond to positive integers. Then $Q(A)$ is a function of the set A. Thus, if $A = \{x; 0 < x < 5\}$, then $Q(A) = 4$; if $A = \{x; x = -2, -1\}$, then $Q(A) = 0$; if $A = \{x; -\infty < x < 6\}$, then $Q(A) = 5$.

EXAMPLE 2. Let A be a set in two-dimensional space and let $Q(A)$ be the area of A, if A has a finite area; otherwise let $Q(A)$ be undefined. Thus, if $A = \{(x, y); x^2 + y^2 \leq 1\}$, then $Q(A) = \pi$; if $A = \{(x, y); (x, y) = (0, 0), (1, 1), (0, 1)\}$, then $Q(A) = 0$; if $A = \{(x, y); 0 \leq x, 0 \leq y, x + y \leq 1\}$, then $Q(A) = \frac{1}{2}$.

EXAMPLE 3. Let A be a set in three-dimensional space and let $Q(A)$ be the volume of A, if A has a finite volume; otherwise, let $Q(A)$ be undefined. Thus, if $A = \{(x, y, z); 0 \leq x \leq 2, 0 \leq y \leq 1, 0 \leq z \leq 3\}$, then $Q(A) = 6$; if $A = \{(x, y, z); x^2 + y^2 + z^2 \geq 1\}$, then $Q(A)$ is undefined.

At this point we introduce the following notations. The symbol

$$\int_A f(x) \, dx$$

will mean the ordinary (Riemann) integral of $f(x)$ over a prescribed one-dimensional set A; the symbol

$$\int_A \int g(x, y)\ dx\ dy$$

will mean the Riemann integral of $g(x, y)$ over a prescribed two-dimensional set A; and so on.   To be sure, unless these sets A are chosen with care, the integrals will frequently fail to exist.   Similarly, the symbol

$$\sum_A f(x)$$

will mean the sum extended over all $x \epsilon A$; the symbol

$$\sum_A \sum g(x, y)$$

will mean the sum extended over all $(x, y) \epsilon A$; and so on.

EXAMPLE 4.   Let A be a set in one-dimensional space and let $Q(A) = \sum_A f(x)$, where

$$f(x) = (\tfrac{1}{2})^x, \quad x = 1, 2, 3, \cdots,$$
$$= 0 \text{ elsewhere.}$$

If $A = \{x; 0 \leq x \leq 3\}$, then

$$Q(A) = \frac{1}{2} + \left(\frac{1}{2}\right)^2 + \left(\frac{1}{2}\right)^3 = \frac{7}{8}.$$

EXAMPLE 5.   Let $Q(A) = \sum_A f(x)$, where

$$f(x) = p^x(1 - p)^{1-x}, \quad x = 0, 1,$$
$$= 0 \text{ elsewhere.}$$

If $A = \{x; x = 0\}$, then

$$Q(A) = \sum_{x=0}^{x=0} p^x(1 - p)^{1-x} = 1 - p;$$

if $A = \{x; 1 \leq x \leq 2\}$, then $Q(A) = f(1) = p$.

EXAMPLE 6.   Let A be a one-dimensional set and let

$$Q(A) = \int_A e^{-x} dx.$$

Thus, if $A = \{x; 0 \leq x < \infty\}$, then

$$Q(A) = \int_0^\infty e^{-x} dx = 1;$$

if $A = \{x; 1 \leq x \leq 2\}$, then

$$Q(A) = \int_1^2 e^{-x} dx = e^{-1} - e^{-2};$$

if $A_1 = \{x; 0 \leq x \leq 1\}$ and $A_2 = \{x; 1 < x \leq 3\}$, then

$$Q(A_1 \cup A_2) = \int_0^3 e^{-x}dx$$

$$= \int_0^1 e^{-x}dx + \int_1^3 e^{-x}dx$$

$$= Q(A_1) + Q(A_2);$$

if $A = A_1 \cup A_2$, where $A_1 = \{x; 0 \leq x \leq 2\}$ and $A_2 = \{x; 1 \leq x \leq 3\}$, then

$$Q(A) = Q(A_1 \cup A_2) = \int_0^3 e^{-x}dx$$

$$= \int_0^2 e^{-x}dx + \int_1^3 e^{-x}dx - \int_1^2 e^{-x}dx$$

$$= Q(A_1) + Q(A_2) - Q(A_1 \cap A_2).$$

EXAMPLE 7. Let A be a set in n-dimensional space and let

$$Q(A) = \int \cdots \int_A dx_1 dx_2 \cdots dx_n.$$

If $A = \{(x_1, x_2, \cdots, x_n); 0 \leq x_1 \leq x_2 \leq \cdots \leq x_n \leq 1\}$, then

$$Q(A) = \int_0^1 \int_0^{x_n} \cdots \int_0^{x_3} \int_0^{x_2} dx_1 dx_2 \cdots dx_{n-1} dx_n$$

$$= \frac{1}{n!}, \text{ where } n! = n(n-1) \cdots 3 \cdot 2 \cdot 1.$$

Exercises

1.6. For every one-dimensional set A for which the integral exists, let $Q(A)$ $= \int_A f(x)dx$, where $f(x) = 6x(1 - x), 0 < x < 1$, zero elsewhere; otherwise, let $Q(A)$ be undefined. If $A_1 = \{x; \frac{1}{4} < x < \frac{3}{4}\}$, $A_2 = \{x; x = \frac{1}{2}\}$ and $A_3 = \{x; 0 < x < 10\}$, find $Q(A_1)$, $Q(A_2)$ and $Q(A_3)$.

1.7 For every one-dimensional set A, let $Q(A)$ be equal to the number of points in A that correspond to positive integers. If $A_1 = \{x; x$ a multiple of 3, less than or equal to 50$\}$ and $A_2 = \{x; x$ a multiple of 7, less than or equal to 50$\}$, find $Q(A_1)$, $Q(A_2)$, $Q(A_1 \cup A_2)$ and $Q(A_1 \cap A_2)$. Show that $Q(A_1 \cup A_2) = Q(A_1) + Q(A_2) - Q(A_1 \cap A_2)$.

1.8. For every two-dimensional set A, let $Q(A)$ be equal to the number of points (x, y) in A for which both x and y are positive integers. Find $Q(A_1)$ and $Q(A_2)$ where $A_1 = \{(x, y); x^2 + y^2 \leq 4\}$ and $A_2 = \{(x, y); x^2 + y^2 \leq 9\}$. Note that $A_1 \subset A_2$ and that $Q(A_1) \leq Q(A_2)$.

1.9. Let $Q(A) = \int\int_A (x^2 + y^2)dx\, dy$ for every two-dimensional set A for which the integral exists; otherwise, let $Q(A)$ be undefined. If $A_1 = \{(x, y); -1 \leq x \leq 1, -1 \leq y \leq 1\}$, $A_2 = \{(x, y); -1 \leq x = y \leq 1\}$, and $A_3 = \{(x, y); x^2 + y^2 \leq 1\}$, find $Q(A_1), Q(A_2)$, and $Q(A_3)$.

o K

(1.10.) Let $Q(A) = \int\int\int_A z\,dx\,dy\,dz$ for every three-dimensional set A for which

the integral exists; otherwise, let $Q(A)$ be undefined. Evaluate the set function for the sets $A_1 = \{(x, y, z); (x, y, z) = (0, 0, 0)\}$ and $A_2 = \{(x, y, z); x^2 + y^2 \leq 4, 0 \leq z \leq 1\}$.

1.3. Probability. Consider an experiment, the outcome X of which cannot be predicted with certainty but is such that the set of the totality of every possible outcome can be described prior to the performance of the experiment. Such, for example, would be the tossing of a coin. We cannot predict tails (which we indicate by $X = 0$) nor heads (indicated by $X = 1$). But the set $\{x; x = 0, 1\}$ is a complete description of the totality of every possible outcome in tossing a coin. Experiments of this sort, which may be repeated under the same conditions, are called *random experiments;* the outcome X, provided it can be represented by a real number, is called a *random variable;* and the set $\mathcal{A}$ of every possible outcome, in accordance with Definition 5, page 3, is called the experimental or *sample space.*

For the coin-tossing experiment, the sample space is $\mathcal{A} = \{x; x = 0, 1\}$. There are but four subsets of this space: $A_1 = 0$, $A_2 = \{x; x = 0\}$, $A_3 = \{x; x = 1\}$, $A_4 = \mathcal{A}$. We should like to associate with each subset A_i a number $P(A_i)$, $i = 1, 2, 3, 4$, which is "indicative" of X being an element of A_i. Obviously, X is never an element of A_1, and equally obviously, X is always an element of A_4. To get some idea about A_2 and A_3 we can make use of the assumption that the experiment may be repeated under the same conditions. If we actually repeat the experiment under the same conditions, n times, we can count the number f_i of times (or the frequency) that X is an element of A_i. Of course we know that we shall have $f_1 = 0$, $f_4 = n$. Suppose the experiment yields $f_3 = k$, so that $f_2 = n - k$. Then in our experiment the numbers $0, (n - k)/n, k/n$, and 1 are respectively the *relative frequencies* with which X was an element of A_i, $i = 1, 2, 3, 4$. Experience seems to indicate that if n is large, relative frequencies in random experiments tend to stabilize. This suggests that we select a non-negative proper fraction p (close to k/n) and associate the numbers $0, 1 - p, p, 1$ with the subsets A_1, A_2, A_3, A_4, respectively. It is quite possible, for instance, that we would choose $p = \frac{1}{2}$, provided k/n is close to $\frac{1}{2}$. To be sure, there is an arbitrariness in this selection of the value of p; but if the choice of p is made in this manner, then $0, 1 - p, p, 1$ can be interpreted as numbers which, in future experiments with the coin, the respective relative frequencies $f_1/n, f_2/n, f_3/n, f_4/n$ will either equal or approximate. This is the sense of the phrase "indicative of X being an element of A_i," which was used above. It is worth noting that if we take

$$f(x) = p^x(1 - p)^{1-x}, \quad x \epsilon \mathcal{A} = \{x; x = 0, 1\},$$

then for every subset A of $\mathcal{A}$ the set function

$$P(A) = \sum_A f(x)$$

is such that $P(A_1) = 0$, $P(A_2) = 1 - p$, $P(A_3) = p$, $P(A_4) = 1$.

Not all random experiments are sufficiently simple to have the outcome denoted by a single symbol X. Suppose, for example, that a card is to be drawn from an ordinary deck of 52 playing cards and that the outcome relates to both the suit and the value of the card. If we let $X = 0, 1, 2, 3$ represent respectively clubs, diamonds, hearts, and spades, and let $Y = 1, 2, 3, \cdots, 10, 11, 12, 13$ represent respectively the ace, two, three, $\cdots$, ten, Jack, Queen, and King, then the outcome can be represented by the two random variables X and Y. In this case the sample space $\mathcal{A}$ (the set of the totality of every possible outcome) is the two-dimensional set $\mathcal{A} = \{(x, y); (x, y) = (0, 1), \cdots, (1, 13), (2, 1), \cdots (3,13)\}$. As in the coin-tossing experiment, we wish to associate with each subset A of $\mathcal{A}$ a number $P(A)$, so that, in particular, $P(0) = 0$ and $P(\mathcal{A}) = 1$. One way to do this is to take

$$f(x, y) = \frac{1}{52}, \quad (x, y) \epsilon \mathcal{A},$$

and define

$$P(A) = \sum_A \sum f(x, y).$$

Thus, if A is the null set, $P(A) = 0$; if A is the set $\{(x, y); (x, y) = (0,1), (0, 2), (1, 1)\}$, $P(A) = 3/52$; and finally if $A = \mathcal{A}$, $P(\mathcal{A}) = 1$. Whether these assignments are realistic from a relative frequency point of view will have to await experimentation.

The sample space $\mathcal{A}$ of every random experiment may not be a set of a finite number of points. Suppose that a rectangle is to be constructed by a random determination of a positive base and a positive height. The outcome of the experiment can be represented by the two random variables X (base) and Y (height). The sample space is $\mathcal{A} = \{(x, y); 0 < x, 0 < y\}$. In this case there will be a great variety of subsets of $\mathcal{A}$; for instance, we could have $A = \{(x, y); 0 < \text{rational } x < 1, 0 < \text{irrational } y < 1\}$; or $A = \{(x, y); 1 \leq x = y \leq 2\}$, and so on. To simplify matters (and to avoid intruding on an advanced course), we shall be content with associating numbers $P(A)$ only with certain subsets A, with $P(0) = 0$ and $P(\mathcal{A}) = 1$. This can be done in many arbitrary ways. For instance, suppose

$$P(A) = \int \int_A e^{-x-y} dx \, dy$$

for all subsets A of $\mathcal{A} = \{(x, y); 0 < x, 0 < y\}$ for which the integral exists.   Thus, if $A = \{(x, y); 0 < x < 1, 0 < y < 1\}$, then

$$P(A) = \int_0^1 \int_0^1 e^{-x-y} dx\, dy = \frac{(e - 1)^2}{e^2}.$$

$$\frac{e^2 - 2e + 1}{e^2} = 1 - \frac{2}{e} + e^{-2}$$

We note that

$$1 - 2e^{-1} + e^{-2}$$

$$P(\mathcal{A}) = \int_0^\infty \int_0^\infty e^{-x-y} dx\, dy = 1.$$

Had we elected to define the set function $P(A)$ in an equally arbitrary way by

$$P(A) = \iint\limits_{A} \frac{4}{\pi^2(1 + x^2)(1 + y^2)}\, dx\, dy,$$

then with $A = \{(x, y); 0 < x < 1, 0 < y < 1\}$, we have $P(A) = \frac{1}{4}$ and $P(\mathcal{A}) = 1$.   The nature of the random experiment by which X and Y are to be determined would have to be taken into account before we could decide whether either of these definitions of the set function is realistic.

The preceding discussion was intended to motivate two definitions: that of a *probability set function* and that of the *probability* that the outcome of a random experiment is an element of a set.   Let $\mathcal{A}$ be the sample space of a random experiment.   If $\mathcal{A}$ is one-dimensional, one random variable X is defined on this space; if $\mathcal{A}$ is two-dimensional, two random variables X and Y are defined on the space; and so on.   Let there be a type of subset of $\mathcal{A}$, including $\mathcal{A}$ itself, such that a set function $P(A)$ is defined for each A of that type.   Henceforth all sets considered will be sets for which $P(A)$ is defined.   The two definitions follow.

Definition 1.   If $P(A)$ is defined for a type of subset of the sample space $\mathcal{A}$, and if

(a) $P(A) \geq 0$,
(b) $P(A_1 \cup A_2 \cup A_3 \cup \cdots) = P(A_1) + P(A_2) + P(A_3) + \cdots$, where the sets A_i, $i = 1, 2, 3, \cdots$, are such that no two have a point in common,   *mutually exclusive sets*
(c) $P(\mathcal{A}) = 1$,

then $P(A)$ is called the *probability set function* of the random variable(s).

Definition 2.   The value of $P(A)$ for each subset A of $\mathcal{A}$ is called the *probability* that the outcome of the random experiment is an element of that set A.

In accordance with these definitions, we shall write

$$P(A) = \text{the probability that } X \epsilon A = Pr(X \epsilon A),$$

when A is one-dimensional (and accordingly there is one random variable X); or

$$P(A) = \text{the probability that } (X, Y) \epsilon A = Pr[(X, Y) \epsilon A],$$

when A is two-dimensional (and accordingly there are two random variables X and Y); or

$$P(A) = Pr[(X_1, X_2, \cdots, X_n)\epsilon A],$$

when A is n-dimensional (and accordingly there are n random variables $X_1, X_2, \cdots, X_n$).

Each of the symbols $X\epsilon A$, $(X, Y)\epsilon A$, and so on, can be thought of as an event; in this sense we can speak of the *event* A (not the set A). Thus the probability Pr of the event A means the probability that the outcome of the random experiment is an element of the set A. Further, if the sets $A_1, A_2, A_3, \ldots$ are such that no two have a point in common, the corresponding events $A_1, A_2, A_3, \ldots$ are said to be *mutually exclusive events*. For instance, if A is one-dimensional and $A_1, A_2, A_3, \cdots$ are mutually exclusive events, we have

$$Pr(X\epsilon A_1 \cup A_2 \cup A_3 \cup \cdots) = Pr(X\epsilon A_1) + Pr(X\epsilon A_2) + Pr(X\epsilon A_3) + \cdots$$

in accordance with (b) of Definition 1.

The following are additional properties of the probability set function that are immediate consequences of Definition 1 and the algebra of sets.

(d) $P(A) = 1 - P(A^*)$. This follows from (c) and (b) of Definition 1 since $1 = P(A) = P(A \cup A^*) = P(A) + P(A^*)$.

(e) $P(0) = 0$. In (d), take $A = 0$ so $A^* = A$.

(f) $A_1 \subset A_2$, then $P(A_1) \leq P(A_2)$. Now $A_2 = A_1 \cup (A^*_1 \cap A_2)$, and hence $P(A_2) = P(A_1) + P(A^*_1 \cap A_2)$ by (b) of Definition 1. However, from (a) of Definition 1, $P(A^*_1 \cap A_2) \geq 0$.

(g) $0 \leq P(A) \leq 1$. Since $0 \subset A \subset A$, then by (f), $P(0) \leq P(A) \leq P(A)$, or $0 \leq P(A) \leq 1$.

The probability set function $P(A)$ of one or more random variables is often called the *probability distribution function* because it tells how the total probability of one is distributed over various sets in the sample space. In this sense we speak of the distribution of one or more random variables, meaning, of course, the distribution of probability. It will be seen later that, in certain cases, this distribution of probability may be given by functions other than the set function $P(A)$.

Comment. In order to have a mathematical model for making inferences about certain phenomena, one frequently assumes that the phenomenon under consideration may be associated with a random experiment, the outcome X of which he takes to be a random variable. For instance, if $X = 0$ denotes female and $X = 1$ denotes male, then in a series of births of children, X is considered to be a random variable. Or, if X and Y denote respectively the weight and the length of a child, then in a series of births of children, X and Y are considered to be two random variables. In a sequence of casts of a die, the number X of spots which show is assumed to be a random variable. In the manufacture of refrigerator doors, the number X of defects on each door is often assumed to be a random variable.

Exercises

1.11. Let the probability set function $P(A)$ be defined by $P(A) = \sum\sum_A f(x, y)$, where $f(x, y) = 1/52$, $(x, y)\epsilon A = \{(x, y); (x, y) = (0, 1), (0, 2) \cdots, (0, 13), (1, 1), \cdots (1, 13), \cdots, (3, 13)\}$. Compute $P(A) = Pr[(X, Y)\epsilon A]$ (a) when $A = \{(x, y); (x, y) = (0, 4), (1, 3), (2, 2)\}$; (b) when $A = \{(x, y); x + y = 4, (x, y)\epsilon A\}$.

1.12. Let the probability set function $P(A)$ be defined by $P(A) = \int_A f(x)\, dx$, where $f(x) = 2x/9$, $x\epsilon A = \{x; 0 < x < 3\}$. Let $A_1 = \{x; 0 < x < 1\}$, $A_2 = \{x; 2 < x < 3\}$. Compute $P(A_1) = Pr[X\epsilon A_1]$, $P(A_2) = Pr[X\epsilon A_2]$, and $P[A_1 \cup A_2] = Pr[X\epsilon A_1 \cup A_2]$.

1.13. Let the sample space $A = \{x; 0 < x < 1\}$. If $A_1 = \{x; 0 < x < \frac{1}{2}\}$ and $A_2 = \{x; \frac{1}{2} \leq x < 1\}$, find $P(A_2)$ if $P(A_1) = \frac{1}{4}$.

1.14. Let the sample space be $A = \{x; 0 < x < 10\}$ and let $P(A_1) = \frac{3}{8}$ and $P(A_2) = \frac{7}{8}$, where $A_1 = \{x; 0 < x \leq 2\}$ and $A_2 = \{x; 0 < x \leq 4\}$. Find $P(A_3)$ where $A_3 = \{x; 0 < x \leq 2 \text{ or } 4 < x < 10\}$.

1.15. If the sample space is $A = A_1 \cup A_2$ and if $P(A_1) = 0.8$ and $P(A_2) = 0.5$, find $P(A_1 \cap A_2)$.

1.16. Let the subsets $A_1 = \{x; \frac{1}{4} < x < \frac{1}{2}\}$ and $A_2 = \{x; \frac{1}{2} \leq x < 1\}$ of the sample space $A = \{x; 0 < x < 1\}$ be such that $P(A_1) = \frac{1}{8}$ and $P(A_2) = \frac{1}{2}$. Find $P(A_1 \cup A_2)$, $P(A^*_1)$, and $P(A^*_1 \cap A^*_2)$.

1.17. If A_1 and A_2 are subsets of the sample space A, show that

$$P(A_1 \cup A_2) = P(A_1) + P(A_2) - P(A_1 \cap A_2).$$

Hint: Write $A_1 \cup A_2 = A_1 \cup (A^*_1 \cap A_2)$ and $A_2 = (A_1 \cap A_2) \cup (A^*_1 \cap A_2)$.

1.18. If A_1 and A_2 are subsets of the sample space A, show that

$$P(A_1 \cap A_2) \leq P(A_1) \leq P(A_1 \cup A_2) \leq P(A_1) + P(A_2).$$

1.19. Let $A_1 = \{(x, y); x \leq 2, y \leq 4\}$, $A_2 = \{(x, y); x \leq 2, y \leq 1\}$, $A_3 = \{(x, y); x \leq 0, y \leq 4\}$, and $A_4 = \{(x, y); x \leq 0, y \leq 1\}$ be subsets of the sample space A which is the entire two-dimensional plane. If $P(A_1) = \frac{7}{8}$, $P(A_2) = 4/8$, $P(A_3) = \frac{3}{8}$, and $P(A_4) = 2/8$, find $P(A_5)$ where $A_5 = \{(x, y); 0 < x \leq 2, 1 < y \leq 4\}$.

1.20. Let A_1, A_2, and A_3 be three mutually exclusive subsets of the sample space A. Find $P[(A_1 \cup A_2) \cap A_3]$ and $P(A^*_1 \cup A^*_2)$.

1.4. Two Simple Types of Random Variables.

In this section we introduce two special kinds of random variables and their distributions. For simplicity of presentation we first consider a distribution of one random variable X.

(a) *The discrete type of random variable.* Let the outcome of a random experiment be represented by the random variable X. Suppose the one-dimensional sample space A is a set of points such that there is a finite number of points of A in every finite interval. Such a set A will be called a set of discrete points. Let a function $f(x)$ be defined so that $f(x) > 0$, $x\epsilon A$, and let

$$\sum_A f(x) = 1.$$

Whenever a probability set function $P(A)$, $A \subset \mathcal{A}$, is defined in terms of such an $f(x)$ by

$$P(A) = Pr(X \epsilon A) = \sum_A f(x),$$

then X is called a random variable of the *discrete type*, and X is said to have a distribution of the discrete type.

EXAMPLE 1. Let X be a random variable of the discrete type with sample space $\mathcal{A} = \{x; x = 0, 1, 2, 3, 4\}$. Let

$$P(A) = \sum_A f(x),$$

where

$$f(x) = \frac{4!}{x!(4-x)!}\left(\frac{1}{2}\right)^4, \quad x \epsilon \mathcal{A},$$

and, as usual, $0! = 1$. Then if $A = \{x; x = 0, 1\}$, we have

$$Pr(X \epsilon A) = \frac{4!}{0!4!}\left(\frac{1}{2}\right)^4 + \frac{4!}{1!3!}\left(\frac{1}{2}\right)^4 = \frac{5}{16}.$$

EXAMPLE 2. Let the sample space $\mathcal{A} = \{x; x = 1, 2, 3, \cdots\}$, and let

$$f(x) = \left(\frac{1}{2}\right)^x, \quad x \epsilon \mathcal{A}.$$

If X is a random variable of the discrete type so that

$$Pr(X \epsilon A) = \sum_A f(x),$$

then if $A = \{x; x = 1, 3, 5, 7, \cdots\}$, we have

$$Pr(X \epsilon A) = \left(\frac{1}{2}\right) + \left(\frac{1}{2}\right)^3 + \left(\frac{1}{2}\right)^5 + \cdots = \frac{2}{3}.$$

(b) *The continuous type of random variable.* Let the one-dimensional set $\mathcal{A}$ be such that the Riemann integral

$$\int_{\mathcal{A}} f(x)\, dx = 1,$$

where (i) $f(x) > 0$, $x \epsilon \mathcal{A}$, and (ii) $f(x)$ has a finite number of discontinuities in every finite interval that is a subset of $\mathcal{A}$. If $\mathcal{A}$ is the sample space of the random variable X and if the probability set function $P(A)$, $A \subset \mathcal{A}$, is defined in terms of such an $f(x)$ by

$$P(A) = Pr(X \epsilon A) = \int_A f(x)\, dx,$$

then X is said to be a random variable of the *continuous type* and to have a distribution of that type.

EXAMPLE 3. Let the sample space $\mathcal{A} = \{x; 0 < x < \infty\}$, and let

$$f(x) = e^{-x}, \quad x \epsilon \mathcal{A}.$$

If X is a random variable of the continuous type so that

$$Pr(X \epsilon A) = \int_A e^{-x} dx,$$

we have, with $A = \{x; 0 < x < 1\}$,

$$Pr(X \epsilon A) = \int_0^1 e^{-x} dx = 1 - e^{-1}.$$

EXAMPLE 4. Let X be a random variable of the continuous type with sample space $A = \{x; 0 < x < 1\}$. Let the probability set function be defined by

$$P(A) = \int_A f(x) \, dx,$$

where

$$f(x) = cx^2, \quad x \epsilon A.$$

Since $P(A)$ is a probability set function, $P(A) = 1$. Hence the constant c is determined by

$$\int_0^1 cx^2 \, dx = 1,$$

or $c = 3$.

It is seen that whether the random variable X is of the discrete type or of the continuous type, the probability $Pr(X \epsilon A)$ is completely determined by a function $f(x)$. In either case $f(x)$ is called the *probability density function* (hereafter abbreviated p.d.f.) of the random variable X. If we restrict ourselves to random variables of either the discrete type or the continuous type, we may work exclusively with the p.d.f. $f(x)$. This affords an enormous simplification; but it should be recognized that this simplification is obtained at considerable cost from a mathematical point of view. Not only shall we exclude from consideration many random variables that do not have these types of distributions, but we shall also exclude many interesting subsets of the sample space. In this book, however, we shall restrict ourselves to these simple types of random variables.

Comments. Let X denote the number of spots that show when a die is cast. We can assume that X is a random variable with $A = \{x; x = 1, 2, \cdots, 6\}$ and with a p.d.f. $f(x) = 1/6$, $x \epsilon A$. Other assumptions can be made to provide different mathematical models for this experiment. Experimental evidence can be used to help one decide which model is the more realistic. Next, let X denote the point at which a balanced pointer comes to rest. If the circumference is graduated $0 \leq x < 1$, a reasonable mathematical model for this experiment is to take X to be a random variable with $A = \{x; 0 \leq x < 1\}$ and with a p.d.f. $f(x) = 1$, $x \epsilon A$.

The notion of the p.d.f. of one random variable X can be extended to the notion of the p.d.f. of two or more random variables. Under certain restrictions on the sample space A and the function $f > 0$ on A (restrictions which will not be enumerated here), we say that the two random variables X and Y are of the discrete type or of the continuous type, and have a distribution of that type, according as the probability set function $P(A)$, $A \subset \mathcal{A}$, is defined by

$$P(A) = Pr[(X, Y)\epsilon A] = \sum_{A}\sum f(x, y),$$

or by

$$P(A) = Pr[(X, Y)\epsilon A] = \int\int_{A} f(x, y) \ dx \ dy.$$

In either case f is called the p.d.f. of the two random variables X and Y. Of necessity, $P(\mathcal{A}) = 1$ in each case. More generally we say that the n random variables $X_1, X_2, \cdots, X_n$ are of the discrete type or of the continuous type, and have a distribution of that type, according as the probability set function $P(A)$, $A \subset \mathcal{A}$, is defined by

$$P(A) = Pr[(X_1, \cdots, X_n)\epsilon A] = \sum_{A} \cdots \sum f(x_1, \cdots, x_n),$$

or by

$$P(A) = Pr[(X_1, \cdots, X_n)\epsilon A] = \int \cdots \int_{A} f(x_1, \cdots, x_n) \ dx_1 \cdots dx_n.$$

The idea to be emphasized is that a function f, whether in one or more variables, essentially satisfies the conditions of being a p.d.f. if $f > 0$ on a sample space $\mathcal{A}$ and if its integral [for the continuous type of random variable(s)] or its sum [for the discrete type of random variable(s)] over $\mathcal{A}$ is one.

Our notation can be considerably simplified when we restrict ourselves to random variables of the continuous or discrete types. Suppose the sample space of a continuous type of random variable X is $\mathcal{A} = \{x; 0 < x < \infty\}$ and that the p.d.f. of X is e^{-x}, $x\epsilon \mathcal{A}$. We shall in no manner alter the distribution of X [that is, alter any $P(A)$, $A \subset \mathcal{A}$] if we extend the definition of the p.d.f. of X by writing

$$f(x) = e^{-x}, \quad 0 < x < \infty,$$
$$= 0 \text{ elsewhere,}$$

and then refer to $f(x)$ as the p.d.f. of X. We have

$$\int_{-\infty}^{\infty} f(x) \ dx = \int_{-\infty}^{0} 0 \ dx + \int_{0}^{\infty} e^{-x}dx = 1.$$

Thus we may treat the entire axis of reals as though it were the sample space. Accordingly we now replace

$$\int_{\mathcal{A}} f(x) \ dx \qquad \text{by} \qquad \int_{-\infty}^{\infty} f(x) \ dx.$$

Similarly, we may extend the definition of a p.d.f. $f(x, y)$ over the entire xy plane; or a p.d.f. $f(x, y, z)$ throughout three-dimensional space; and so on. We shall do this consistently so that tedious, repetitious references to the sample space can be avoided. Once this is done, we replace

$$\iint_{\mathcal{A}} f(x, y)\ dx\ dy \qquad \text{by} \qquad \int_{-\infty}^{\infty} \int_{-\infty}^{\infty} f(x, y)\ dx\ dy,$$

and so on. Similarly, after extending the definition of a p.d.f. of the discrete type, we replace, for one random variable,

$$\sum_{\mathcal{A}} f(x) \qquad \text{by} \qquad \sum_{x} f(x),$$

and, for two random variables,

$$\sum_{\mathcal{A}} \sum f(x, y) \qquad \text{by} \qquad \sum_{y} \sum_{x} f(x, y),$$

and so on.

In accordance with this convention (of extending the definition of a p.d.f.), it is seen that a point function f, whether in one or more variables, essentially satisfies the conditions of being a p.d.f. if (a) f is defined and is not negative for all real values of its argument(s) and if (b) its integral [for the continuous type of random variable(s)] or its sum [for the discrete type of random variable(s)] over all real values of its argument(s) is one.

If $f(x)$ is the p.d.f. of a continuous type of random variable X and if A is the set $\{x; a < x < b\}$, then $P(A) = Pr(X \epsilon A)$ can be written as

$$Pr(a < X < b) = \int_{a}^{b} f(x)\ dx.$$

Moreover, if $A = \{x; x = a\}$, then

$$P(A) = Pr(X \epsilon A) = Pr(X = a) = \int_{a}^{a} f(x)\ dx = 0,$$

since the integral $\int_{a}^{a} f(x)\ dx$ is defined in calculus to be zero. That is, if X is a random variable of the continuous type, the probability of every set consisting of a single point is zero. This fact enables us to write, say,

$$Pr(a < X < b) = Pr(a \leq X \leq b).$$

More importantly, this fact allows us to change the value of the p.d.f. of a continuous type of random variable X at a single point without altering the distribution of X. For instance, the p.d.f.

$$f(x) = e^{-x}, \quad 0 < x < \infty,$$
$$= 0 \text{ elsewhere,}$$

can be written as

$$f(x) = e^{-x}, \quad 0 \leq x < \infty,$$
$$= 0 \text{ elsewhere,}$$

without changing any $P(A)$. We observe that these two functions differ only at $x = 0$ and $Pr(X = 0) = 0$. More generally, if two probability density functions of random variables of the continuous type differ only on a set having probability zero, the two corresponding probability set functions are exactly the same. Unlike the continuous type, the p.d.f. of a discrete type of random variable may not be changed at any point, since a change in such a p.d.f. alters the distribution of probability.

Finally, if a p.d.f. in one or more variables is explicitly defined, we can see by inspection whether the random variables are of the continuous or discrete type. For example, it seems obvious that the p.d.f.

$$f(x, y) = \frac{9}{4^{x+y}}, \quad \begin{matrix} x = 1, 2, 3, \cdots \\ y = 1, 2, 3, \cdots, \end{matrix}$$
$$= 0 \text{ elsewhere,}$$

is a p.d.f. of two discrete-type random variables X and Y, while the p.d.f.

$$f(x, y) = 4xye^{-x^2-y^2}, \quad 0 < x < \infty, \quad 0 < y < \infty,$$
$$= 0 \text{ elsewhere,}$$

is clearly a p.d.f. of two continuous-type random variables X and Y. In such cases it seems unnecessary to specify which of the two simpler types of random variables is under consideration.

EXAMPLE 5. Let the random variable X have the p.d.f.

$$f(x) = 2x, \quad 0 < x < 1,$$
$$= 0 \text{ elsewhere.}$$

Find $Pr(\frac{1}{2} < X < \frac{3}{4})$ and $Pr(-\frac{1}{2} < X < \frac{1}{2})$. First,

$$Pr(\tfrac{1}{2} < X < \tfrac{3}{4}) = \int_{1/2}^{3/4} f(x) \, dx = \int_{1/2}^{3/4} 2x \, dx = \frac{5}{16}.$$

Next,

$$Pr(-\tfrac{1}{2} < X < \tfrac{1}{2}) = \int_{-1/2}^{1/2} f(x) \, dx$$

$$= \int_{-1/2}^{0} 0 \, dx + \int_{0}^{1/2} 2x \, dx$$

$$= 0 + \frac{1}{4} = \frac{1}{4}.$$

EXAMPLE 6. Let

$$f(x, y) = 6x^2y, \quad 0 < x < 1, 0 < y < 1,$$
$$= 0 \text{ elsewhere,}$$

be the p.d.f. of two random variables X and Y. We have, for instance,

$$Pr(0 < X < \tfrac{3}{4}, \tfrac{1}{3} < Y < 2) = \int_{1/3}^{2} \int_{0}^{3/4} f(x, y) \, dx \, dy$$

$$= \int_{1/3}^{1} \int_{0}^{3/4} 6x^2y \, dx \, dy + \int_{1}^{2} \int_{0}^{3/4} 0 \, dx \, dy$$

$$= \frac{3}{8} + 0 = \frac{3}{8}.$$

Exercises

1.21. For each of the following, find the constant c so that $f(x)$ satisfies the conditions of being a p.d.f. of one random variable X.

(a) $f(x) = c(\frac{2}{3})^x$, $x = 1, 2, 3, \cdots$, zero elsewhere.

(b) $f(x) = cxe^{-x}$, $0 < x < \infty$, zero elsewhere.

1.22. Let $f(x) = x/15$, $x = 1, 2, 3, 4, 5$, zero elsewhere, be the p.d.f. of X. Find $Pr[X = 1 \text{ or } 2]$, $Pr[\frac{1}{2} < X < 5/2]$, and $Pr[1 \leq X \leq 2]$.

1.23. Let $f(x) = 1/x^2$, $1 < x < \infty$, zero elsewhere, be the p.d.f. of X. If $A_1 = \{x; 1 < x < 2\}$ and $A_2 = \{x; 4 < x < 5\}$, find $P(A_1 \cup A_2)$ and $P(A_1 \cap A_2)$.

1.24. Let $f(x_1, x_2) = 4x_1 x_2$, $0 < x_1 < 1$, $0 < x_2 < 1$, zero elsewhere, be the p.d.f. of X_1 and X_2. Find $Pr(0 < X_1 < \frac{1}{2}, \frac{1}{4} < X_2 < 1)$, $Pr(X_1 = X_2)$, $Pr(X_1 < X_2)$, and $Pr(X_1 \leq X_2)$.

1.25. Let $f(x_1, x_2, x_3) = e^{-(x_1 + x_2 + x_3)}$, $0 < x_1 < \infty$, $0 < x_2 < \infty$, $0 < x_3 < \infty$, zero elsewhere, be the p.d.f. of X_1, X_2, X_3. Compute $Pr(X_1 < X_2 < X_3)$ and $Pr(X_1 = X_2 < X_3)$.

1.26. A *mode* of a distribution of one random variable X of the continuous or discrete type is a value of x that maximizes the p.d.f. $f(x)$. If there is only one such x, it is called the *mode of the distribution*. Find the mode of each of the following distributions:

(a) $f(x) = (\frac{1}{2})^x$, $x = 1, 2, 3, \cdots$, zero elsewhere.

(b) $f(x) = 12x^2(1 - x)$, $0 < x < 1$, zero elsewhere.

(c) $f(x) = (\frac{1}{2})x^2 e^{-x}$, $0 < x < \infty$, zero elsewhere.

1.27. A *median* of a distribution of one random variable X of the discrete or continuous type is a value of x such that $Pr(X < x) \leq \frac{1}{2}$ and $Pr(X \leq x) \geq \frac{1}{2}$. If there is only one such x, it is called the *median of the distribution*. Find the median of each of the following distributions:

(a) $f(x) = \dfrac{4!}{x!(4 - x)!}\left(\dfrac{1}{4}\right)^x\left(\dfrac{3}{4}\right)^{4-x}$, $x = 0, 1, 2, 3, 4$, zero elsewhere.

(b) $f(x) = 3x^2$, $0 < x < 1$, zero elsewhere.

(c) $f(x) = \dfrac{1}{\pi(1 + x^2)}$, $-\infty < x < \infty$.

1.28. Let $f(x) = 12x^2(1 - x)$, $0 < x < 1$, zero elsewhere, be the p.d.f. of X. Let $Pr(a < X < b) = \frac{1}{2}$. Find an additional condition on a and b so that the difference $(b - a)$ is a minimum.

1.29. Given that the non-negative function $g(x)$ has the property that

$$\int_0^\infty g(x)\, dx = 1.$$

Show that $f(x_1, x_2) = \dfrac{2g(\sqrt{x_1^2 + x_2^2})}{\pi\sqrt{x_1^2 + x_2^2}}$, $0 < x_1 < \infty$, $0 < x_2 < \infty$, zero elsewhere,

satisfies the conditions of being a p.d.f. of two continuous-type random variables X_1 and X_2.

1.5. Mathematical Expectation. One of the more useful concepts in problems involving distributions of random variables is that of mathematical expectation.   Let X be a random variable having a p.d.f. $f(x)$, and let $u(X)$ be a function of X such that

$$\int_{-\infty}^{\infty} u(x)f(x)\ dx$$

exists, if X is a continuous type of random variable, or such that

$$\sum_{x} u(x)f(x)$$

exists, if X is a discrete type of random variable.   The integral, or the sum, as the case may be, is called the *mathematical expectation* (or expected value) of $u(X)$ and is denoted by $E[u(X)]$.   That is,

$$E[u(X)] = \int_{-\infty}^{\infty} u(x)f(x)\ dx,$$

if X is a continuous type of random variable, or

$$E[u(X)] = \sum_{x} u(x)f(x),$$

if X is a discrete type of random variable.

Comments.   The usual definition of $E[u(X)]$ requires that the integral (or sum) converge absolutely.   However, in this book, each $u(x)$ is of such a character that if the integral (or sum) exists, the convergence is absolute.   Accordingly, we have not burdened the student with this additional provision.

The terminology "mathematical expectation" or "expected value" has its origin in games of chance.   This can be illustrated as follows: Three small similar discs, numbered 1, 2, and 2, respectively, are placed in a bowl and are mixed.   A player is to be blindfolded and is to draw a disc from the bowl.   If he draws the disc numbered 1, he will receive nine dollars; if he draws either disc numbered 2, he will receive three dollars.   It seems reasonable to assume that the player has a "$\frac{1}{3}$ claim" on the nine dollars and a "$\frac{2}{3}$ claim" on the three dollars.   His "total claim" is $9(\frac{1}{3}) + 3(\frac{2}{3})$, or five dollars.   If we take X to be a random variable having the p.d.f. $f(x) = x/3$, $x = 1, 2$, zero elsewhere, and $u(x) = 15 - 6x$, then $E[u(X)] = \sum_{x} u(x)f(x) = \sum_{x=1}^{2} (15 - 6x)(x/3) = 5.$ That is, the mathematical expectation of $u(X)$ is precisely the player's "claim" or expectation.

More generally, let $X_1,\ X_2, \cdots, X_n$ be random variables having p.d.f. $f(x_1, x_2, \cdots, x_n)$ and let $u(X_1, X_2, \cdots, X_n)$ be a function of these variables such that the n-fold integral

$$(1)\qquad \int_{-\infty}^{\infty} \cdots \int_{-\infty}^{\infty} u(x_1, x_2, \cdots, x_n)f(x_1, x_2, \cdots, x_n)\ dx_1\ dx_2 \cdots dx_n$$

exists, if the random variables are of the continuous type, or such that the n-fold sum

$$(2)\qquad \sum_{x_n} \cdots \sum_{x_1} u(x_1, x_2, \cdots, x_n)f(x_1, x_2, \cdots, x_n)$$

exists if the random variables are of the discrete type.   The n-fold integral (or the n-fold sum, as the case may be) is called the *mathematical expectation*, denoted by $E[u(X_1, X_2, \cdots, X_n)]$, of the function $u(X_1, X_2, \cdots, X_n)$.

In this paragraph we shall point out some fairly obvious but useful facts about mathematical expectations when they exist.

(a) If k is a constant, then $E(k) = k$.   This follows from expression (1) [or (2)] upon setting $u = k$ and recalling that an integral (or sum) of a constant times a function is the constant times the integral (or sum) of the function.   Of course the integral (or sum) of the function f is one.

(b) If k is a constant and v is a function, then $E(kv) = kE(v)$.   This follows from expression (1) [or (2)] upon setting $u = kv$ and rewriting expression (1) [or (2)] as k times the integral (or sum) of the product vf.

(c) If k_1 and k_2 are constants and v_1 and v_2 are functions, then $E(k_1v_1+k_2v_2) = k_1E(v_1) + k_2E(v_2)$.   This too follows from expression (1) [or (2)] upon setting $u = k_1v_1 + k_2v_2$ because the integral (or sum) of $(k_1v_1 + k_2v_2)f$ is equal to the integral (or sum) of k_1v_1f plus the integral (or sum) of k_2v_2f. Repeated application of this property shows that if $k_1, k_2, \cdots, k_m$ are constants and $v_1, v_2, \cdots, v_m$ are functions, then

$$E(k_1v_1 + k_2v_2 + \cdots + k_mv_m) = k_1E(v_1) + k_2E(v_2) + \cdots + k_mE(v_m).$$

This property of mathematical expectation leads us to characterize the symbol E as a linear operator; that is, the mathematical expectation of a finite sum is equal to the sum of the mathematical expectations, provided, of course, the expectations exist.

EXAMPLE 1.   Let X have the p.d.f.
$$f(x) = 2(1 - x), \quad 0 < x < 1,$$
$$= 0 \text{ elsewhere.}$$
Then
$$E(X) = \int_{-\infty}^{\infty} xf(x) \, dx = \int_{0}^{1} (x)2(1 - x) \, dx = \frac{1}{3},$$

$$E(X^2) = \int_{-\infty}^{\infty} x^2f(x) \, dx = \int_{0}^{1} (x^2)2(1 - x) \, dx = \frac{1}{6},$$

and, of course,
$$E(6X + 3X^2) = 6\left(\frac{1}{3}\right) + 3\left(\frac{1}{6}\right) = \frac{5}{2}. \quad = 6\,E(x) + 3\,E(x^2)$$

EXAMPLE 2.   Let X have the p.d.f.
$$f(x) = \frac{x}{6}, \quad x = 1, 2, 3,$$
$$= 0 \text{ elsewhere.}$$
Then
$$E(X^3) = \sum_{x} x^3f(x) = \sum_{x=1}^{3} x^3\left(\frac{x}{6}\right)$$
$$= \frac{1}{6} + \frac{16}{6} + \frac{81}{6} = \frac{98}{6}.$$

EXAMPLE 3. Let X and Y have the p.d.f.

$$f(x, y) = x + y, \quad 0 < x < 1, 0 < y < 1,$$
$$= 0 \text{ elsewhere.}$$

Accordingly,

$$E(XY^2) = \int_{-\infty}^{\infty} \int_{-\infty}^{\infty} xy^2 f(x, y) \, dx \, dy$$

$$= \int_0^1 \int_0^1 xy^2(x + y) \, dx \, dy$$

$$= \frac{17}{72}.$$

Exercises

1.30. Let X have the p.d.f. $f(x) = (x + 2)/18$, $-2 < x < 4$, zero elsewhere. Find $E[X]$, $E[(X + 2)^3]$, and $E[6X - 2(X + 2)^3]$.

1.31. Suppose $f(x) = 1/5$, $x = 1, 2, 3, 4, 5$, zero elsewhere, is the p.d.f. of the discrete type of random variable X. Compute $E[X]$ and $E[X^2]$. Using these two results, find $E[(X + 2)^2]$ by writing $(X + 2)^2 = X^2 + 4X + 4$.

1.32. If X and Y have the p.d.f. $f(x, y) = \frac{1}{3}$, $(x, y) = (0, 0), (0, 1), (1, 1)$, zero elsewhere, find $E[(X - \frac{1}{3})(Y - \frac{2}{3})]$.

1.33. Let the p.d.f. of X and Y be $f(x, y) = e^{-x-y}$, $0 < x < \infty$, $0 < y < \infty$, zero elsewhere. Let $u(X, Y) = X$, $v(X, Y) = Y$, and $w(X, Y) = XY$. Show that $E[u(X, Y)] \cdot E[v(X, Y)] = E[w(X, Y)]$.

1.34. Let the p.d.f. of X and Y be $f(x, y) = 2$, $0 < x < y$, $0 < y < 1$, zero elsewhere. Let $u(X, Y) = X$, $v(X, Y) = Y$ and $w(X, Y) = XY$. Show that $E[u(X, Y)] \cdot E[v(X, Y)] \neq E[w(X, Y)]$.

1.6. Some Special Mathematical Expectations. Certain mathematical expectations, if they exist, have special names and symbols to represent them. We shall mention now only those associated with one random variable. First, let $u(X) = X$, where X is a random variable of the discrete type having a p.d.f. $f(x)$. Then

$$E(X) = \sum_x x f(x).$$

If the discrete points of the sample space having positive probability are $a_1, a_2, a_3, \cdots$, then

$$E(X) = a_1 f(a_1) + a_2 f(a_2) + a_3 f(a_3) + \cdots.$$

This sum of products is seen to be a "weighted average" of the values $a_1, a_2, a_3, \cdots$, the "weight" associated with each a_i being $f(a_i)$. This suggests that we call $E(X)$ the arithmetic mean of the values of X, or, more simply, the *mean value* of X (or the mean value of the distribution).

The mean value μ of a random variable X is defined, when it exists, to be $\mu = E(X)$, whether X is a random variable of the discrete or of the continuous type.

$$E(XY^2) = \int_{-\infty}^{+\infty}\int_{-\infty}^{+\infty} xy^2 f(xy)\, dx\, dy$$

$$= \int_0^1\int_0^1 xy^2(x+y)\, dx\, dy$$

$$\int_0^1 \left[\int_0^1 x^2y^2 + xy^3\, dx \right] dy$$

$$\frac{x^3 y^2}{3} + \frac{x^2 y^3}{2} \Big|_0^1 = \frac{y^2}{3} + \frac{y^3}{2} - 0$$

$$\int_0^1 \left(\frac{y^2}{3} + \frac{y^3}{2} \right) dy = \frac{y^3}{9} + \frac{y^4}{8} \Big|_0^1$$

$$= \frac{1}{9} + \frac{1}{8} = \frac{17}{72}$$

Yee!

COLOMBIÈRE COLLEGE

CLARKSTON • MICHIGAN

A as well as A an event   p. 10

1.14   A₃ — be got ... or point   p. 11

1.15

B. 15

Being X

Battonof 14 Cap 15

$$\frac{d(e^x)}{dx} = e^x$$

$$\frac{d\{e^{x(t-1)}\}}{dx} = (t-1)\, e^{x(t-1)}$$

NOVITIATE OF THE DETROIT PROVINCE OF THE SOCIETY OF JESUS

$$e^{m(e^t - 1)}$$

$$\frac{d}{dt}(e^t) = e^t \frac{d\phi}{dt}$$

$$e^{m(e^t - 1)} \quad \frac{d[m(e^t - 1)]}{dt}$$

$$\downarrow$$

$$m e^t - 0$$

$$e^{m(e^t - 1)} \, m e^t$$

$$\begin{array}{ll} 10 & 15 \\ 15 & 25 \end{array} \qquad 5\,1/2$$

$$1015$$

$$325 \qquad \begin{array}{l} 48+ \\ \underline{15} \\ 53 \end{array} \qquad \begin{array}{r} 36 \\ 16\ 1/2 \\ \hline 52\ 1/2 \end{array}$$

$$x^{-2} e^x -$$

$$\int dx \, x^{-2} + (x^{-2} x -) x$$

$$\left(\int dx \, x^{-2} + (x^{-2} - x) \right) = (x^{-2} x) \phi$$

Another special mathematical expectation is obtained by taking $u(X) = (X - \mu)^2$. If, initially, X is a random variable of the discrete type having a p.d.f. $f(x)$, then

$$E[(X - \mu)^2] = \sum_x (x - \mu)^2 f(x)$$
$$= (a_1 - \mu)^2 f(a_1) + (a_2 - \mu)^2 f(a_2) + \cdots,$$

if $a_1, a_2, \cdots$ are the discrete points of the sample space having positive probability. This sum of products may be interpreted as a "weighted average" of the squares of the deviations of the numbers $a_1, a_2, \cdots$ from the mean value μ of those numbers where the "weight" associated with each $(a_i - \mu)^2$ is $f(a_i)$. This suggests that we may appropriately call $E[(X - \mu)^2]$ the mean value of the square of the deviation of X from its mean value; however, we shall call it the *variance* of X (or the variance of the distribution).

The variance of X will be denoted by σ^2, and we define σ^2, if it exists, by $\sigma^2 = E[(X - \mu)^2]$, whether X is a discrete or a continuous type of random variable.

It is worthwhile to observe that

$$\sigma^2 = E[(X - \mu)^2] = E[X^2 - 2\mu X + \mu^2];$$

and since E is a linear operator,

$$\sigma^2 = E(X^2) - 2\mu E(X) + \mu^2$$
$$= E(X^2) - 2\mu^2 + \mu^2$$
$$= E(X^2) - \mu^2.$$

This frequently affords an easier way of computing the variance of X.

It is customary to call σ (the positive square root of the variance) the *standard deviation* of X (or the standard deviation of the distribution). The number σ is sometimes interpreted as a measure of the dispersion of the points of the sample space relative to the mean value μ. We note that if the sample space contains only one point x for which $f(x) > 0$, then $\sigma = 0$.

Comment. Let the random variable X of the continuous type have the p.d.f. $f(x) = 1/(2a)$, $-a < x < a$, zero elsewhere, so that $\sigma = a/\sqrt{3}$ is the standard deviation of the distribution of X. Next, let the random variable Y of the continuous type have the p.d.f. $g(y) = 1/(4a)$, $-2a < y < 2a$, zero elsewhere, so that $\sigma = 2a/\sqrt{3}$ is the standard deviation of the distribution of Y. Here the standard deviation of Y is greater than that of X; this reflects the fact that the probability for Y is more widely distributed (relative to the mean zero) than is the probability for X.

We next define a third special mathematical expectation called the *moment-generating function* of a random variable X. Suppose there is a positive number h such that for $-h < t < h$ the mathematical expectation $E(e^{tX})$ exists. Thus

$$E(e^{tX}) = \int_{-\infty}^{\infty} e^{tx}f(x)\,dx,$$

if X is a continuous type of random variable, or

$$E(e^{tX}) = \sum_{x} e^{tx}f(x),$$

if X is a discrete type of random variable. This expectation is called the moment-generating function of X (or of the distribution) and is denoted by $M_X(t)$. That is,

$$M_X(t) = E(e^{tX}).$$

It is evident that if we set $t = 0$, we have $M_X(0) = 1$. As will be seen by example, not every distribution has a moment-generating function. But it is difficult to overemphasize the importance of a moment-generating function when it does exist. This importance stems from the fact that the moment-generating function is unique and completely determines the distribution of the random variable; thus, if two random variables have the same moment-generating function, they have the same distribution. This property of a moment-generating function will be very useful in subsequent chapters. Proof of the uniqueness of the moment-generating function is based on the theory of transforms in analysis, and therefore we merely assert this uniqueness.

Although the fact that a moment-generating function (when it exists) completely determines a distribution of one random variable will not be proved, it does seem desirable to try to make the assertion plausible. This can be done if the random variable is of the discrete type. For example, let it be given that

$$M_X(t) = \frac{1}{10}e^{t} + \frac{2}{10}e^{2t} + \frac{3}{10}e^{3t} + \frac{4}{10}e^{4t}$$

is, for all real values of t, the moment-generating function of a random variable X of the discrete type. If we let $f(x)$ be the p.d.f. of X and let $a_1, a_2, a_3, \cdots$ be the discrete points in the sample space at which $f(x) > 0$, then

$$M_X(t) = \sum_{x} e^{tx}f(x),$$

or

$$\frac{1}{10}e^{t} + \frac{2}{10}e^{2t} + \frac{3}{10}e^{3t} + \frac{4}{10}e^{4t} = f(a_1)e^{a_1 t} + f(a_2)e^{a_2 t} + \cdots.$$

Because this is an identity for all real values of t, it seems that the right-hand member should consist of but four terms and that each of the four should equal, respectively, one of those in the left-hand member; hence, we may take $a_1 = 1$, $f(a_1) = 1/10$; $a_2 = 2$, $f(a_2) = 2/10$; $a_3 = 3$, $f(a_3) = 3/10$; $a_4 = 4$, $f(a_4) = 4/10$. Or, more simply, the p.d.f. of X is

$$f(x) = \frac{x}{10}, \quad x = 1, 2, 3, 4,$$
$$= 0 \text{ elsewhere.}$$

On the other hand, let X be a random variable of the continuous type and let it be given that

$$M_X(t) = \frac{1}{1 - t}, \quad t < 1$$

is the moment-generating function of X. That is, we are given

$$\frac{1}{1 - t} = \int_{-\infty}^{\infty} e^{tx} f(x) \, dx, \quad t < 1.$$

It is not at all obvious how $f(x)$ is found. However, it is easy to see that a distribution with p.d.f.

$$f(x) = e^{-x}, \quad 0 < x < \infty,$$
$$= 0 \text{ elsewhere}$$

has the moment-generating function $M_X(t) = (1 - t)^{-1}, t < 1$. Thus the random variable X has a distribution with this p.d.f. in accordance with the assertion of the uniqueness of the moment-generating function.

Since a distribution that has a moment-generating function $M_X(t)$ is completely determined by $M_X(t)$, it would not be surprising if we could obtain some properties of the distribution directly from $M_X(t)$. For example, the existence of $M_X(t)$ for $-h < t < h$ implies that derivatives of all order exist at $t = 0$. Thus

$$\frac{dM_X(t)}{dt} = M'_X(t) = \int_{-\infty}^{\infty} x e^{tx} f(x) \, dx,$$

if X is of the continuous type, or

$$\frac{dM_X(t)}{dt} = M'_X(t) = \sum_x x e^{tx} f(x),$$

if X is of the discrete type. Upon setting $t = 0$, we have in either case

$$M'_X(0) = E(X) = \mu.$$

The second derivative of $M_X(t)$ is

$$M''_X(t) = \int_{-\infty}^{\infty} x^2 e^{tx} f(x) \, dx, \quad \left(\text{or} \sum_x x^2 e^{tx} f(x) \right),$$

so that $M''_X(0) = E(X^2)$. Accordingly,

$$\sigma^2 = E(X^2) - \mu^2 = M''_X(0) - [M'_X(0)]^2.$$

For example, if $M_X(t) = (1 - t)^{-1}$, $t < 1$, as in the illustration above, then

$$M'_X(t) = (1 - t)^{-2},$$

and

$$M''_X(t) = 2(1 - t)^{-3}.$$

Hence

$$\mu = M'_X(0) = 1,$$

and

$$\sigma^2 = M''_X(0) - \mu^2 = 2 - 1 = 1.$$

Of course we could have computed μ and σ^2 from the p.d.f. by

$$\mu = \int_{-\infty}^{\infty} xf(x)\ dx \qquad \text{and} \qquad \sigma^2 = \int_{-\infty}^{\infty} x^2 f(x)\ dx - \mu^2,$$

respectively.   Sometimes one way is easier than the other.

In general, if m is a positive integer and if $M^{(m)}_X(t)$ means the mth derivative of $M_X(t)$, we have, by repeated differentiation with respect to t,

$$M^{(m)}_X(0) = E(X^m).$$

Now

$$E(X^m) = \int_{-\infty}^{\infty} x^m f(x)\,dx, \quad \left(\text{or } \sum_x x^m f(x)\right),$$

and integrals (or sums) of this sort are, in mechanics, called *moments*. Since $M_X(t)$ generates the values of $E(X^m)$, $m = 1, 2, 3, \cdots$, it is called the moment-generating function.

EXAMPLE 1.   Let X have the p.d.f.

$$f(x) = \frac{1}{2}(x + 1), \quad -1 < x < 1,$$
$$= 0 \text{ elsewhere.}$$

Then the mean value of X is

$$\mu = \int_{-\infty}^{\infty} xf(x)\ dx = \int_{-1}^{1} x\left(\frac{x + 1}{2}\right) dx = \frac{1}{3}$$

while the variance of X is

$$\sigma^2 = \int_{-\infty}^{\infty} x^2 f(x)\ dx - \mu^2 = \int_{-1}^{1} x^2\left(\frac{x + 1}{2}\right) dx - \left(\frac{1}{3}\right)^2 = \frac{2}{9}.$$

EXAMPLE 2.   If X has the p.d.f.

$$f(x) = \frac{1}{x^2}, \quad 1 < x < \infty,$$
$$= 0 \text{ elsewhere,}$$

then the mean value of X does not exist, since

$$\int_{1}^{\infty} x\left(\frac{1}{x^2}\right) dx = \lim_{b \to \infty} \int_{1}^{b} \frac{1}{x}\ dx$$
$$= \lim_{b \to \infty} [\ln b - \ln 1]$$

does not exist.

EXAMPLE 3.   Given that the series

$$\frac{1}{1^2} + \frac{1}{2^2} + \frac{1}{3^2} + \cdots = \frac{\pi^2}{6}.$$

Then

$$f(x) = \frac{6}{\pi^2 x^2}, \quad x = 1, 2, 3, \cdots$$
$$= 0 \text{ elsewhere,}$$

is the p.d.f. of a discrete type of random variable X.   The moment-generating function of this distribution, if it exists, is given by

$$M_X(t) = E(e^{tX}) = \sum_x e^{tx} f(x)$$
$$= \sum_{x=1}^{\infty} \frac{6 e^{tx}}{\pi^2 x^2}.$$

The ratio test may be used to show that this series converges only if $t \leq 0$.   Thus there does not exist a positive number h such that $M_X(t)$ exists for $-h < t < h$. Accordingly the distribution having the p.d.f. $f(x)$ of this example does not have a moment-generating function.

Exercises

1.35.   Find the mean and variance, if they exist, of each of the random variables having the indicated probability density functions.

(a) $f(x) = \dfrac{3!}{x!(3-x)!}\left(\dfrac{1}{2}\right)^3$, $x = 0, 1, 2, 3$, zero elsewhere.

(b) $f(x) = 6x(1-x)$, $0 < x < 1$, zero elsewhere.

(c) $f(x) = 1$, $x = 0$, zero elsewhere.

(d) $f(x) = 2/x^3$, $1 < x < \infty$, zero elsewhere.

1.36.   Let $f(x) = (\frac{1}{2})^x$, $x = 1, 2, 3, \cdots$, zero elsewhere, be the p.d.f. of the random variable X.   Find the moment-generating function, the mean, and the variance of X.

1.37.   For each of the following probability density functions, compute $Pr(\mu - 2\sigma < X < \mu + 2\sigma)$.

(a) $f(x) = 6x(1-x)$, $0 < x < 1$, zero elsewhere.

(b) $f(x) = (\frac{1}{2})^x$, $x = 1, 2, 3, \cdots$, zero elsewhere.

1.38.   If the variance of the random variable X exists, show that $E(X^2) \geq [E(X)]^2$.

1.39.   Let a random variable X of the continuous type have a p.d.f. $f(x)$ whose graph is symmetric with respect to $x = c$.   If the mean value of X exists, show that $E(X) = c$.

1.40.   Let the random variable X have mean μ, standard deviation σ, and moment-generating function $M_X(t)$, $-h < t < h$.   Show that

$$E\left(\frac{X-\mu}{\sigma}\right) = 0, \quad E\left[\left(\frac{X-\mu}{\sigma}\right)^2\right] = 1,$$

and

$$E\left[e^{t\left(\frac{X-\mu}{\sigma}\right)}\right] = e^{-\frac{\mu t}{\sigma}} M_X\left(\frac{t}{\sigma}\right), \quad -h\sigma < t < h\sigma.$$

1.41. Show that the moment-generating function of the random variable X having the p.d.f. $f(x) = \frac{1}{3}$, $-1 < x < 2$, zero elsewhere, is

$$M_X(t) = \frac{e^{2t} - e^{-t}}{3t}, \quad t \neq 0,$$

$$= 1, \quad t = 0.$$

1.42. Let X be a random variable so that $E[(X - b)^2]$ exists for all real b. Show that $E[(X - b)^2]$ is a minimum when $b = E(X)$.

1.43. Let $f(x_1, x_2) = 2x_1$, $0 < x_1 < 1$, $0 < x_2 < 1$, zero elsewhere, be the p.d.f. of X_1 and X_2. Compute $E(X_1 + X_2)$ and $E\{[X_1 + X_2 - E(X_1 + X_2)]^2\}$.

1.44. Let $f(x_1, x_2, x_3) = e^{-x_1-x_2-x_3}$, $0 < x_1 < \infty$, $0 < x_2 < \infty$, $0 < x_3 < \infty$, zero elsewhere, be the p.d.f. of the random variables X_1, X_2, X_3. Find $E[e^{t(x_1+x_2+x_3)}]$, $t < 1$.

CHAPTER TWO

SOME SPECIAL DISTRIBUTIONS

In this chapter we shall discuss some important distributions of one random variable that are frequently used in statistics. It is not our purpose at this time to go very far into questions of how these distributions arise or how they are used. We wish primarily to establish their names and some of their properties.

2.1. Two Discrete-Type Distributions. In this section we introduce the binomial and Poisson distributions.

(a) *The binomial distribution.* Recall that if n is a positive integer,

$$(a + b)^n = \sum_{x=0}^{n} \frac{n!}{x!(n-x)!} b^x a^{n-x},$$

provided we agree to interpret the symbol 0! to be 1. Consider the function defined by

$$f(x) = \frac{n!}{x!(n-x)!} p^x (1-p)^{n-x}, \quad x = 0, 1, 2, \cdots, n$$

$$= 0 \text{ elsewhere,}$$

where n is a positive integer and $0 < p < 1$. Under these conditions it is clear that $f(x) \geq 0$ and that

$$\sum_x f(x) = \sum_{x=0}^{n} \frac{n!}{x!(n-x)!} p^x (1-p)^{n-x}$$

$$= [(1-p) + p]^n = 1.$$

That is, $f(x)$ satisfies the conditions of being a p.d.f. of a random variable X of the discrete type. A random variable X that has a p.d.f. of the form of $f(x)$ is said to have a *binomial* distribution, and any such $f(x)$ is called a *binomial p.d.f.*

Comment. The binomial distribution serves as an excellent mathematical model in a number of experimental situations. Consider an experiment, the outcome of which can be classified in but one of two ways (head or tail, life or death, effective or noneffective, etc.). Let p denote the probability of a head (or life, or effective) in an experiment, and let X denote the number of heads in n such experiments. Under certain assumptions, listed in Chapter Three, X has a binomial distribution.

The moment-generating function of a binomial distribution is easily found. It is

$$M_X(t) = \sum_x e^{tx}f(x) = \sum_{x=0}^{n} e^{tx}\frac{n!}{x!(n-x)!}p^x(1-p)^{n-x}$$

$$= \sum_{x=0}^{n} \frac{n!}{x!(n-x)!}(pe^t)^x(1-p)^{n-x}$$

$$= [(1-p) + pe^t]^n$$

for all real values of t. The mean μ and variance σ^2 of X may be computed from $M_X(t)$. Since

$$M'_X(t) = n[(1-p) + pe^t]^{n-1}(pe^t)$$

and

$$M''_X(t) = n[(1-p)+pe^t]^{n-1}(pe^t)+n(n-1)[(1-p)+pe^t]^{n-2}(pe^t)^2,$$

it follows that

$$\boxed{\mu = M'_X(0) = np,}$$

and

$$\boxed{\sigma^2 = M''_X(0) - \mu^2 = np + n(n-1)p^2 - (np)^2 = np(1-p).}$$

EXAMPLE 1. The binomial distribution with p.d.f.

$$f(x) = \frac{7!}{x!(7-x)!}\left(\frac{1}{2}\right)^x\left(1-\frac{1}{2}\right)^{7-x}, \quad x = 0, 1, 2, \cdots, 7,$$

$$= 0 \text{ elsewhere}$$

has the moment-generating function

$$M_X(t) = \left(\frac{1}{2} + \frac{1}{2}e^t\right)^7,$$

has mean $\mu = np = 7/2$, and has variance $\sigma^2 = np(1-p) = 7/4$. Further, if X is the random variable with this distribution, we have

$$Pr(0 \leq X \leq 1) = \sum_{x=0}^{1} f(x) = \frac{1}{128} + \frac{7}{128} = \frac{8}{128}$$

and

$$Pr(X = 5) = f(5)$$

$$= \frac{7!}{5!2!}\left(\frac{1}{2}\right)^5\left(\frac{1}{2}\right)^2 = \frac{21}{128}.$$

EXAMPLE 2. If the moment-generating function of a random variable X is

$$M_X(t) = \left(\frac{2}{3} + \frac{1}{3}e^t\right)^5,$$

then X has a binomial distribution with $n = 5$ and $p = \frac{1}{3}$; that is, the p.d.f. of X is

$$f(x) = \frac{5!}{x!(5-x)!}\left(\frac{1}{3}\right)^x\left(\frac{2}{3}\right)^{5-x}, \quad x = 0, 1, 2, \cdots, 5$$

$$= 0 \text{ elsewhere.}$$

Here $\mu = np = 5/3$ and $\sigma^2 = np(1-p) = 10/9$.

(b) *The Poisson distribution.* Recall that the series

$$1 + m + \frac{m^2}{2!} + \frac{m^3}{3!} + \cdots = \sum_{x=0}^{\infty} \frac{m^x}{x!} \qquad \lim_{x \to \infty} \sum \frac{u^x}{x!} = e^u$$

converges, for all values of m, to e^m. Consider the function $f(x)$ defined by

$$f(x) = \frac{m^x e^{-m}}{x!}, \quad x = 0, 1, 2, \cdots$$

$$= 0 \text{ elsewhere,}$$

where $m > 0$. Since $m > 0$, then $f(x) \geq 0$ and

$$\sum_x f(x) = \sum_{x=0}^{\infty} \frac{m^x e^{-m}}{x!} = e^{-m} \sum_{x=0}^{\infty} \frac{m^x}{x!} = e^{-m}e^m = 1;$$

that is, $f(x)$ satisfies the conditions of being a p.d.f. of a discrete type of random variable. A random variable X which has a p.d.f. of the form of $f(x)$ is said to have a *Poisson* distribution, and any such $f(x)$ is called a *Poisson p.d.f.*

Comment. Experience indicates that the Poisson p.d.f. may be used in a number of applications with quite satisfactory results. For example, let X denote the number of alpha particles emitted by a radioactive substance that enter a prescribed region during a prescribed interval of time. With a suitable value of m, it is found that X may be assumed to have a Poisson distribution. Again let X denote the number of defects on a manufactured article, such as a refrigerator door. Upon examining many of these doors, it is found, with an appropriate value of m, that X may be said to have a Poisson distribution. The number of railroad accidents in some unit of time (or the number of insurance claims in some unit of time) is often assumed to be a random variable which has a Poisson distribution.

The moment generating function of a Poisson distribution is given by

$$M_X(t) = \sum_x e^{tx}f(x) = \sum_{x=0}^{\infty} e^{tx}\frac{m^x e^{-m}}{x!}$$

$$= e^{-m} \sum_{x=0}^{\infty} \frac{(me^t)^x}{x!}$$

$$= e^{-m} e^{me^t} = e^{m(e^t-1)}$$

for all real values of t. Since

$$M'_X(t) = e^{m(e^t-1)}(me^t),$$

and

$$M''_X(t) = e^{m(e^t-1)}(me^t) + e^{m(e^t-1)}(me^t)^2,$$

then

$$\boxed{\mu = M'_X(0) = m,}$$

and

$$\boxed{\sigma^2 = M''_X(0) - \mu^2 = m + m^2 - m^2 = m.}$$

That is, a Poisson distribution has $\mu = \sigma^2 = m > 0$. On this account, a Poisson p.d.f. is frequently written

$$f(x) = \frac{\mu^x e^{-\mu}}{x!}, \quad x = 0, 1, 2, \cdots$$

$$= 0 \text{ elsewhere.}$$

EXAMPLE 3. Suppose X has a Poisson distribution with $\mu = 2$. Then the p.d.f. of X is

$$f(x) = \frac{2^x e^{-2}}{x!}, \quad x = 0, 1, 2, \cdots,$$

$$= 0 \text{ elsewhere.}$$

The variance of this distribution is $\sigma^2 = \mu = 2$. If we wish to compute $Pr(1 \leq X)$, we have

$$Pr(1 \leq X) = 1 - Pr(X = 0)$$
$$= 1 - f(0) = 1 - e^{-2}.$$

EXAMPLE 4. If the moment-generating function of a random variable X is

$$M_X(t) = e^{4(e^t-1)},$$

then X has a Poisson distribution with $\mu = 4$. Accordingly, by way of example,

$$Pr(X = 3) = \frac{4^3 e^{-4}}{3!} = \frac{32}{3} e^{-4}.$$

Exercises

2.1. If the moment-generating function of a random variable X is $[\frac{1}{3} + (\frac{2}{3})e^t]^5$, find $Pr(X = 2 \text{ or } 3)$.

2.2. If the random variable X has a Poisson distribution such that $Pr(X = 1) = Pr(X = 2)$, find $Pr(X = 4)$.

2.3. The moment-generating function of a random variable X is $e^{4(e^t-1)}$. Show that $Pr(\mu - 2\sigma < X < \mu + 2\sigma) = \sum_{x=1}^{7} \frac{4^x e^{-4}}{x!}$.

2.4. The moment-generating function of a random variable X is $[\frac{2}{3} + (\frac{1}{3})e^t]^9$. Show that

$$Pr(\mu - 2\sigma < X < \mu + 2\sigma) = \sum_{x=1}^{5} \frac{9!}{x!(9-x)!}\left(\frac{1}{3}\right)^x\left(\frac{2}{3}\right)^{9-x}$$

2.5. Let X have a binomial distribution. Show that

$$E\left(\frac{X - np}{\sqrt{np(1-p)}}\right) = 0, \qquad E\left[\left(\frac{X - np}{\sqrt{np(1-p)}}\right)^2\right] = 1,$$

and

$$E\left[e^{t\left(\frac{X-np}{\sqrt{np(1-p)}}\right)}\right] = \left[(1-p)e^{-t\sqrt{\frac{p}{n(1-p)}}} + pe^{t\sqrt{\frac{1-p}{np}}}\right]^n$$

2.6. Let X have a Poisson distribution with mean μ. Show that

$$E\left(\frac{X - \mu}{\sqrt{\mu}}\right) = 0, \qquad E\left[\left(\frac{X - \mu}{\sqrt{\mu}}\right)^2\right] = 1,$$

and

$$E\left[e^{t\left(\frac{X-\mu}{\sqrt{\mu}}\right)}\right] = e^{\mu\left(e^{\frac{t}{\sqrt{\mu}}} - 1 - \frac{t}{\sqrt{\mu}}\right)}.$$

2.7. If X has a binomial distribution, show that

$$E\left(\frac{X}{n}\right) = p \quad \text{and} \quad E\left[\left(\frac{X}{n} - p\right)^2\right] = \frac{p(1-p)}{n}.$$

2.8. Let $\qquad f(x) = \frac{2!}{x!(2-x)!}p^x(1-p)^{2-x}, \quad x = 0, 1, 2, \text{ zero elsewhere,}$

and $\qquad g(y) = \frac{4!}{y!(4-y)!}p^y(1-p)^{4-y}, \quad y = 0, 1, 2, 3, 4, \text{ zero elsewhere,}$

be the probability density functions of the random variables X and Y. If $Pr(X \geq 1) = 5/9$, find $Pr(Y \geq 1)$.

2.9. If $x = r$ is the unique mode of the binomial distribution having mean np and variance $np(1 - p)$, show that

$$(n + 1)p - 1 < r < (n + 1)p.$$

2.2. Two Continuous-Type Distributions. In this section we introduce two distributions of random variables of the continuous type called the *normal* and *chi-square distributions*.

(a) *The normal distribution.* It is shown in some books on calculus that the integral

$$\int_{-\infty}^{\infty} e^{-\frac{y^2}{2}}\,dy = \sqrt{2\pi}.$$

If we introduce a new variable of integration (say, x) by writing

$$y = \frac{x - a}{b}, \quad b > 0,$$

the integral becomes

$$\int_{-\infty}^{\infty} e^{-\frac{(x-a)^2}{2b^2}} \left(\frac{1}{b}\right) dx = \sqrt{2\pi}.$$

Thus

$$\int_{-\infty}^{\infty} \frac{1}{b\sqrt{2\pi}} e^{-\frac{(x-a)^2}{2b^2}} dx = 1.$$

Since $b > 0$, this implies that

$$f(x) = \frac{1}{b\sqrt{2\pi}} e^{-\frac{(x-a)^2}{2b^2}}, \quad -\infty < x < \infty$$

satisfies the conditions of being a p.d.f. of a continuous type of random variable. A random variable of the continuous type that has a p.d.f. of the form of $f(x)$ is said to have a *normal* distribution, and any $f(x)$ of this form is called a normal p.d.f.

We can find the moment-generating function of a normal distribution as follows. In

$$M_X(t) = \int_{-\infty}^{\infty} e^{tx} \frac{1}{b\sqrt{2\pi}} e^{-\frac{(x-a)^2}{2b^2}} dx$$

let $x = by + b^2t + a$. Then $M_X(t)$ becomes

$$M_X(t) = \int_{-\infty}^{\infty} e^{t(by+b^2t+a)} \frac{1}{b\sqrt{2\pi}} e^{-\frac{(by+b^2t)^2}{2b^2}} (b) \, dy$$

$$= e^{at + \frac{b^2 t^2}{2}} \int_{-\infty}^{\infty} \frac{1}{\sqrt{2\pi}} e^{-\frac{y^2}{2}} dy$$

$$= e^{at + \frac{b^2 t^2}{2}}$$

for all real values of t.

The mean μ and variance σ^2 of a normal distribution will be calculated from $M_X(t)$. Now

$$M'_X(t) = e^{at + \frac{b^2 t^2}{2}} (a + b^2t),$$

and

$$M''_X(t) = e^{at + \frac{b^2 t^2}{2}} (b^2) + e^{at + \frac{b^2 t^2}{2}} (a + b^2t)^2.$$

Thus

$$\mu = M'_X(0) = a,$$

and

$$\sigma^2 = M''_X(0) - \mu^2 = b^2 + a^2 - a^2 = b^2.$$

This permits us to write a normal p.d.f. in the form of

$$f(x) = \frac{1}{\sigma\sqrt{2\pi}}e^{-\frac{(x-\mu)^2}{2\sigma^2}}, \quad -\infty < x < \infty,$$

a form which shows explicitly the values of μ and σ^2. The moment-generating function $M_X(t)$ can be written

$$M_X(t) = e^{\mu t + \frac{\sigma^2 t^2}{2}}.$$

EXAMPLE 1.   If X has the moment-generating function
$$M_X(t) = e^{2t+32t^2},$$

then X has a normal distribution with $\mu = 2$, $\sigma^2 = 64$.

The normal p.d.f. occurs so frequently in certain parts of statistics that we denote it, for brevity, by $n(x; \mu, \sigma^2)$. Thus, if we say the random variable X is $n(x; 0, 1)$, we mean that X has a normal distribution with mean $\mu = 0$ and variance $\sigma^2 = 1$, so that the p.d.f. of X is

$$f(x) = \frac{1}{\sqrt{2\pi}}e^{-\frac{x^2}{2}}, \quad -\infty < x < \infty.$$

If we say that X is $n(x; 5, 4)$, we mean that X has a normal distribution with mean $\mu = 5$ and variance $\sigma^2 = 4$, so that the p.d.f. of X is

$$f(x) = \frac{1}{2\sqrt{2\pi}}e^{-\frac{(x-5)^2}{2(4)}}, \quad -\infty < x < \infty.$$

Moreover, if

$$M_X(t) = e^{\frac{t^2}{2}},$$

then X is $n(x; 0,1)$.

The graph of

$$f(x) = \frac{1}{\sigma\sqrt{2\pi}}e^{-\frac{(x-\mu)^2}{2\sigma^2}}, \quad -\infty < x < \infty,$$

is seen (1) to be symmetric about a vertical axis through $x = \mu$; (2) to have its maximum of $1/(\sigma\sqrt{2\pi})$ at $x = \mu$; and (3) to have the x-axis as a horizontal asymptote. It should be verified that (4) there are points of inflection at $x = \mu \pm \sigma$.

Comment. The normal distribution is one of the more widely used distributions in applications of statistical methods. Variables that are often assumed to be random variables having normal distributions (with appropriate values of μ and σ) are the diameter of a hole made by a drill press, the score on a test, the yield of a grain on a plot of ground, and the length of a newborn child.

We now consider a very useful function of a random variable X which is $n(x; \mu, \sigma^2)$. The probability

$$Pr(\mu + a\sigma < X < \mu + b\sigma) = \int_{\mu+a\sigma}^{\mu+b\sigma} \frac{1}{\sigma\sqrt{2\pi}} e^{-\frac{(x-\mu)^2}{2\sigma^2}} dx$$

is defined for every $a < b$. The event

$$a < \frac{X - \mu}{\sigma} < b$$

occurs when, and only when, the event

$$\mu + a\sigma < X < \mu + b\sigma$$

occurs; so, the two events are completely equivalent. The latter event, however, has its probability defined for every $a < b$, and thus the event

$$a < \frac{X - \mu}{\sigma} < b$$

has the same probability of occurrence. In other words, $(X - \mu)/\sigma$ is itself a random variable and has its own p.d.f. We seek the p.d.f. of this new random variable, say, $W = (X - \mu)/\sigma$. The moment-generating function of W, say, $M_W(t)$, is

$$M_W(t) = E\left(e^{t\frac{X-\mu}{\sigma}}\right)$$

$$= E\left(e^{\frac{tX}{\sigma}}e^{-\frac{t\mu}{\sigma}}\right)$$

$$= e^{-\frac{\mu t}{\sigma}}E\left(e^{\frac{t}{\sigma}X}\right),$$

since $e^{-\mu t/\sigma}$ is not a function of X. Now we know that

$$E(e^{tX}) = e^{\mu t + \frac{\sigma^2 t^2}{2}}$$

for all real values of t; hence $E[e^{(t/\sigma)X}]$ can be obtained from $E(e^{tX})$ by replacing t by t/σ. That is,

$$E\left(e^{\frac{tX}{\sigma}}\right) = e^{\mu\frac{t}{\sigma} + \frac{t^2}{2}}.$$

Finally,

$$M_W(t) = e^{-\frac{\mu t}{\sigma}}e^{\mu\frac{t}{\sigma} + \frac{t^2}{2}} = e^{\frac{t^2}{2}}.$$

But this is the moment-generating function of a random variable that has a normal distribution with zero mean and unit variance; consequently W is $n(w; 0, 1)$. We state this result as a theorem.

THEOREM 1. If the random variable X has a normal distribution with mean μ and variance σ^2, then the random variable $W = (X - \mu)/\sigma$ is normally distributed with mean zero and variance one.

This fact considerably simplifies calculations of probabilities concerning normally distributed variables, as will be seen presently. Suppose that X is $n(x; \mu, \sigma^2)$. Then, with $c_1 < c_2$ we have, since $Pr(X = c_1) = 0$,

$$Pr(c_1 < X < c_2) = Pr(X < c_2) - Pr(X < c_1)$$

$$= Pr\left(\frac{X - \mu}{\sigma} < \frac{c_2 - \mu}{\sigma}\right) - Pr\left(\frac{X - \mu}{\sigma} < \frac{c_1 - \mu}{\sigma}\right)$$

$$= \int_{-\infty}^{\frac{c_2 - \mu}{\sigma}} \frac{1}{\sqrt{2\pi}} e^{-\frac{w^2}{2}} dw - \int_{-\infty}^{\frac{c_1 - \mu}{\sigma}} \frac{1}{\sqrt{2\pi}} e^{-\frac{w^2}{2}} dw$$

because $W = (X - \mu)/\sigma$ is $n(w; 0, 1)$. That is, probabilities concerning X, which is $n(x; \mu, \sigma^2)$, can be expressed in terms of probabilities concerning W, which is $n(w; 0, 1)$. However, an integral like

$$\int_{-\infty}^{k} \frac{1}{\sqrt{2\pi}} e^{-\frac{w^2}{2}} dw$$

cannot be evaluated by the fundamental theorem of calculus because an "anti-derivative" of $e^{-w^2/2}$ is not expressible as an elementary function. Instead, tables of the approximate value of this integral for various values of k have been prepared and are partially reproduced in Table I, in the Appendix. We use the notation (for normal)

$$N(x) = \int_{-\infty}^{x} \frac{1}{\sqrt{2\pi}} e^{-\frac{w^2}{2}} dw;$$

thus, if X is $n(x; \mu, \sigma^2)$, then

$$Pr(c_1 < X < c_2) = Pr\left(\frac{X - \mu}{\sigma} < \frac{c_2 - \mu}{\sigma}\right) - Pr\left(\frac{X - \mu}{\sigma} < \frac{c_1 - \mu}{\sigma}\right)$$

$$= N\left(\frac{c_2 - \mu}{\sigma}\right) - N\left(\frac{c_1 - \mu}{\sigma}\right).$$

EXAMPLE 2. Let X be $n(x; 2, 25)$. Then, by Table I,

$$Pr(0 < X < 10) = N\left(\frac{10 - 2}{5}\right) - N\left(\frac{0 - 2}{5}\right)$$

$$= N(1.6) - N(-0.4)$$

$$= 0.945 - (1 - 0.655) = 0.600,$$

and

$$Pr(-8 < X < 1) = N\left(\frac{1 - 2}{5}\right) - N\left(\frac{-8 - 2}{5}\right)$$

$$= N(-0.2) - N(-2)$$

$$= (1 - 0.579) - (1 - 0.977) = 0.398.$$

EXAMPLE 3.   Let X be $n(x; \mu, \sigma^2)$.   Then, by Table I,

$$Pr(\mu - 2\sigma < X < \mu + 2\sigma) = N\left(\frac{\mu + 2\sigma - \mu}{\sigma}\right) - N\left(\frac{\mu - 2\sigma - \mu}{\sigma}\right)$$

$$= N(2) - N(-2)$$

$$= 0.977 - (1 - 0.977) = 0.954.$$

(b)   *The chi-square distribution*.   It is proved in books on advanced calculus that the integral

$$\int_0^\infty y^{k-1}e^{-y}dy$$

exists for $k > 0$ and that the value of the integral is a positive number. The integral is called the gamma function of k and we write

$$\Gamma(k) = \int_0^\infty y^{k-1}e^{-y}dy.$$

If $k = 1$, clearly

$$\Gamma(1) = \int_0^\infty e^{-y}dy = 1.$$

If $k > 1$, an integration by parts shows that

$$\Gamma(k) = (k - 1)\int_0^\infty y^{k-2}e^{-y}dy = (k - 1)\Gamma(k - 1).$$

Accordingly, if k is a positive integer greater than one, $\Gamma(k) = (k - 1)(k - 2) \cdots 3.2.1 = (k - 1)!$ Since $\Gamma(1) = 1$, this suggests we take $0! = 1$ as we did in our study of the binomial and Poisson distributions.

In the integral which defines $\Gamma(k)$, let us introduce a new variable x by $y = x/2$.   Then

$$\Gamma(k) = \int_0^\infty \left(\frac{x}{2}\right)^{k-1}e^{-\frac{x}{2}}\left(\frac{1}{2}\right)dx;$$

consequently

$$1 = \int_0^\infty \frac{1}{\Gamma(k)2^k}x^{k-1}e^{-\frac{x}{2}}\,dx.$$

Since $\Gamma(k) > 0$, this implies that

$$f(x) = \frac{1}{\Gamma(k)2^k}x^{k-1}e^{-\frac{x}{2}}, \quad 0 < x < \infty,$$

$$= 0 \text{ elsewhere}$$

is a p.d.f. of a random variable of the continuous type.   In particular, when $k = r/2$, where r is a positive integer, a random variable X having the p.d.f.

$$f(x) = \frac{1}{\Gamma\left(\frac{r}{2}\right)2^{\frac{r}{2}}}x^{\frac{r}{2}-1}e^{-\frac{x}{2}}, \quad 0 < x < \infty,$$

$$= 0 \text{ elsewhere}$$

is said to have a *chi-square* distribution, and any $f(x)$ of this form is called a chi-square p.d.f.

We now find the moment-generating function of a chi-square distribution. Since

$$M_X(t) = E(e^{tX}) = \int_0^\infty e^{tx} \frac{1}{\Gamma\left(\frac{r}{2}\right)2^{\frac{r}{2}}} x^{\frac{r}{2}-1} e^{-\frac{x}{2}} \, dx$$

$$= \int_0^\infty \frac{1}{\Gamma\left(\frac{r}{2}\right)2^{\frac{r}{2}}} x^{\frac{r}{2}-1} e^{-\frac{x(1-2t)}{2}} \, dx,$$

we may set $y = x(1 - 2t)/2$, $t < \frac{1}{2}$, to obtain

$$M_X(t) = \int_0^\infty \frac{1}{\Gamma\left(\frac{r}{2}\right)2^{\frac{r}{2}}} \left(\frac{2y}{1-2t}\right)^{\frac{r}{2}-1} e^{-y} \left(\frac{2}{1-2t}\right) dy$$

$$= \frac{1}{(1-2t)^{\frac{r}{2}}} \int_0^\infty \frac{1}{\Gamma\left(\frac{r}{2}\right)} y^{\frac{r}{2}-1} e^{-y} \, dy$$

$$= \frac{1}{(1-2t)^{\frac{r}{2}}}, \quad t < \frac{1}{2}.$$

Since

$$M'_X(t) = \left(-\frac{r}{2}\right)(1-2t)^{-\frac{r}{2}-1}(-2)$$

and

$$M''_X(t) = \left(-\frac{r}{2}\right)\left(-\frac{r}{2}-1\right)(1-2t)^{-\frac{r}{2}-2}(-2)^2,$$

we have, for a chi-square distribution,

$$\mu = M'_X(0) = r$$

and

$$\sigma^2 = M''_X(0) - \mu^2 = r(r+2) - r^2 = 2r.$$

We can write the chi-square p.d.f. $f(x)$, with r replaced by μ; instead, for no obvious reason, we retain r and call r the number of degrees of freedom of the chi-square distribution (or of the chi-square p.d.f.). Like the normal distribution, a chi-square distribution has an important role in statistics.

EXAMPLE 4. If X has the p.d.f.

$$f(x) = \frac{1}{4}xe^{-\frac{x}{2}}, \quad 0 < x < \infty,$$

$$= 0 \text{ elsewhere,}$$

then X has a chi-square distribution with four degrees of freedom; hence, $\mu = 4$ and $\sigma^2 = 8$ and $M_X(t) = (1 - 2t)^{-2}$, $t < \frac{1}{2}$.

EXAMPLE 5. If X has the moment-generating function $M_X(t) = (1 - 2t)^{-8}$, $t < \frac{1}{2}$, then the p.d.f. of X is chi-square with 16 degrees of freedom.

If the random variable X has a chi-square distribution with r degrees of freedom, then, with $c_1 < c_2$, we have, since $Pr(X = c_1) = 0$,

$$Pr(c_1 < X < c_2) = Pr(X < c_2) - Pr(X < c_1).$$

To compute such a probability, we need the value of an integral like

$$Pr(X < x) = \int_0^x \frac{1}{\Gamma\left(\frac{r}{2}\right)2^{\frac{r}{2}}} w^{\frac{r}{2} - 1} e^{-\frac{w}{2}} \, dw.$$

As with the normal distribution, tables of this integral for selected values of r and x have been prepared and are partially reproduced in Table II, in the Appendix.

EXAMPLE 6. Let X have a chi-square distribution with ten degrees of freedom. Then, by Table II, with $r = 10$,

$$Pr(3.25 < X < 20.5) = Pr(X < 20.5) - Pr(X < 3.25)$$
$$= 0.975 - 0.025 = 0.95.$$

Again, by way of example, if $Pr(a < X) = 0.05$, then $Pr(X < a) = 0.95$, since $Pr(X = a) = 0$, and thus $a = 18.3$ from Table II with $r = 10$.

Let the random variable X be $n(x; \mu, \sigma^2)$. It has been seen that the random variable $W = (X - \mu)/\sigma$ is $n(w; 0, 1)$. We are now to find the p.d.f. of $V = W^2 = [(X - \mu)/\sigma]^2$. The moment-generating function of V, say, $M_V(t)$, is

$$M_V(t) = E(e^{tW^2}) = \int_{-\infty}^{\infty} e^{tw^2} \frac{1}{\sqrt{2\pi}} e^{-\frac{w^2}{2}} \, dw,$$

since W is $n(w; 0, 1)$. That is,

$$M_V(t) = \int_{-\infty}^{\infty} \frac{1}{\sqrt{2\pi}} e^{-\frac{w^2(1-2t)}{2}} \, dw.$$

If a new variable, $y = w\sqrt{1 - 2t}$, $t < \frac{1}{2}$, is introduced, it is seen that

$$M_V(t) = \int_{-\infty}^{\infty} \frac{1}{\sqrt{2\pi}} e^{-\frac{y^2}{2}} \left(\frac{1}{\sqrt{1 - 2t}} \right) dy$$

$$= \frac{1}{(1 - 2t)^{1/2}}, \quad t < \frac{1}{2}.$$

Thus, the moment-generating function of V is that of a chi-square distribution with $r = $ one degree of freedom. Accordingly, we state the following theorem.

THEOREM 2.   If the random variable X has a normal distribution with mean μ and variance σ^2, then the random variable

$$V = \left(\frac{X - \mu}{\sigma}\right)^2$$

has a chi-square distribution with one degree of freedom.

Exercises

2.10.   If

$$N(x) = \int_{-\infty}^{x} \frac{1}{\sqrt{2\pi}} e^{-\frac{w^2}{2}} dw,$$

show that $N(-x) = 1 - N(x)$.

2.11.   If X is $n(x; 75, 100)$, find $Pr(X < 60)$ and $Pr(70 < X < 100)$.

2.12.   If X is $n(x; \mu, \sigma^2)$, find b so that $Pr(-b < (X - \mu)/\sigma < b) = 0.90$.

2.13.   Let X be $n(x; \mu, \sigma^2)$ so that $Pr(X < 89) = 0.90$ and $Pr(X < 94) = 0.95$. Find μ and σ^2.

2.14.   Determine the constant c so that $f(x) = ce^{-x^2+4x}$, $-\infty < x < \infty$, satisfies the conditions of being a p.d.f.

2.15.   Show that a p.d.f. $n(x; \mu, \sigma^2)$ has points of inflection at $x = \mu - \sigma$ and $x = \mu + \sigma$.

2.16.   If e^{3t+8t^2} is the moment-generating function of the random variable X, find $Pr(-1 < X < 9)$.

2.17.   Let the random variable X have the p.d.f.

$$f(x) = \frac{2}{\sqrt{2\pi}} e^{-\frac{x^2}{2}}, \quad 0 < x < \infty, \quad \text{zero elsewhere.}$$

Find the mean and variance of X.

2.18.   Let X be $n(x; \mu, \sigma^2)$.   Find the p.d.f. of $Z = aX + b$, where a and b are constants.   Hint: Show that $M_Z(t) = e^{(a\mu+b)t + a^2\sigma^2 t^2/2}$.

2.19.   If $(1 - 2t)^{-6}$, $t < \frac{1}{2}$, is the moment-generating function of the random variable X, find $Pr(X < 5.23)$.

2.20.   If X has a chi-square distribution with five degrees of freedom, determine a and b so that $Pr(a < X < b) = 0.95$ and $Pr(X < a) = 0.025$.

2.21.   Let X be $n(x; 5, 10)$.   Find $Pr[0.04 < (X - 5)^2 < 38.4]$.

2.22.   Let X have a chi-square distribution with r degrees of freedom.   Show that

$$E\left(\frac{X - r}{\sqrt{2r}}\right) = 0 \qquad E\left[\left(\frac{X - r}{\sqrt{2r}}\right)_i^2\right] = 1,$$

and

$$E\left[e^{t\left(\frac{X-r}{\sqrt{2r}}\right)}\right] = \left(e^{+t\sqrt{\frac{2}{r}}} - t\sqrt{\frac{2}{r}} e^{+t\sqrt{\frac{2}{r}}}\right)^{-\frac{r}{2}}, \quad t < \sqrt{\frac{r}{2}}.$$

2.23. A random variable X of the continuous type that has a p.d.f. of the form

$$f(x) = \frac{1}{\Gamma(\alpha)\beta^\alpha} x^{\alpha-1} e^{-\frac{x}{\beta}}, \quad 0 < x < \infty$$

$$= 0 \text{ elsewhere,}$$

where $\alpha > 0$, $\beta > 0$, is said to have a *gamma* distribution. Show that $M_X(t) = (1 - \beta t)^{-\alpha}$, $t < 1/\beta$. Using this result, obtain $\mu = \alpha\beta$ and $\sigma^2 = \alpha\beta^2$.

2.24. If X has a gamma distribution with $\alpha = 3$ and $\beta = 4$, find $Pr(3.28 < X < 25.2)$. Hint: Determine the distribution of $Y = X/2$ and consider the probability of the equivalent event $1.64 < X/2 < 12.6$.

2.3. Parameters of a Distribution. In each of the four special distributions introduced in Sections 2.1 and 2.2, certain constants enter the p.d.f. $f(x)$. In the binomial distribution, these constants were a positive integer n and a number p, $0 < p < 1$; in the Poisson distribution there was a positive number m, later identified with μ; in the normal distribution, there were two constants a and $b > 0$, later identified with μ and σ, respectively; and in the chi-square distribution a positive integer r, which was called the number of degrees of freedom of the chi-square distribution. Any such constant which enters into a p.d.f. is called a *parameter*. No distribution is completely determined until all parameters have been specified. For example, the statement that X has a normal distribution tells us something about X, but the statement that X has a normal distribution with $\mu = 0$ and $\sigma = 1$ tells us everything. One of the interesting problems in mathematical statistics is to leave one or more parameters in a p.d.f. unassigned and to study ways and means of eliciting information about the parameter from the numerical results of random experiments. Various aspects of this problem will be investigated in the subsequent chapters.

Exercises

2.25. Determine the mean and variance of the random variable X if its p.d.f. is $f(x) = \theta x^{\theta-1}$, $0 < x < 1$, zero elsewhere, where the parameter $\theta > 0$.

2.26. Let X have the p.d.f. $f(x) = \theta(1 - x)^{\theta-1}$, $0 < x < 1$, zero elsewhere, where the parameter $\theta > 0$. If $Pr(X < \frac{1}{2}) = \frac{7}{8}$, find the parameter θ and the median of the distribution.

2.27. Let X have a gamma distribution with the p.d.f.

$$f(x) = \frac{1}{\beta^2} x e^{-\frac{x}{\beta}}, \quad 0 < x < \infty, \text{ zero elsewhere.}$$

If $x = 2$ is the mode of the distribution, find the parameter β and $Pr(X < 9.49)$.

2.28. Let X have the uniform distribution with p.d.f. $f(x) = 1/(2\theta_2)$, $\theta_1 - \theta_2 < x < \theta_1 + \theta_2$, zero elsewhere, where $-\infty < \theta_1 < \infty$, $0 < \theta_2$. Compute the mean and variance of X in terms of the parameters θ_1 and θ_2.

2.29. Let X have the uniform distribution of Exercise 2.28. If $Pr(X < 10) = 0.25$ and $Pr(X < 15) = 0.60$, find the values of the parameters θ_1 and θ_2.

CHAPTER THREE

INTRODUCTION TO SAMPLING THEORY

Although we were primarily concerned in Chapters One and Two with definitions and descriptive properties of random variables and their distributions, we did solve two problems on the distribution of a function of a random variable. Specifically in Section 2.2 it was shown that if X is $n(x; \mu, \sigma^2)$, then the functions of X, $W = (X - \mu)/\sigma$ and $V = (X - \mu)^2/\sigma^2$, have respectively a normal distribution with zero mean and unit variance and a chi-square distribution with one degree of freedom. In this chapter we shall investigate the distributions of certain functions of one or more random variables. For example, suppose that $f(x_1, x_2)$ is the p.d.f. of two random variables X_1 and X_2. Then $Y = X_1 + X_2$ and $Z = X_1 X_2$ are functions of the random variables X_1 and X_2, and we may be interested in finding the distribution of Y or Z. As a matter of fact, problems of this sort will not frequently appear in this book unless the random variables X_1 and X_2 are of a character presently to be described as stochastically independent. The concepts of marginal probability density and stochastic independence will be introduced in Section 3.1.

3.1. Marginal Probability Density Functions and Stochastic Independence. Let $f(x_1, x_2)$ be the p.d.f. of two random variables X_1 and X_2. From this point on, for emphasis and clarity, we shall call $f(x_1, x_2)$ the joint p.d.f. of X_1 and X_2. Consider the event $a < X_1 < b, a < b$. This event can occur when and only when the event $a < X_1 < b, -\infty < X_2 < \infty$ occurs; that is, the two events are equivalent, so that they have the same probability. But the probability of the latter event has been defined and is given by

$$Pr(a < X_1 < b, -\infty < X_2 < \infty) = \int_a^b \int_{-\infty}^{\infty} f(x_1, x_2) \, dx_2 \, dx_1$$

for the continuous case, and by

$$Pr(a < X_1 < b, -\infty < X_2 < \infty) = \sum_{a < x_1 < b} \sum_{x_2} f(x_1, x_2)$$

for the discrete case.   Now each of

$$\int_{-\infty}^{\infty} f(x_1, x_2) \, dx_2 \qquad \text{and} \qquad \sum_{x_2} f(x_1, x_2)$$

is a function of x_1 alone, say, $f_1(x_1)$.   Thus, for every $a < b$, we have

$$Pr(a < X_1 < b) = \int_a^b f_1(x_1) \, dx_1 \qquad \text{(continuous case)},$$

$$= \sum_{a < x_1 < b} f_1(x_1) \qquad \text{(discrete case)},$$

so that $f_1(x_1)$ is the p.d.f. of X_1 alone.   Since $f_1(x_1)$ is found by summing (or integrating) the joint p.d.f. $f(x_1, x_2)$ over all x_2 for a fixed x_1, we can think of recording this sum in the "margin" of the $x_1 x_2$ plane.   Accordingly, $f_1(x_1)$ is called the marginal p.d.f. of X_1.   In like manner

$$f_2(x_2) = \int_{-\infty}^{\infty} f(x_1, x_2) \, dx_1 \qquad \text{(continuous case)},$$

$$= \sum_{x_1} f(x_1, x_2) \qquad \text{(discrete case)},$$

is called the marginal p.d.f. of X_2.

In some instances we find that $f(x_1, x_2) = f_1(x_1) f_2(x_2)$.   Such instances are covered by the following definition.

Definition.   Let the random variables X_1 and X_2 have the joint p.d.f. $f(x_1, x_2)$ and the marginal probability density functions $f_1(x_1)$ and $f_2(x_2)$, respectively.   The random variables X_1 and X_2 are said to be stochastically independent if, and only if, $f(x_1, x_2) \equiv f_1(x_1) f_2(x_2)$.   Random variables that are not stochastically independent are said to be stochastically dependent.

Comment.   The identity in the preceding definition should be interpreted as follows.   There may be certain points (x_1, x_2) at which $f(x_1, x_2) \neq f_1(x_1) f_2(x_2)$.   However, if A is the set of points (x_1, x_2) at which equality does not hold, then $P(A) = 0$.   In a subsequent generalization of the definition of stochastic independence of two random variables, the identity should be interpreted in an analogous manner.

EXAMPLE 1.   Let the joint p.d.f. of X_1 and X_2 be
$$f(x_1, x_2) = x_1 + x_2, \quad 0 < x_1 < 1, \quad 0 < x_2 < 1,$$
$$= 0 \text{ elsewhere.}$$

It will be shown that X_1 and X_2 are stochastically dependent.   Here the marginal probability density functions are

$$f_1(x_1) = \int_{-\infty}^{\infty} f(x_1, x_2) \, dx_2 = \int_0^1 (x_1 + x_2) \, dx_2 = x_1 + \frac{1}{2}, \quad 0 < x_1 < 1,$$
$$= 0 \text{ elsewhere,}$$

and

$$f_2(x_2) = \int_{-\infty}^{\infty} f(x_1, x_2) \, dx_1 = \int_0^1 (x_1 + x_2) \, dx_1 = \frac{1}{2} + x_2, \, 0 < x_2 < 1,$$
$$= 0 \text{ elsewhere.}$$

Since $f(x_1, x_2) \neq f_1(x_1)f_2(x_2)$, the random variables X_1 and X_2 are stochastically dependent.

We now give a theorem that frequently simplifies the calculations of probabilities of events which involve stochastically independent variables.

THEOREM 1.   If X_1 and X_2 are stochastically independent random variables with marginal probability density functions $f_1(x_1)$ and $f_2(x_2)$, respectively, then

$$Pr(a < X_1 < b, c < X_2 < d) = Pr(a < X_1 < b) \, Pr(c < X_2 < d)$$

for every $a < b$ and $c < d$, where a, b, c, and d are constants.

PROOF.   From the stochastic independence of X_1 and X_2, the joint p.d.f. of X_1 and X_2 is $f_1(x_1)f_2(x_2)$. Accordingly, in the continuous case,

$$Pr(a < X_1 < b, c < X_2 < d) = \int_a^b \int_c^d f_1(x_1)f_2(x_2) \, dx_2 \, dx_1$$
$$= \left(\int_a^b f_1(x_1) \, dx_1 \right) \left(\int_c^d f_2(x_2) \, dx_2 \right)$$
$$= Pr(a < X_1 < b) Pr(c < X_2 < d);$$

or, in the discrete case,

$$Pr(a < X_1 < b, c < X_2 < d) = \sum_{a<x_1<b} \sum_{c<x_2<d} f_1(x_1)f_2(x_2)$$
$$= \left(\sum_{a<x_1<b} f_1(x_1) \right) \left(\sum_{c<x_2<d} f_2(x_2) \right)$$
$$= Pr(a < X_1 < b) Pr(c < X_2 < d)$$

as was to be shown.

EXAMPLE 2.   In Example 1, X_1 and X_2 were found to be stochastically dependent. There, in general,

$$Pr(a < X_1 < b, c < X_2 < d) \neq Pr(a < X_1 < b) \, Pr(c < X_2 < d).$$

For instance,

$$Pr\left(0 < X_1 < \frac{1}{2}, 0 < X_2 < \frac{1}{2} \right) = \int_0^{1/2} \int_0^{1/2} (x_1 + x_2) \, dx_1 \, dx_2 = \frac{1}{8}$$

whereas

$$Pr\left(0 < X_1 < \frac{1}{2} \right) = \int_0^{1/2} \left(x_1 + \frac{1}{2} \right) dx_1 = \frac{3}{8}$$

and

$$Pr\left(0 < X_2 < \frac{1}{2} \right) = \int_0^{1/2} \left(\frac{1}{2} + x_2 \right) dx_2 = \frac{3}{8}.$$

$$\frac{9}{64} > \frac{1}{8}$$

EXAMPLE 3. Let X_1 and X_2 have the joint p.d.f.
$$f(x_1, x_2) = 6x_1x_2^2, \quad 0 < x_1 < 1, \quad 0 < x_2 < 1,$$
$$= 0 \text{ elsewhere.}$$

It will be shown that X_1 and X_2 are stochastically independent. The marginal probability density functions are respectively

$$f_1(x_1) = \int_0^1 6x_1x_2^2 \, dx_2 = 2x_1, \quad 0 < x_1 < 1,$$
$$= 0 \text{ elsewhere}$$

and

$$f_2(x_2) = \int_0^1 6x_1x_2^2 \, dx_1 = 3x_2^2, \quad 0 < x_2 < 1,$$
$$= 0 \text{ elsewhere.}$$

Consequently, $f(x_1, x_2) \equiv f_1(x_1)f_2(x_2)$, and X_1 and X_2 are stochastically independent. We would then have, for instance,

$$Pr\left(\frac{1}{4} < X_1 < \frac{1}{2}, \; \frac{1}{2} < X_2 < 1\right) = Pr\left(\frac{1}{4} < X_1 < \frac{1}{2}\right)Pr\left(\frac{1}{2} < X_2 < 1\right)$$
$$= \left(\int_{1/4}^{1/2} 2x_1 \, dx_1\right)\left(\int_{1/2}^1 3x_2^2 \, dx_2\right)$$
$$= \left(\frac{3}{16}\right)\left(\frac{7}{8}\right) = \frac{21}{128}.$$

Not merely are calculations of some probabilities usually simpler when we have stochastically independent random variables, but many mathematical expectations, including certain moment-generating functions, have comparably simpler computations. The following result will prove so useful that we state it in form of a theorem.

THEOREM 2. Let the stochastically independent random variables X_1 and X_2 have the marginal probability density functions $f_1(x_1)$ and $f_2(x_2)$, respectively. The expected value of the product of a function $u(X_1)$ of X_1 alone and a function $v(X_2)$ of X_2 alone is, subject to their existence, equal to the product of the expected value of $u(X_1)$ and the expected value of $v(X_2)$; that is,

$$E[u(X_1)v(X_2)] = E[u(X_1)]E[v(X_2)].$$

PROOF. The stochastic independence of X_1 and X_2 implies that the joint p.d.f. of X_1 and X_2 is $f_1(x_1)f_2(x_2)$. Thus, we have, by definition of mathematical expectation, in the continuous case,

$$E[u(X_1)v(X_2)] = \int_{-\infty}^{\infty} \int_{-\infty}^{\infty} u(x_1)v(x_2)f_1(x_1)f_2(x_2) \, dx_1 \, dx_2$$
$$= \left(\int_{-\infty}^{\infty} u(x_1)f_1(x_1) \, dx_1\right)\left(\int_{-\infty}^{\infty} v(x_2)f_2(x_2) \, dx_2\right)$$
$$= E[u(X_1)]E[v(X_2)];$$

or, in the discrete case,

$$E[u(X_1)v(X_2)] = \sum_{x_2}\sum_{x_1} u(x_1)v(x_2)f_1(x_1)f_2(x_2)$$

$$= \left(\sum_{x_1} u(x_1)f_1(x_1)\right)\left(\sum_{x_2} v(x_2)f_2(x_2)\right)$$

$$= E[u(X_1)]E[v(X_2)],$$

as stated in the theorem.

EXAMPLE 4. In Example 3, X_1 and X_2 were found to be stochastically independent. We would then have, for instance,

$$E(X_1X_2) = E(X_1)E(X_2)$$

$$= \left(\int_0^1 x_1(2x_1)\ dx_1\right)\left(\int_0^1 x_2(3x_2^2)\ dx_2\right)$$

$$= \left(\frac{2}{3}\right)\left(\frac{3}{4}\right) = \frac{1}{2}.$$ *or this the joint mean ?*

EXAMPLE 5. Let X_1 and X_2 be any two stochastically independent random variables. Then

$$E[e^{t(X_1+X_2)}] = E(e^{tX_1}e^{tX_2}) = E(e^{tX_1})E(e^{tX_2}),$$

provided these expectations exist.

The preceding definitions and theorems can be directly generalized to the case of n random variables. Let the random variables $X_1, X_2, \cdots, X_n$ have the joint p.d.f. $f(x_1, x_2, \cdots, x_n)$. If $f_1(x_1)$ is defined by the $n-1$ fold integral (or sum)

$$f_1(x_1) = \int_{-\infty}^{\infty}\cdots\int_{-\infty}^{\infty} f(x_1, x_2, \cdots, x_n)\ dx_2\cdots dx_n \quad \text{(continuous case)},$$

$$= \sum_{x_n}\cdots\sum_{x_2} f(x_1, x_2, \cdots, x_n) \quad \text{(discrete case)},$$

then by an argument similar to the two-variable case, we have

$$Pr(a < X_1 < b) = \int_a^b f_1(x_1)\ dx_1 \quad \text{(continuous case)},$$

$$= \sum_{a<x_1<b} f_1(x_1) \quad \text{(discrete case)},$$

for every $a < b$, and accordingly $f_1(x_1)$ is the p.d.f. of the one random variable X_1 alone. It is called the marginal p.d.f. of X_1. The marginal probability density functions $f_2(x_2), \cdots, f_n(x_n)$ of $X_2, \cdots, X_n$, respectively, are similar $n-1$ fold integrals (or sums). The definition of the stochastic independence of X_1 and X_2 is generalized to the mutual stochastic independence of $X_1, X_2, \cdots, X_n$ as follows: The random variables $X_1, X_2,$

$\cdots$, X_n are said to be mutually stochastically independent if, and only if, $f(x_1, x_2, \cdots, x_n) \equiv f_1(x_1)f_2(x_2) \cdots f_n(x_n)$. It follows immediately from this definition of the mutual stochastic independence of $X_1, X_2, \cdots, X_n$ that

$$Pr(a_1 < X_1 < b_1, a_2 < X_2 < b_2, \cdots, a_n < X_n < b_n)$$

$$= Pr(a_1 < X_1 < b_1)Pr(a_2 < X_2 < b_2) \cdots Pr(a_n < X_n < b_n)$$

$$= \prod_{i=1}^{n} Pr(a_i < X_i < b_i)$$

where the symbol $\prod_{i=1}^{n} \phi(i)$ is defined to be

$$\prod_{i=1}^{n} \phi(i) = \phi(1)\phi(2) \cdots \phi(n).$$

The theorem that $E[u(X_1)v(X_2)] = E[u(X_1)]E[v(X_2)]$ for stochastically independent random variables X_1 and X_2 becomes, for mutually stochastically independent random variables $X_1, X_2, \cdots, X_n$,

$$E[u_1(X_1)u_2(X_2) \cdots u_n(X_n)] = E[u_1(X_1)]E[u_2(X_2)] \cdots E[u_n(X_n)],$$

or

$$E\left[\prod_{i=1}^{n} u_i(X_i) \right] = \prod_{i=1}^{n} E[u_i(X_i)].$$

In particular, for these mutually stochastically independent random variables $X_1, X_2, \cdots, X_n$, we have

$$E[e^{t(X_1+X_2+ \cdots +X_n)}] = E(e^{tX_1}e^{tX_2} \cdots e^{tX_n})$$

$$= E(e^{tX_1})E(e^{tX_2}) \cdots E(e^{tX_n}),$$

provided these expectations exist.

Exercises

3.1. Show that the random variables X_1 and X_2 with joint p.d.f. $f(x_1, x_2) = 12x_1x_2(1 - x_2)$, $0 < x_1 < 1$, $0 < x_2 < 1$, zero elsewhere, are stochastically independent.

3.2. If the random variables X_1 and X_2 have the joint p.d.f. $f(x_1, x_2) = 2e^{-x_1-x_2}$; $0 < x_1 < x_2$, $0 < x_2 < \infty$, zero elsewhere, show that X_1 and X_2 are stochastically dependent.

3.3. Let $f(x_1, x_2) = 1/16$, $x_1 = 1, 2, 3, 4$, and $x_2 = 1, 2, 3, 4$, zero elsewhere, be the joint p.d.f. of X_1 and X_2. Show that X_1 and X_2 are stochastically independent.

3.4. Find $Pr(0 < X_1 < \frac{1}{3}, 0 < X_2 < \frac{1}{3})$ if the random variables X_1 and X_2 have the joint p.d.f. $f(x_1, x_2) = 4x_1(1 - x_2)$, $0 < x_1 < 1$, $0 < x_2 < 1$, zero elsewhere.

3.5. Find the probability of the union of the events $a < X_1 < b$, $-\infty < X_2 < \infty$ and $-\infty < X_1 < \infty$, $c < X_2 < d$ if X_1 and X_2 are two stochastically independent variables with $Pr(a < X_1 < b) = \frac{2}{3}$ and $Pr(c < X_2 < d) = \frac{5}{8}$.

$\circ K$

3.6. If $f(x_1, x_2) = e^{-x_1 - x_2}$, $0 < x_1 < \infty$, $0 < x_2 < \infty$, zero elsewhere, is the joint p.d.f. of the random variables X_1 and X_2, show that X_1 and X_2 are stochastically independent and that

$$E[e^{t(X_1 + X_2)}] = (1 - t)^{-2}, \quad t < 1.$$

3.7. Given that

$$f(x_1, x_2) = \frac{1}{2\pi\sqrt{1 - \rho^2}} e^{-\frac{1}{2(1-\rho^2)}(x_1{}^2 - 2\rho x_1 x_2 + x_2{}^2)}, \quad -\infty < x_1 < \infty, \quad -\infty < x_2 < \infty,$$

is the joint p.d.f. of two continuous-type random variables X_1 and X_2, provided $-1 < \rho < 1$. Find the marginal probability density functions $f_1(x_1)$ and $f_2(x_2)$, and show that in general X_1 and X_2 are stochastically dependent. Determine when, and only when, X_1 and X_2 are stochastically independent. Find the mean values μ_1, μ_2 and variances $\sigma_1{}^2$, $\sigma_2{}^2$ of X_1 and X_2, respectively. Compute

$$E\left[\left(\frac{X_1 - \mu_1}{\sigma_1}\right)\left(\frac{X_2 - \mu_2}{\sigma_2}\right)\right].$$

3.2. Linear Functions of Stochastically Independent Random Variables.

This section will consist of a number of examples which are intended to illustrate the nature of the problem (and methods of solving the problem) of finding the distribution of functions of random variables. In the interest of simplicity, we shall here restrict ourselves to linear functions.

EXAMPLE 1. Let the stochastically independent random variables X_1 and X_2 have the same p.d.f.

$$f(x) = \frac{x}{6}, \quad x = 1, 2, 3$$

$$= 0 \text{ elsewhere};$$

that is, the p.d.f. of X_1 is $f(x_1)$ and that of X_2 is $f(x_2)$; and so the joint p.d.f. of X_1 and X_2 is

$$f(x_1)f(x_2) = \frac{x_1 x_2}{36}, \quad x_1 = 1, 2, 3, \quad x_2 = 1, 2, 3$$

$$= 0 \text{ elsewhere}.$$

A probability, such as $Pr(X_1 = 2, X_2 = 3)$, can be seen immediately to be $(2)(3)/36 = 1/6$. However, consider a probability such as $Pr(X_1 + X_2 = 3)$. The computation can be made by first observing that the event $X_1 + X_2 = 3$ is the union, exclusive of the events with probability zero, of the two mutually exclusive events $(X_1 = 1, X_2 = 2)$ and $(X_1 = 2, X_2 = 1)$. Thus

$$Pr(X_1 + X_2 = 3) = Pr(X_1 = 1, X_2 = 2) + Pr(X_1 = 2, X_2 = 1)$$

$$= \frac{(1)(2)}{36} + \frac{(2)(1)}{36} = \frac{4}{36}.$$

More generally, let y represent any of the numbers 2, 3, 4, 5, 6. The probability of each of the events $X_1 + X_2 = y$, $y = 2, 3, 4, 5, 6$, can be computed as in the case $y = 3$. Let $g(y) = Pr(X_1 + X_2 = y)$. Then the table

y	2	3	4	5	6
$g(y)$	$\dfrac{1}{36}$	$\dfrac{4}{36}$	$\dfrac{10}{36}$	$\dfrac{12}{36}$	$\dfrac{9}{36}$

gives the values of $g(y)$ for $y = 2, 3, 4, 5, 6$. For all other values of y, $g(y) = 0$. What we have actually done is to define a new random variable Y by $Y = X_1 + X_2$, and we have found the p.d.f. $g(y)$ of this random variable Y. We shall now solve the same problem, but by another technique.

To this end it should be recalled that if X is a random variable of the discrete type having p.d.f. $f(x) \neq 0$, $x = a_1, a_2, \cdots$, and $f(x) = 0$ elsewhere, the moment-generating function of X is

$$M_X(t) = \sum_x e^{tx} f(x) = f(a_1)e^{ta_1} + f(a_2)e^{ta_2} + \cdots$$

Conversely, if the moment-generating function of a random variable X is of the form

$$M_X(t) = k_1 e^{tb_1} + k_2 e^{tb_2} + \cdots,$$

then X is of the discrete type and has the p.d.f.

$$f(x) = k_i, \quad x = b_i,$$
$$= 0 \text{ elsewhere.}$$

This suggests that we can first find the moment-generating function of $Y = X_1 + X_2$ and let this result tell us what the p.d.f. $g(y)$ of Y is. Now the moment-generating function of Y is

$$M_Y(t) = E[e^{t(X_1 + X_2)}]$$
$$= E(e^{tX_1} e^{tX_2})$$
$$= E(e^{tX_1})E(e^{tX_2})$$

since X_1 and X_2 are stochastically independent. In this example X_1 and X_2 have the same distribution, so they have the same moment-generating function; that is,

$$E(e^{tX_1}) = E(e^{tX_2}) = \frac{1}{6}e^t + \frac{2}{6}e^{2t} + \frac{3}{6}e^{3t}.$$

Thus

$$M_Y(t) = \left(\frac{1}{6}e^t + \frac{2}{6}e^{2t} + \frac{3}{6}e^{3t}\right)^2$$

$$= \frac{1}{36}e^{2t} + \frac{4}{36}e^{3t} + \frac{10}{36}e^{4t} + \frac{12}{36}e^{5t} + \frac{9}{36}e^{6t}.$$

This form of $M_Y(t)$ tells us immediately that the p.d.f. $g(y)$ of Y is zero except at $y = 2, 3, 4, 5, 6$, and that $g(y)$ assumes the values 1/36, 4/36, 10/36, 12/36, 9/36, respectively, at these points where $g(y) > 0$. This is, of course, the same result that was obtained in the first solution. There appears here to be little, if any, preference for one solution over the other. But in more complicated situations, and particularly with random variables of the continuous type, the moment-generating function technique can prove very powerful.

EXAMPLE 2. Let X_1 and X_2 be stochastically independent with normal distributions $n(x_1; \mu_1, \sigma_1^2)$ and $n(x_2; \mu_2, \sigma_2^2)$, respectively. Define the random variable Y by $Y = X_1 - X_2$. The problem is to find $g(y)$, the p.d.f. of Y. This will be done by first finding the moment-generating function of Y. Here

$$M_Y(t) = E[e^{t(X_1 - X_2)}]$$

$$= E[e^{tX_1} e^{-tX_2}]$$

$$= E(e^{tX_1})E(e^{-tX_2}),$$

since X_1 and X_2 are stochastically independent. It is known that

$$E(e^{tX_1}) = e^{\mu_1 t + \frac{\sigma_1^2 t^2}{2}}$$

and that

$$E(e^{tX_2}) = e^{\mu_2 t + \frac{\sigma_2^2 t^2}{2}}$$

for all real t. Then $E(e^{-tX_2})$ can be obtained from $E(e^{tX_2})$ by replacing t by $-t$. That is,

$$E(e^{-tX_2}) = e^{-\mu_2 t + \frac{\sigma_2^2 t^2}{2}}.$$

Finally then,

$$M_Y(t) = \left(e^{\mu_1 t + \frac{\sigma_1^2 t^2}{2}}\right)\left(e^{-\mu_2 t + \frac{\sigma_2^2 t^2}{2}}\right)$$

$$= e^{(\mu_1 - \mu_2)t + \frac{(\sigma_1^2 + \sigma_2^2)t^2}{2}}.$$

The distribution of Y is completely determined by its moment-generating function $M_Y(t)$, and it is seen that Y has the p.d.f. $g(y)$ which is $n(y; \mu_1 - \mu_2, \sigma_1^2 + \sigma_2^2)$. That is, the difference between two stochastically independent, normally distributed, random variables is itself a random variable that is normally distributed with mean equal to the difference of the means (in the order indicated) and the variance equal to the sum of the variances.

EXAMPLE 3. Let the random variable Y be the sum of two stochastically independent random variables X_1 and X_2 which have chi-square distributions with r_1 and r_2 degrees of freedom, respectively. It will be shown that Y has itself a chi-square distribution with $r = r_1 + r_2$ degrees of freedom. The moment-generating function technique will be used. It is known that

$$E(e^{tX_1}) = (1 - 2t)^{-\frac{r_1}{2}}, \quad t < \frac{1}{2},$$

and that

$$E(e^{tX_2}) = (1 - 2t)^{-\frac{r_2}{2}}, \quad t < \frac{1}{2}.$$

Now

$$M_Y(t) = E[e^{t(X_1 + X_2)}]$$

$$= E(e^{tX_1})E(e^{tX_2})$$

$$= (1 - 2t)^{-\frac{r_1 + r_2}{2}}, \quad t < \frac{1}{2},$$

which is the moment-generating function of a chi-square distribution with $r_1 + r_2$ degrees of freedom. Accordingly, Y has this chi-square distribution. The reader should extend this proposition to the sum of n mutually stochastically independent chi-square variables.

EXAMPLE 4. Let each of the mutually stochastically independent random variables $X_1, X_2, \cdots, X_n$ have the same p.d.f.

$$f(x) = p^x(1 - p)^{1-x}, \quad x = 0, 1, \quad 0 < p < 1,$$
$$= 0 \text{ elsewhere.}$$

Then

$$E(e^{tX_1}) = E(e^{tX_2}) = \cdots = E(e^{tX_n}) = (1 - p) + pe^t.$$

Let the random variable Y be defined by $Y = X_1 + X_2 + \cdots + X_n$. The moment-generating function of Y is

$$M_Y(t) = E[e^{t(X_1 + X_2 + \cdots + X_n)}]$$

$$= E(e^{tX_1})E(e^{tX_2}) \cdots E(e^{tX_n})$$

$$= [(1 - p) + pe^t]^n.$$

But this is the moment-generating function of a binomial distribution with parameters n and p. Thus, the p.d.f. of Y is

$$g(y) = \frac{n!}{y!(n - y)!}p^y(1 - p)^{n-y}, \quad y = 0, 1, 2, \cdots, n,$$
$$= 0 \text{ elsewhere.}$$

This result can be given a concrete interpretation which shows why a binomial distribution is an important distribution. The interpretation is as follows: A random experiment is to be repeated n independent times, and on each repetition the experiment will terminate in one of two mutually exclusive ways, say, success or failure. Assume further that the probability of success, say, p, is the same on each repetition of the experiment; so, of course, the probability of failure on each repetition is $1 - p$. Let the random variable X_i represent the outcome of the ith independent repetition of the random experiment, where $i = 1, 2, \cdots, n$. Now X_i can be either a success, which we now denote by $X_i = 1$, or a failure, denoted by $X_i = 0$. Since $Pr(X_i = 1) = p$ and $Pr(X_i = 0) = 1 - p$, each X_i has the p.d.f. $f(x)$ of this example, and it has been assumed that the experiment is to be repeated n independent times so the X_i are mutually stochastically independent. According to the definition of X_i, the sum $Y = X_1 + X_2 + \cdots + X_n$ is the number of successes throughout the n repetitions of the random experiment. Thus, under the conditions stated, the number Y of successes has a binomial distribution with parameters n and p.

EXAMPLE 5.   Let $X_1, X_2, \cdots, X_n$ denote n mutually stochastically independent random variables having respectively the marginal probability density functions $f_1(x_1), f_2(x_2), \cdots, f_n(x_n)$.   Further, let the moment-generating functions

$$M_{X_i}(t) = E(e^{tX_i}), \quad i = 1, 2, \cdots, n$$

exist, and let

$$\mu_i = E(X_i), \quad \sigma_i^2 = E[(X_i - \mu_i)^2], \quad i = 1, 2, \cdots, n.$$

Define the random variable Y by $Y = k_1X_1 + k_2X_2 + \cdots + k_nX_n$, where $k_1, k_2, \cdots, k_n$ are real constants, not all zero, to avoid a trivial case.   In numerous instances it is quite difficult to find $g(y)$, the p.d.f. of Y.   It is the purpose of this example to point out that even though $g(y)$ is not immediately available, we always have

$$E\,[k_1\,X_1 + \cdots + k_n\,X_n]$$

(i) $$\mu_Y = E(Y) = k_1\mu_1 + k_2\mu_2 + \cdots + k_n\mu_n = \sum_1^n k_i\mu_i;$$

$$E(k_1 X_1) = k_1\,E(X_1) = k_1\mu_1.$$

(ii) $$\sigma_Y^2 = E[(Y - \mu_Y)^2] = k_1^2\sigma_1^2 + k_2^2\sigma_2^2 + \cdots + k_n^2\sigma_n^2 = \sum_1^n k_i^2\sigma_i^2;$$

(iii) $$M_Y(t) = E[e^{t(k_1X_1 + k_2X_2 + \cdots + k_nX_n)}]$$

$$= M_{X_1}(k_1t)M_{X_2}(k_2t) \cdots M_{X_n}(k_nt)$$

$$= \prod_{i=1}^n M_{X_i}(k_it).$$

The relation (i) follows from

$$\mu_Y = E(k_1X_1 + k_2X_2 + \cdots + k_nX_n)$$
$$= k_1E(X_1) + k_2E(X_2) + \cdots + k_nE(X_n),$$

since E is a linear operator.   That is,

$$\mu_Y = \sum_1^n k_i\mu_i$$

since $\mu_i = E(X_i)$, $i = 1, 2, \cdots, n$.   The variance of Y is given by

$$\sigma_Y^2 = E\{[(k_1X_1 + k_2X_2 + \cdots + k_nX_n) - (k_1\mu_1 + k_2\mu_2 + \cdots + k_n\mu_n)]^2\}$$
$$= E\{[k_1(X_1 - \mu_1) + k_2(X_2 - \mu_2) + \cdots + k_n(X_n - \mu_n)]^2\}$$
$$= E\{k_1^2(X_1 - \mu_1)^2 + k_2^2(X_2 - \mu_2)^2 + \cdots + k_n^2(X_n - \mu_n)^2$$
$$+ 2k_1k_2(X_1 - \mu_1)(X_2 - \mu_2) + \cdots + 2k_{n-1}k_n(X_{n-1} - \mu_{n-1})(X_n - \mu_n)\}$$
$$= \sum_{i=1}^n k_i^2 E[(X_i - \mu_i)^2] + 2\sum_{i<j}\sum k_ik_j E[(X_i - \mu_i)(X_j - \mu_j)].$$

Consider $E[(X_i - \mu_i)(X_j - \mu_j)]$, $i \neq j$.   Since X_i and X_j are stochastically independent,

$$E[(X_i - \mu_i)(X_j - \mu_j)] = E(X_i - \mu_i)E(X_j - \mu_j).$$

But

$$E(X_i - \mu_i) = E(X_i) - \mu_i = 0.$$

Hence

$$2\sum_{i<j}\sum k_ik_j E[(X_i - \mu_i)(X_j - \mu_j)] = 0,$$

and

$$\sigma_Y^2 = \sum_{i=1}^{n} k_i^2 E[(X_i - \mu_i)^2] = \sum_1^n k_i^2 \sigma_i^2$$

as stated in relation (ii). That $M_Y(t)$ is as given in relation (iii) follows from

$$M_Y(t) = E[e^{t(k_1 X_1 + k_2 X_2 + \cdots + k_n X_n)}]$$

$$= E(e^{tk_1 X_1}) E(e^{tk_2 X_2}) \cdots E(e^{tk_n X_n}),$$

since $X_1, X_2, \cdots, X_n$ are mutually stochastically independent. Now

$$E(e^{tX_i}) = M_{X_i}(t);$$

so

$$E(e^{tk_i X_i}) = M_{X_i}(k_i t).$$

Thus

$$M_Y(t) = \prod_{i=1}^{n} M_{X_i}(k_i t)$$

as stated.

Some very useful results are obtained if we make the following modification in the assumptions of this example: Let the n mutually stochastically independent random variables $X_1, X_2, \cdots, X_n$ have the same p.d.f. $f(x)$. In the notation of this example we now have, for $i = 1, 2, \cdots, n$, $f_i(x_i) = f(x_i)$; $M_{X_i}(t) = M_X(t)$, say; $\mu_i = \mu$, say; and $\sigma_i^2 = \sigma^2$, say. For this special case, relations (i), (ii), and (iii) then become

(i)′ $$\mu_Y = \left(\sum_1^n k_i \right) \mu;$$

(ii)′ $$\sigma_Y^2 = \left(\sum_1^n k_i^2 \right) \sigma^2;$$

(iii)′ $$M_Y(t) = \prod_{i=1}^{n} M_X(k_i t).$$

These special results are useful in the next section.

Exercises

3.8. Let the stochastically independent random variables X_1 and X_2 have the same p.d.f. $f(x) = 1/6$, $x = 1, 2, 3, 4, 5, 6$, zero elsewhere. Find the p.d.f. of $Y = X_1 + X_2$. Note, under appropriate assumptions, that Y may be interpreted as the sum of the spots which appear when two dice are cast.

3.9. Let X_1 and X_2 be stochastically independent with normal distributions $n(x_i; \mu_i, \sigma_i^2)$, $i = 1, 2$. Show that $Y = k_1 X_1 + k_2 X_2$ is $n(y; k_1\mu_1 + k_2\mu_2, k_1^2\sigma_1^2 + k_2^2\sigma_2^2)$.

3.10. Let X_1 and X_2 be stochastically independent with normal distributions $n(x_1; 6, 1)$ and $n(x_2; 7, 1)$, respectively. Find $Pr(X_1 > X_2)$. Hint: Write $Pr(X_1 > X_2) = Pr(X_1 - X_2 > 0)$ and determine the distribution of $X_1 - X_2$.

3.11. Let X have the p.d.f. $f(x)$, the moment-generating function $M_X(t)$, the mean μ, and the variance σ^2. If the random variable $Y = aX + b$, show that $\mu_Y = a\mu + b$, $\sigma_Y^2 = a^2\sigma^2$, and $M_Y(t) = e^{bt}M_X(at)$.

3.12. Let X_1 and X_2 be stochastically independent random variables. Let X_1 and $Y = X_1 + X_2$ have chi-square distributions with r_1 and r degrees of freedom, respectively. Here $r_1 < r$. Show that X_2 has a chi-square distribution with $r - r_1$ degrees of freedom. Hint: Write $M_Y(t) = E[e^{t(X_1+X_2)}]$ and make use of the stochastic independence of X_1 and X_2.

3.13. Let Y be the sum of n mutually stochastically independent chi-square variables $X_1, X_2, \cdots, X_n$ with $r_1, r_2, \cdots, r_n$ degrees of freedom, respectively. Show that Y has a chi-square distribution with $r_1 + r_2 + \cdots + r_n$ degrees of freedom.

3.14. Let the mutually stochastically independent random variables X_1, X_2, X_3 have the same p.d.f. $f(x) = 3x^2$, $0 < x < 1$, zero elsewhere. Find the probability that exactly two of these three variables exceed $\frac{1}{2}$.

3.15. Let Y be the number of successes in n independent repetitions of a random experiment having the probability of success $p = 2/3$. If $n = 3$, compute $Pr(2 \leq Y)$; if $n = 5$, compute $Pr(3 \leq Y)$.

3.16. Let Y be the number of successes throughout n independent repetitions of a random experiment having probability of success $p = \frac{1}{4}$. Determine the smallest value of n so that $Pr(1 \leq Y) \geq 0.70$.

3.17. Let the stochastically independent random variables X_1 and X_2 have binomial distributions with parameters $n_1 = 3$, $p_1 = \frac{2}{3}$ and $n_2 = 4$, $p_2 = \frac{1}{2}$, respectively. Compute $Pr(X_1 = X_2)$.

3.18. Let X_1, X_2, X_3, X_4 be four mutually stochastically independent random variables having the same p.d.f. $f(x) = 2x$, $0 < x < 1$, zero elsewhere. Find the mean and variance of the sum Y of these four random variables.

3.19. Let X_1 and X_2 be two stochastically independent random variables so that the variances of X_1 and X_2 are $\sigma_1^2 = k$ and $\sigma_2^2 = 2$, respectively. Given that the variance of $Y = 3X_2 - X_1$ is 25, find k.

3.20. If the stochastically independent variables X_1 and X_2 have means μ_1, μ_2 and variances σ_1^2, σ_2^2, respectively, show that the mean and variance of the product $Y = X_1 X_2$ are $\mu_1\mu_2$ and $\sigma_1^2\sigma_2^2 + \mu_1^2\sigma_2^2 + \mu_2^2\sigma_1^2$, respectively.

3.21. Let the stochastically independent random variables X_1 and X_2 have binomial distributions with parameters $n_1, p_1 = \frac{1}{2}$ and $n_2, p_2 = \frac{1}{2}$, respectively. Show that $Y = X_1 - X_2 + n_2$ has a binomial distribution with parameters $n = n_1 + n_2, p = \frac{1}{2}$.

3.22. Let the stochastically independent random variables X_1 and X_2 have chi-square distributions with r_1 and r_2 degrees of freedom, respectively. Define the random variable Y by $Y = k_1 X_1 + k_2 X_2$, where k_1 and k_2 are real constants not equal to zero. When, and only when, will Y have a chi-square distribution?

3.3. Random Sampling. In the preceding section, the notion of finding the p.d.f. of a function of several mutually stochastically independent random variables $X_1, X_2, \cdots, X_n$ was introduced by examples. One aspect of this problem is called _random sampling distribution theory._ We shall first discuss the concept of a random sample.

In many situations confronting us, the distribution of the outcome X of a random experiment is not completely known. For instance, we may know the distribution except for the value of an unknown parameter. To obtain more information about this distribution (or the unknown parameter), we shall repeat under identical conditions the random experiment n independent times. Let the outcome of these n repetitions be denoted respectively by the random variables $X_1, X_2, \cdots, X_n$. Then we call $X_1, X_2, \cdots, X_n$ the items of a random sample from the distribution under consideration.

Comments. Let it be assumed that the diameter X of a hole to be drilled by a certain drill press is a random variable that has a normal distribution. Past experience with many drill presses makes this assumption plausible; but the assumption does not specify the mean μ nor the variance σ^2 of this normal distribution. The only way to obtain information about μ and σ^2 is to have recourse to experimentation. Thus we shall drill a number, say, $n = 20$, of these holes whose diameters will be $X_1, X_2, \cdots, X_{20}$. Then $X_1, X_2, \cdots, X_{20}$ is a random sample from the normal distribution under consideration. Once the holes have been drilled and the diameters measured, the 20 numbers may be used, as will be seen later, to elicit information about μ and σ^2.

The term random sample is now defined in a more formal manner.

Definition 1. Let $X_1, X_2, \cdots, X_n$ denote n mutually stochastically independent random variables, each of which has the same but possibly unknown p.d.f. $f(x)$; that is, the probability density functions of $X_1, X_2, \cdots, X_n$ are respectively $f_1(x_1) = f(x_1)$, $f_2(x_2) = f(x_2)$, $\cdots, f_n(x_n) = f(x_n)$, so that the joint p.d.f. is $f(x_1) f(x_2) \cdots f(x_n)$. The random variables $X_1, X_2, \cdots, X_n$ are then said to constitute a *random sample* from a distribution having p.d.f. $f(x)$.

Sometimes it is convenient to refer to a random sample of size n from a given distribution and, as has been remarked, to refer to $X_1, X_2, \cdots, X_n$ as the items of the random sample. A re-examination of Examples 1 and 4 and the latter part of 5 of the preceding section will reveal that the notion of a random sample from a given distribution was actually introduced there. In Example 1 we had under consideration a random sample of size $n = 2$ from a distribution having p.d.f.

$$f(x) = \frac{x}{6}, \quad x = 1,2,3,$$
$$= 0 \text{ elsewhere.}$$

In Example 4 we considered a random sample $X_1, X_2, \cdots, X_n$ from a distribution having p.d.f.

$$f(x) = p^x(1 - p)^{1-x}, \quad x = 0, 1, \quad 0 < p < 1,$$
$$= 0 \text{ elsewhere.}$$

And in the latter part of Example 5 we considered a random sample $X_1, X_2, \cdots, X_n$ from an arbitrary distribution having mean μ, variance σ^2, and moment-generating function $M_X(t)$.   In the first of these examples the p.d.f. of the random variable $Y = X_1 + X_2$ was obtained; here Y is the sum of the two items of the random sample.   In Example 4 we found the p.d.f. of the sum $Y = X_1 + X_2 + \cdots + X_n$ of the n items of the random sample.   And in the latter part of Example 5 we investigated some of the properties of the distribution of an arbitrary linear function $Y = k_1X_1 + k_2X_2 + \cdots + k_nX_n$ of the n items of the random sample.

Random sampling distribution theory means the general problem of finding distributions of functions of the items $X_1, X_2, \cdots, X_n$ of a random sample from a given distribution having p.d.f. $f(x)$.   Certain functions of the items of a random sample are given a special name, as indicated by the following definition.

Definition 2.   Let $X_1, X_2, \cdots, X_n$ denote a random sample from a given distribution.   Let $Y = u(X_1, X_2, \cdots, X_n)$ denote a function of $X_1, X_2, \cdots, X_n$ alone.   Then the random variable $Y = u(X_1, X_2, \cdots, X_n)$ is called a *statistic*.

In this definition the word "alone" requires that a statistic be a function of $X_1, X_2, \cdots, X_n$ that does not depend upon an unknown parameter. The point to emphasize is that once the random experiment has been performed n times, and it has been found that $X_1 = x_1, X_2 = x_2, \cdots, X_n = x_n$, then $y = u(x_1, x_2, \cdots, x_n)$ is a known number.   For example, suppose $X_1, X_2, \cdots, X_n$ is a random sample from some normal distribution $n(x; \mu, 1)$. Then each of $Y = (X_1 + X_2 + \cdots + X_n)/n$ and $Z = Y - \mu$ is a random variable and has its own p.d.f.   But Y is a statistic, whereas Z is not a statistic unless the value of μ is a known constant.   We next define two important statistics.

Definition 3.   Let $X_1, X_2, \cdots, X_n$ denote a random sample from a given distribution.   The statistic

$$\bar{X} = \frac{1}{n}(X_1 + X_2 + \cdots + X_n) = \frac{1}{n}\sum_1^n X_i$$

is called the *mean* of the random sample, and the statistic

$$S^2 = \frac{1}{n}\sum_1^n (X_i - \bar{X})^2 = \frac{1}{n}\sum_1^n X_i^2 - \bar{X}^2$$

is called the *variance* of the random sample.

Much of random sampling distribution theory is devoted to finding the distributions of various statistics.   If the random sample is from any distribution having a mean μ and a variance σ^2, it follows from relations, (i)' and (ii)', page 52, upon setting $k_1 = k_2 = \cdots = k_n = 1/n$, that the distribution of $\bar{X}$ has mean μ and variance σ^2/n.

In this section we shall find the p.d.f. of the statistic $\bar{X}$ when the random sample is from a normal distribution $n(x; \mu, \sigma^2)$.   The distribution of the statistic S^2 for this random sample will be obtained in Chapter Six. We shall use the results of the latter part of Example 5, page 52, to obtain the p.d.f. of $\bar{X}$. In that example, take $X_1, X_2, \cdots, X_n$ to be a random sample from a distribution that is $n(x; \mu, \sigma^2)$, and take $k_1 = k_2 = \cdots = k_n = 1/n$. Then

$$Y = \frac{1}{n}(X_1 + X_2 + \cdots + X_n) = \bar{X}.$$

By relation (iii)' of that example,

$$M_Y(t) = M_{\bar{x}}(t) = \left[M_X\left(\frac{t}{n}\right) \right]^n.$$

$E\{e^{yt}\} = E\{e^{\frac{1}{n}(X_1 + \cdots + X_n)t}\}$

Since X is $n(x; \mu, \sigma^2)$, we have

$$M_X(t) = e^{\mu t + \frac{\sigma^2 t^2}{2}}.$$

$E\{e^{\frac{1}{n}X_1 t}\} \cdots E\{e^{\frac{1}{n}X_n t}\}$

Accordingly,

$$M_{\bar{x}}(t) = \left[e^{\mu\left(\frac{t}{n}\right) + \frac{\sigma^2\left(\frac{t}{n}\right)^2}{2}} \right]^n$$

$$= e^{\mu t + \frac{\left(\frac{\sigma^2}{n}\right)t^2}{2}}.$$

This shows that the statistic $\bar{X}$ is $n(\bar{x}; \mu, \sigma^2/n)$. This important result may be summarized as follows:

THEOREM. Let $X_1, X_2, \cdots, X_n$ denote a random sample from a normal distribution with mean μ and variance σ^2. The statistic $\bar{X}$ has a normal distribution with mean μ and variance σ^2/n.

It may be observed that the information from relations (i)' and (ii)' of the Example 5 cited is contained in relation (iii)', as would be expected.

As an example of the theorem, let $\bar{X}$ be the mean of a random sample of size 25 from a distribution that is $n(x; 75, 100)$. Thus $\bar{X}$ is $n(\bar{x}; 75, 4)$. Then, for instance,

$$Pr(71 < \bar{X} < 79) = N\left(\frac{79 - 75}{2}\right) - N\left(\frac{71 - 75}{2}\right)$$
$$= N(2) - N(-2) = 0.954.$$

Exercises

3.23. Show that
$$S^2 = \frac{1}{n}\sum_1^n (X_i - \bar{X})^2 = \frac{1}{n}\sum_1^n X_i^2 - \bar{X}^2,$$
where $\bar{X} = \sum_1^n X_i/n$.

3.24. If a random experiment has been performed five times and it has been found that $X_1 = 2.1$, $X_2 = 2.5$, $X_3 = 2.2$, $X_4 = 2.5$, $X_5 = 2.7$, compute the mean $\bar{x}$ and variance s^2 of this sample.

3.25. Find the probability that exactly four items of a random sample of size 5 from the distribution having p.d.f. $f(x) = (x + 1)/2$, $-1 < x < 1$, zero elsewhere, exceed zero.

3.26. Let X_1, X_2, X_3 be a random sample of size 3 from a normal distribution $n(x; 6, 4)$. Determine the probability that the largest sample item exceeds 8.

3.27. Show that the moment-generating function of the sum Y of the items of a random sample of size n from a distribution having p.d.f. $f(x) = e^{-x}, 0 < x < \infty$, zero elsewhere, is $(1 - t)^{-n}$, $t < 1$. Find the mean and variance of Y.

3.28. Find the mean and variance of the sum Y of the items of a random sample of size 5 from the distribution having p.d.f. $f(x) = 6x(1 - x)$, $0 < x < 1$, zero elsewhere.

3.29. Determine the mean and variance of the mean $\bar{X}$ of a random sample of size 9 from a distribution having p.d.f. $f(x) = 4x^3$, $0 < x < 1$, zero elsewhere.

3.30. Let X_1, X_2 be a random sample from the distribution having p.d.f. $f(x) = 2x, 0 < x < 1$, zero elsewhere. Find $Pr(X_1/X_2 \leq \frac{1}{2})$.

3.31. Find the moment-generating function of the sum Y of the items of a random sample of size 4 from the Poisson distribution with $\mu = 1$. Use this result to find $Pr(Y = 2)$.

3.32. Let $\bar{X}$ be the mean of a random sample of size 5 from a normal distribution with $\mu = 0$ and $\sigma^2 = 125$. Determine c so that $Pr(\bar{X} < c) = 0.90$.

3.33. If $\bar{X}$ is the mean of a random sample of size n from a normal distribution with mean μ and variance 100, find n so that $Pr(\mu - 5 < \bar{X} < \mu + 5) = 0.954$.

3.34. Let X_1, X_2, $\cdots$, X_{25} and Y_1, Y_2, $\cdots$, Y_{25} be two random samples from two independent normal distributions $n(x; 0, 16)$ and $n(y; 1, 9)$, respectively. Let $\bar{X}$ and $\bar{Y}$ denote the corresponding sample means. Compute $Pr(\bar{X} > \bar{Y})$.

3.4. An Example of Statistical Inference.

In the introductory remarks to Chapter One, a reference was made to statistical inference. We are now in position to give an example of the meaning of this expression. Our illustration will be that of finding a *confidence interval* for an unknown parameter in a p.d.f.

Suppose we are willing to accept as a fact that the outcome X of a random experiment is a random variable that has a normal distribution with known variance σ^2 but unknown mean μ. That is, μ is some constant, but its value is unknown. To elicit some information about μ, we decide to repeat the random experiment n independent times, n being a fixed positive integer, and under identical conditions. Let the random variables X_1, X_2, $\cdots$, X_n denote respectively the outcome to be obtained on each of these n repetitions of the experiment. If our assumptions are fulfilled, we then have under consideration a random sample X_1, X_2, $\cdots$, X_n from a distribution that is $n(x; \mu, \sigma^2)$, σ^2 known. Consider the statistic $\bar{X}$ $= \left(\sum_{1}^{n} X_i \right)/n$. The p.d.f. of $\bar{X}$ has been seen to be $n(\bar{x}; \mu, \sigma^2/n)$. On page 34 it was found that the deviation of a normal random variable from its mean, divided by its standard deviation, is itself normal with zero mean and unit variance. Thus

$$\frac{\bar{X} - \mu}{\frac{\sigma}{\sqrt{n}}}$$

is normally distributed with mean zero and variance one, regardless of the values of μ and σ^2. From the tables of the normal distribution, Table I, the probability that such a normal variable is between -2 and $+2$ is 0.954. Thus we write

$$Pr\left(-2 < \frac{\bar{X} - \mu}{\frac{\sigma}{\sqrt{n}}} < 2\right) = 0.954.$$

The inequalities

$$-2 < \frac{\bar{X} - \mu}{\frac{\sigma}{\sqrt{n}}} < 2 \quad \text{and} \quad \bar{X} - \frac{2\sigma}{\sqrt{n}} < \mu < \bar{X} + \frac{2\sigma}{\sqrt{n}}$$

are equivalent in the sense that the first set is satisfied when, and only when, the latter set is satisfied. Thus the events

$$-2 < \frac{\bar{X} - \mu}{\frac{\sigma}{\sqrt{n}}} < 2 \quad \text{and} \quad \bar{X} - \frac{2\sigma}{\sqrt{n}} < \mu < \bar{X} + \frac{2\sigma}{\sqrt{n}}$$

are equivalent and have the same probability. That is,

$$Pr\left(\bar{X} - \frac{2\sigma}{\sqrt{n}} < \mu < \bar{X} + \frac{2\sigma}{\sqrt{n}}\right) = 0.954.$$

Since σ is a known number, each of the random variables $\bar{X} - (2\sigma/\sqrt{n})$ and $\bar{X} + (2\sigma/\sqrt{n})$ is a statistic. The interval $[\bar{X} - (2\sigma/\sqrt{n}), \bar{X} + (2\sigma/\sqrt{n})]$ is called a random interval: that is, an interval at least one of whose endpoints is a random variable. In this case both end points of the interval are random variables (here, statistics). The immediately preceding probability statement can be read: Prior to the repeated independent performances of the random experiment, the probability is (approximately) 0.95 that the random interval $[\bar{X} - (2\sigma/\sqrt{n}), \bar{X} + (2\sigma/\sqrt{n})]$ includes the unknown fixed point (parameter) μ.

Up to this point, only probability has been involved; the determination of the p.d.f. of $\bar{X}$ and the determination of the random interval were problems of probability. Now the problem becomes statistical. Suppose the experiment yields $X_1 = x_1, X_2 = x_2, \cdots, X_n = x_n$. Then the sample value of $\bar{X}$ is $\bar{x} = (x_1 + x_2 + \cdots + x_n)/n$, a known number.   Moreover, since σ is known, the interval $[\bar{x} - (2\sigma/\sqrt{n}), \bar{x} + (2\sigma/\sqrt{n})]$ has known end points.   Obviously we cannot say that 0.95 is the probability that the particular interval $[\bar{x} - (2\sigma/\sqrt{n}), \bar{x} + (2\sigma/\sqrt{n})]$ includes the parameter μ, for μ, although unknown, is some constant, and this particular interval either does or does not include μ.   However, the fact that we had such a high degree of probability, prior to the performance of the experiment, that the random interval $[\bar{X} - (2\sigma/\sqrt{n}), \bar{X} + (2\sigma/\sqrt{n})]$ includes the fixed point (parameter) μ, leads us to have some reliance on the particular interval $[\bar{x} - (2\sigma/\sqrt{n}), \bar{x} + (2\sigma/\sqrt{n})]$.   This reliance is reflected by calling the known interval $[\bar{x} - (2\sigma/\sqrt{n}), \bar{x} + (2\sigma/\sqrt{n})]$ a 95 per cent confidence interval for μ.   The number 0.95 is called the _confidence coefficient_.   The confidence coefficient is equal to the probability that the random interval includes the parameter.   One may, of course, obtain a 90 per cent or a 99 per cent confidence interval for μ.

If σ were not known, the end points of the random interval would not be statistics.   Although the probability statement about the random interval remains valid, the sample data would not yield an interval with known end points.   That is, if σ were not known, we would be unable at this time to make this statistical inference about μ.

EXAMPLE 1.   If in the preceding discussion $n = 40$, $\sigma^2 = 10$, and $\bar{x} = 7.164$, then $(7.164 - 1.282\sqrt{10/40},\ 7.164 + 1.282\sqrt{10/40})$, or $(6.523, 7.805)$, is an 80 per cent confidence interval for μ.

Next, consider the problem of finding a confidence interval for the unknown variance σ^2 of a normal distribution with known mean μ.   Let $X_1, X_2, \cdots, X_n$ denote a random sample from the distribution $n(x; \mu, \sigma^2)$, μ known, and define the random variable Y by

$$Y = \sum_1^n \left(\frac{X_i - \mu}{\sigma}\right)^2.$$

The moment-generating function of Y is given by

$$M_Y(t) = E\left\{e^{t\left[\left(\frac{X_1-\mu}{\sigma}\right)^2 + \left(\frac{X_2-\mu}{\sigma}\right)^2 + \cdots + \left(\frac{X_n-\mu}{\sigma}\right)^2\right]}\right\}$$
$$= E\left\{e^{t\left(\frac{X_1-\mu}{\sigma}\right)^2} e^{t\left(\frac{X_2-\mu}{\sigma}\right)^2} \cdots e^{t\left(\frac{X_n-\mu}{\sigma}\right)^2}\right\}.$$

Thus $M_Y(t)$ is the expected value of a product of n factors: The first factor is a function of X_1, the second factor is a function of X_2, and so on.   In accordance with Theorem 2, and its generalization, of Section 3.1, page

46, the expectation of a product of such functions is equal to the product of the expectations of these functions when $X_1, X_2, \cdots, X_n$ are mutually stochastically independent. Thus

$$M_Y(t) = \prod_{i=1}^{n} E\left[e^{t\left(\frac{X_i-\mu}{\sigma}\right)^2}\right]$$

$$= \left\{E\left[e^{t\left(\frac{X-\mu}{\sigma}\right)^2}\right]\right\}^n,$$

since $X_1, X_2, \cdots, X_n$ have the same distribution. However, on page 38 it was proved that

$$E\left[e^{t\left(\frac{X-\mu}{\sigma}\right)^2}\right] = \frac{1}{(1-2t)^{1/2}}, \quad t < \frac{1}{2};$$

thus we have

$$M_Y(t) = \frac{1}{(1-2t)^{n/2}}, \quad t < \frac{1}{2}.$$

It is seen that $M_Y(t)$ is the moment-generating function of a chi-square distribution with n degrees of freedom; thus $Y = \sum_{1}^{n}(X_i - \mu)^2/\sigma^2$ has this distribution. Now let us select a probability, say, 0.95, and for the fixed positive integer n determine values of a and b, $a < b$, from Table II of the chi-square distribution, such that

$$Pr(a < Y < b) = 0.95,$$

or

$$Pr\left[a < \frac{\sum_{1}^{n}(X_i - \mu)^2}{\sigma^2} < b\right] = 0.95$$

or

$$Pr\left[\frac{\sum_{1}^{n}(X_i - \mu)^2}{b} < \sigma^2 < \frac{\sum_{1}^{n}(X_i - \mu)^2}{a}\right] = 0.95.$$

Since μ, a, and b are known constants, each of $\sum_{1}^{n}(X_i - \mu)^2/b$ and $\sum_{1}^{n}(X_i - \mu)^2/a$ is a statistic. Moreover, the interval

$$\left[\frac{\sum_{1}^{n}(X_i - \mu)^2}{b}, \frac{\sum_{1}^{n}(X_i - \mu)^2}{a}\right]$$

is a random interval having probability of 0.95 that it includes the unknown fixed point (parameter) σ^2. Once the random experiment has been performed, and it is found that $X_1 = x_1$, $X_2 = x_2$, $\cdots$, $X_n = x_n$, then the particular interval

$$\left[\frac{\sum_1^n (x_i - \mu)^2}{b}, \ \frac{\sum_1^n (x_i - \mu)^2}{a} \right]$$

is a 95 per cent confidence interval for σ^2.

The student will immediately observe that there are no unique numbers $a < b$ such that $Pr(a < Y < b) = 0.95$. A common method of procedure is to find a and b such that $Pr(Y < a) = 0.025$ and $Pr(b < Y) = 0.025$. That procedure will be followed in this book.

EXAMPLE 2. If in the preceding discussion $\mu = 0$, $n = 10$, and $\sum_1^{10} x_i^2 = 106.6$, then the interval $(106.6/20.5, 106.6/3.25)$, or $(5.2, 32.8)$, is a 95 per cent confidence interval for the variance σ^2, since $Pr(Y < 3.25) = 0.025$ and $Pr(20.5 < Y) = 0.025$, provided Y has a chi-square distribution with ten degrees of freedom.

Comment. The following question is often asked in connection with the immediately preceding determination of the p.d.f. of $Y = \sum_1^n (X_i - \mu)^2/\sigma^2$, where $X_1, X_2, \cdots, X_n$ represent a random sample from a distribution that is $n(x; \mu, \sigma^2)$. Theorem 2 of Section 2.2, page 39, asserts that if X is $n(x; \mu, \sigma^2)$, then $(X - \mu)^2/\sigma^2$ has a chi-square distribution with one degree of freedom; and Example 3, page 49, with Exercise 3.13, page 53, show (in particular) that the sum of n mutually stochastically independent random variables, each having a chi-square distribution with one degree of freedom, is itself a random variable that has a chi-square distribution with n degrees of freedom. Why then, under the conditions stated, may it not be asserted immediately that $Y = \sum_1^n (X_i - \mu)^2/\sigma^2$ has a chi-square distribution with n degrees of freedom? The answer is that although $X_1, X_2, \cdots, X_n$ are themselves mutually stochastically independent, up to this point there is no way of proving, regardless of intuitive appeal, that the random variables $(X_1 - \mu)^2/\sigma^2$, $(X_2 - \mu)^2/\sigma^2$, $\cdots$, $(X_n - \mu)^2/\sigma^2$ are mutually stochastically independent. That these random variables actually are mutually stochastically independent will follow easily from certain considerations in Chapter Four.

Exercises

3.35. Let the observed value of the mean $\bar{X}$ of a random sample of size 20 from a distribution that is $n(x; \mu, 80)$ be 81.2. Find a 95 per cent confidence interval for μ.

3.36. Let $\bar{X}$ be the mean of a random sample of size n from a distribution that is $n(x; \mu, 9)$. Find n such that $Pr(\bar{X} - 1 < \mu < \bar{X} + 1) = 0.90$, approximately.

3.37. If 8.6, 7.9, 8.3, 6.4, 8.4, 9.8, 7.2, 7.8, 7.5 are the observed values of a random sample of size 9 from a distribution that is $n(x; 8, \sigma^2)$, construct a 90 per cent confidence interval for σ^2.

3.38. Let $X_1, X_2, \cdots, X_n$ be a random sample from the distribution $n(x; \mu, \sigma^2)$. Let $0 < a < b$. Show that the mathematical expectation of the length of the random interval $\left(\sum_1^n (X_i - \mu)^2/b, \ \sum_1^n (X_i - \mu)^2/a \right)$ is $(b - a)(n\sigma^2/ab)$.

CHAPTER FOUR

TRANSFORMATIONS OF VARIABLES

In Chapter Three we used the moment-generating function technique to find the p.d.f. of some relatively simple functions of mutually stochastically independent random variables $X_1, X_2, \cdots, X_n$. This technique affords a rather elegant solution to some distribution problems, but it may also lead to complications. This can be illustrated by the following example: Let X_1 and X_2 be stochastically independent random variables, each having a chi-square distribution with two degrees of freedom. Define the random variable Y by $Y = (\frac{1}{2})(X_1 - X_2)$. Now

$$M_Y(t) = E\left[e^{\frac{t(X_1 - X_2)}{2}}\right]$$

$$= E\left(e^{\frac{t}{2}X_1}\right)E\left(e^{-\frac{t}{2}X_2}\right)$$

because X_1 and X_2 are stochastically independent. We recall, since both X_1 and X_2 have chi-square distributions with two degrees of freedom, that

$$E(e^{tX_1}) = E(e^{tX_2}) = (1 - 2t)^{-1}, \quad t < \frac{1}{2}.$$

Accordingly

$$E\left(e^{\frac{t}{2}X_1}\right) = (1 - t)^{-1}, \quad t < 1,$$

and

$$E\left(e^{-\frac{t}{2}X_2}\right) = (1 + t)^{-1}, \quad -1 < t;$$

hence

$$M_Y(t) = (1 - t^2)^{-1}, \quad -1 < t < 1.$$

Up to this point a distribution having this moment-generating function has not been encountered, and it is not an elementary problem to discover that the p.d.f. of Y is actually

$$g(y) = \frac{1}{2}e^{-|y|}, \quad -\infty < y < \infty.$$

4.1. Transformations of Variables of the Discrete Type. An alternative method of finding the distribution of a function of one or more random variables is called the *change of variable technique.* There are some delicate questions (with particular reference to random variables of the continuous type) involved in this technique, and these make it desirable for us first to consider special cases.

Let X have the Poisson p.d.f.

$$f(x) = \frac{\mu^x e^{-\mu}}{x!}, \quad x = 0, 1, 2, \cdots$$
$$= 0 \text{ elsewhere.}$$

As we have done before, let A denote the space $A = \{x; x = 0, 1, 2, \cdots\}$ so that A is the set where $f(x) > 0$. Define a new random variable Y by $Y = 4X$. We wish to find the p.d.f. of Y by the change of variable technique. Let $y = 4x$. We call $y = 4x$ a transformation from x to y, and we say that the transformation maps the space A into the space $B = \{y; y = 0, 4, 8, 12, \cdots\}$. The space B is obtained by transforming each point in A in accordance with $y = 4x$. We note two things about this transformation: It is such that to each point in A there corresponds one, and only one, point in B; and conversely, to each point in B there corresponds one, and only one, point in A. That is, the transformation $y = 4x$ sets up a one-to-one correspondence between the points of A and those of B. Any function $y = u(x)$ (not merely $y = 4x$) that maps a space A (not merely our A) into a space B (not merely our B) such that there is a one-to-one correspondence between the points of A and those of B is called a *one-to-one transformation.* It is important to note that a one-to-one tranformation, $y = u(x)$, implies that y is a single-valued function of x, and that x is a single-valued function of y. In our case this is obviously true, since $y = 4x$ and $x = (\frac{1}{4})y$.

Our problem is that of finding the p.d.f. $g(y)$ of the discrete type of random variable $Y = 4X$. Now $g(y) = Pr(Y = y)$. Because there is a one-to-one correspondence between the points of A and those of B, the event $Y = y$ or $4X = y$ can occur when, and only when, the event $X = (\frac{1}{4})y$ occurs. That is, the two events are equivalent and have the same probability. Hence

$$g(y) = Pr(Y = y) = Pr\left(X = \frac{y}{4}\right) = \frac{\mu^{\frac{y}{4}} e^{-\mu}}{\left(\frac{y}{4}\right)!}, \quad y = 0, 4, 8, \cdots$$
$$= 0 \text{ elsewhere.}$$

The foregoing detailed discussion should make the subsequent text easier to read. Let X be a random variable of the discrete type, having p.d.f. $f(x)$. Let A denote the set of discrete points, at each of which

$f(x) > 0$, and let $y = u(x)$ define a one-to-one transformation that maps A into B. If we solve $y = u(x)$ for x in terms of y, say, $x = w(y)$, then for each $y \epsilon B$, we have $x = w(y) \epsilon A$. Consider the random variable $Y = u(X)$. If $y \epsilon B$, then $x = w(y) \epsilon A$, and the events $Y = y$ [or $u(X) = y$] and $X = w(y)$ are equivalent. Accordingly, the p.d.f. of Y is

$$g(y) = Pr(Y = y) = Pr[X = w(y)] = f[w(y)], \quad y \epsilon B,$$
$$= 0 \text{ elsewhere.}$$

EXAMPLE 1.   Let X have the binomial p.d.f.

$$f(x) = \frac{3!}{x!(3-x)!} \left(\frac{2}{3}\right)^x \left(\frac{1}{3}\right)^{3-x}, \quad x = 0, 1, 2, 3,$$

$$= 0 \text{ elsewhere.}$$

We seek the p.d.f. $g(y)$ of the random variable $Y = X^2$. The transformation $y = u(x) = x^2$ maps $A = \{x; x = 0, 1, 2, 3\}$ into $B = \{y; y = 0, 1, 4, 9\}$. In general, $y = x^2$ does not define a one-to-one transformation; here, however, it does, for there are no negative values of x in $A = \{x; x = 0, 1, 2, 3\}$. That is, we have the single-valued inverse function $x = w(y) = \sqrt{y}$ (not $-\sqrt{y}$), and so

$$g(y) = f(\sqrt{y}) = \frac{3!}{(\sqrt{y})!(3-\sqrt{y})!} \left(\frac{2}{3}\right)^{\sqrt{y}} \left(\frac{1}{3}\right)^{3-\sqrt{y}}, \quad y = 0, 1, 4, 9,$$

$$= 0 \text{ elsewhere.}$$

There are no essential difficulties involved in a problem like the following: Let $f(x_1, x_2)$ be the joint p.d.f. of two discrete-type random variables X_1 and X_2 with A the (two-dimensional) set of points at which $f(x_1, x_2) > 0$. Let $y_1 = u_1(x_1, x_2)$ and $y_2 = u_2(x_1, x_2)$ define a one-to-one transformation which maps A into B. The joint p.d.f. of the two new random variables $Y_1 = u_1(X_1, X_2)$ and $Y_2 = u_2(X_1, X_2)$ is given by

$$g(y_1, y_2) = f[w_1(y_1, y_2), w_2(y_1, y_2)], \quad (y_1, y_2) \epsilon B,$$

$$= 0 \text{ elsewhere,}$$

where $x_1 = w_1(y_1, y_2)$ and $x_2 = w_2(y_1, y_2)$ are the single-valued inverses of $y_1 = u_1(x_1, x_2)$ and $y_2 = u_2(x_1, x_2)$. From this joint p.d.f. $g(y_1, y_2)$ we may obtain the marginal p.d.f. of Y_1 by summing on y_2 or the marginal p.d.f. of Y_2 by summing on y_1.

Perhaps it should be emphasized that the technique of change of variables involves the introduction of as many "new" variables as there were "old" variables. That is, suppose $f(x_1, x_2, x_3)$ is the joint p.d.f. of X_1, X_2, and X_3, with A the set where $f(x_1, x_2, x_3) > 0$. Let us say we seek the p.d.f. of $Y_1 = u_1(X_1, X_2, X_3)$. We would then define (if possible) $Y_2 = u_2(X_1, X_2, X_3)$ and $Y_3 = u_3(X_1, X_2, X_3)$, so that $y_1 = u_1(x_1, x_2, x_3)$, y_2

$= u_2(x_1, x_2, x_3)$, $y_3 = u_3(x_1, x_2, x_3)$ define a one-to-one transformation of $\mathcal{A}$ into $\mathcal{B}$. This would enable us to find the joint p.d.f. of Y_1, Y_2, and Y_3 from which we would get the marginal p.d.f. of Y_1 by summing on y_2 and y_3.

Exercises

4.1. Let X have the p.d.f. $f(x) = \frac{1}{3}$, $x = 1, 2, 3$, zero elsewhere. Find the p.d.f. of $Y = 2X + 1$.

4.2. If $f(x_1, x_2) = (\frac{2}{3})^{x_1+x_2}(\frac{1}{3})^{2-x_1-x_2}$; $(x_1, x_2) = (0, 0)$, $(0, 1)$, $(1, 0)$, $(1, 1)$, zero elsewhere, is the joint p.d.f. of X_1 and X_2, find the joint p.d.f. of $Y_1 = X_1 - X_2$ and $Y_2 = X_1 + X_2$.

4.3. Let X have the p.d.f. $f(x) = (\frac{1}{2})^x$, $x = 1, 2, 3, \cdots$, zero elsewhere. Find the p.d.f. of $Y = X^3$.

4.4. Let X_1 and X_2 have the joint p.d.f. $f(x_1, x_2) = x_1 x_2/36$, $x_1 = 1, 2, 3$, and $x_2 = 1, 2, 3$, zero elsewhere. Find first the joint p.d.f. of $Y_1 = X_1 X_2$ and $Y_2 = X_2$, and then find the marginal p.d.f. of Y_1.

4.2. Transformations of Variables of the Continuous Type. In the preceding section, we introduced the notion of a one-to-one transformation and the mapping of a set $\mathcal{A}$ into a set $\mathcal{B}$ under that transformation. Those ideas were sufficient to enable us to find the distribution of a function of several random variables of the discrete type. In this section we shall examine the same problem when the random variables are of the continuous type. It is again helpful to begin with a special problem.

EXAMPLE 1. Let X be a random variable of the continuous type, having p.d.f.

$$f(x) = 2x, \quad 0 < x < 1,$$
$$= 0 \text{ elsewhere.}$$

Here $\mathcal{A}$ is the space $\{x; 0 < x < 1\}$ where $f(x) > 0$. Define the random variable Y by $Y = 8X^3$ and consider the transformation $y = 8x^3$. Under the transformation $y = 8x^3$, the set $\mathcal{A}$ is mapped into the set $\mathcal{B} = \{y; 0 < y < 8\}$, and moreover, the transformation is one-to-one. For every $0 < a < b < 8$, the event $a < Y < b$ will occur when, and only when, the event $(\frac{1}{2}) \sqrt[3]{a} < X < (\frac{1}{2}) \sqrt[3]{b}$ occurs, for there is a one-to-one correspondence between the points of $\mathcal{A}$ and $\mathcal{B}$. Thus

$$Pr(a < Y < b) = Pr\left(\frac{1}{2}\sqrt[3]{a} < X < \frac{1}{2}\sqrt[3]{b}\right)$$

$$= \int_{\frac{1}{2}\sqrt[3]{a}}^{\frac{1}{2}\sqrt[3]{b}} 2x \, dx.$$

Let us re-write this integral by changing the variable of integration from x to y by writing $y = 8x^3$ or $x = (\frac{1}{2}) \sqrt[3]{y}$. Now

$$\frac{dx}{dy} = \frac{1}{6y^{2/3}},$$

and accordingly we have

$$Pr(a < Y < b) = \int_a^b 2\left(\frac{\sqrt[3]{y}}{2}\right)\left(\frac{1}{6y^{2/3}}\right) dy$$

$$= \int_a^b \frac{1}{6y^{1/3}} \, dy.$$

Since this is true for every $0 < a < b < 8$, the p.d.f. $g(y)$ of Y is the integrand; that is,

$$g(y) = \frac{1}{6y^{1/3}}, \quad 0 < y < 8,$$

$$= 0 \text{ elsewhere.}$$

It is worth noting that we found the p.d.f. of the random variable $Y = 8X^3$ by using a theorem on the change of variable in a definite integral. However, to obtain $g(y)$ we actually need only two things: (1) the set $\mathcal{B}$ of points y where $g(y) > 0$ and (2) the integrand of the integral on y to which $Pr(a < Y < b)$ is equal. These can be found by two simple rules:

(a)   Verify that the transformation $y = 8x^3$ maps $\mathcal{A} = \{x; 0 < x < 1\}$ into $\mathcal{B} = \{y; 0 < y < 8\}$ and that the transformation is one-to-one.

(b)   Determine $g(y)$ on this set $\mathcal{B}$ by substituting $(\frac{1}{2}) \sqrt[3]{y}$ for x in $f(x)$ and then multiplying this result by the derivative of $(\frac{1}{2}) \sqrt[3]{y}$. That is,

$$g(y) = f\left(\frac{\sqrt[3]{y}}{2}\right)\frac{d[(\frac{1}{2}) \sqrt[3]{y}]}{dy} = \frac{1}{6y^{1/3}}, \quad 0 < y < 8,$$

$$= 0 \text{ elsewhere.}$$

We shall accept a theorem in analysis on the change of variable in a definite integral to enable us to state a more general result. Let X be a random variable of the continuous type having p.d.f. $f(x)$. Let $\mathcal{A}$ be the one-dimensional space on the x-axis where $f(x) > 0$. Consider the random variable $Y = u(X)$, where $y = u(x)$ defines a one-to-one transformation which maps the set $\mathcal{A}$ into the set $\mathcal{B}$ on the y-axis. Let the inverse of $y = u(x)$ be denoted by $x = w(y)$, and let the derivative $dx/dy = w'(y)$ be continuous and not vanish for all points y in $\mathcal{B}$. Then the p.d.f. of the random variable $Y = u(X)$ is given by

$$g(y) = f[w(y)] \cdot |w'(y)|, \quad y \epsilon \mathcal{B},$$

$$= 0 \text{ elsewhere,}$$

where $|w'(y)|$ represents the absolute value of $w'(y)$. This is precisely what we did in Example 1 of this section except there we deliberately chose $y = 8x^3$ to be an increasing function so that

$$\frac{dx}{dy} = w'(y) = \frac{1}{6y^{2/3}}, \quad 0 < y < 8$$

is positive, and hence

$$\left|\frac{1}{6y^{2/3}}\right| = \frac{1}{6y^{2/3}}, \quad 0 < y < 8.$$

Henceforth, we shall refer to $dx/dy = w'(y)$ as the Jacobian (denoted by J) of the transformation. In most mathematical areas, $J = w'(y)$ is referred to as the Jacobian of the inverse transformation $x = w(y)$, but in this book it will be called the Jacobian of the transformation, simply for convenience.

EXAMPLE 2. Let X have the p.d.f.

$$f(x) = 1, \quad 0 < x < 1,$$
$$= 0 \text{ elsewhere.}$$

We are to show that the random variable $Y = -2 \ln X$ has a chi-square distribution with two degrees of freedom. Here the transformation is $y = u(x) = -2 \ln x$, so that $x = w(y) = e^{-\frac{y}{2}}$. The space A is $A = \{x; 0 < x < 1\}$, which the one-to-one transformation $y = -2 \ln x$ maps into $B = \{y; 0 < y < \infty\}$. The Jacobian of the transformation is

$$J = \frac{dx}{dy} = w'(y) = -\frac{1}{2}e^{-\frac{y}{2}}.$$

Accordingly, the p.d.f. $g(y)$ of $Y = -2 \ln X$ is

$$g(y) = f(e^{-\frac{y}{2}})|J| = \frac{1}{2}e^{-\frac{y}{2}}, \quad 0 < y < \infty,$$
$$= 0 \text{ elsewhere,}$$

a p.d.f. which is chi-square with two degrees of freedom.

This method of finding the p.d.f. of a function of one random variable of the continuous type will now be extended to functions of two random variables of this type. Again, only functions which define a one-to-one transformation will be considered at this time. Let $y_1 = u_1(x_1, x_2)$ and $y_2 = u_2(x_1, x_2)$ define a one-to-one transformation which maps a (two-dimensional) set A in the x_1x_2 plane into a (two-dimensional) set B in the y_1y_2 plane. If we express each of x_1 and x_2 in terms of y_1 and y_2, we can write $x_1 = w_1(y_1, y_2)$, $x_2 = w_2(y_1, y_2)$. The determinant of order two

$$\begin{vmatrix} \dfrac{\partial x_1}{\partial y_1} & \dfrac{\partial x_1}{\partial y_2} \\[2ex] \dfrac{\partial x_2}{\partial y_1} & \dfrac{\partial x_2}{\partial y_2} \end{vmatrix}$$

is called the Jacobian of the transformation and will be denoted by the symbol J. It will be assumed that these first-order partial derivatives are continuous and that the Jacobian J is not identically equal to zero in $\mathcal{B}$. An illustrative example may be desirable before we proceed with the extension of the change of variable technique to two random variables of the continuous type.

EXAMPLE 3. Let $\mathcal{A}$ be the set $\mathcal{A} = \{(x_1, x_2), 0 < x_1 < 1, 0 < x_2 < 1\}$ which is depicted in Figure 4-1. We wish to determine the set $\mathcal{B}$ in the $y_1 y_2$ plane which is

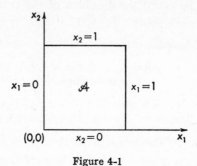

Figure 4-1

the mapping of $\mathcal{A}$ under the one-to-one transformation

$$y_1 = u_1(x_1, x_2) = x_1 + x_2,$$
$$y_2 = u_2(x_1, x_2) = x_1 - x_2,$$

and we wish to compute the Jacobian of the transformation. Now

$$x_1 = w_1(y_1, y_2) = \frac{1}{2}(y_1 + y_2),$$

$$x_2 = w_2(y_1, y_2) = \frac{1}{2}(y_1 - y_2).$$

To determine the set $\mathcal{B}$ in the $y_1 y_2$ plane into which $\mathcal{A}$ is mapped under the transformation, note that the boundaries of $\mathcal{A}$ are transformed as follows into the boundaries of $\mathcal{B}$:

$$x_1 = 0 \quad \text{into} \quad 0 = \frac{1}{2}(y_1 + y_2),$$

$$x_1 = 1 \quad \text{into} \quad 1 = \frac{1}{2}(y_1 + y_2),$$

$$x_2 = 0 \quad \text{into} \quad 0 = \frac{1}{2}(y_1 - y_2),$$

$$x_2 = 1 \quad \text{into} \quad 1 = \frac{1}{2}(y_1 - y_2).$$

Accordingly, $\mathcal{B}$ is as shown in Figure 4–2.

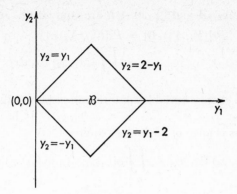

Figure 4-2

Finally,

$$J = \begin{vmatrix} \dfrac{\partial x_1}{\partial y_1} & \dfrac{\partial x_1}{\partial y_2} \\[2ex] \dfrac{\partial x_2}{\partial y_1} & \dfrac{\partial x_2}{\partial y_2} \end{vmatrix} = \begin{vmatrix} \dfrac{1}{2} & \dfrac{1}{2} \\[2ex] \dfrac{1}{2} & -\dfrac{1}{2} \end{vmatrix} = -\dfrac{1}{2}.$$

We now proceed with the problem of finding the joint p.d.f. of two functions of two continuous-type random variables.   Let X_1 and X_2 be random variables of the continuous type, having joint p.d.f. $\phi(x_1, x_2)$.   Let $\mathcal{A}$ be the two-dimensional set in the x_1x_2 plane where $\phi(x_1, x_2) > 0$.   Let $Y_1 = u_1(X_1, X_2)$ be a random variable whose p.d.f. is to be found.   If $y_1 = u_1(x_1, x_2)$ and $y_2 = u_2(x_1, x_2)$ define a one-to-one transformation of $\mathcal{A}$ into a set $\mathcal{B}$ in the y_1y_2 plane (with nonidentically vanishing Jacobian), we can find, by use of a theorem in analysis, the joint p.d.f. of $Y_1 = u_1(X_1, X_2)$ and $Y_2 = u_2(X_1, X_2)$.   Let A be a subset of $\mathcal{A}$, and let B denote the mapping of A under the one-to-one transformation (see Figure 4-3).

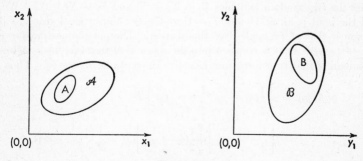

Figure 4-3

The events $(X_1, X_2) \epsilon A$ and $(Y_1, Y_2) \epsilon B$ are equivalent. Hence

$$Pr[(Y_1, Y_2) \epsilon B] = Pr[(X_1, X_2) \epsilon A]$$
$$= \iint_A \phi(x_1, x_2) \, dx_1 \, dx_2.$$

We wish now to change variables of integration by writing $y_1 = u_1(x_1, x_2)$, $y_2 = u_2(x_1, x_2)$, or $x_1 = w_1(y_1, y_2)$, $x_2 = w_2(y_1, y_2)$. It has been proved in analysis that this change of variables requires

$$\iint_A \phi(x_1, x_2) \, dx_1 \, dx_2 = \iint_B \phi[w_1(y_1, y_2), w_2(y_1, y_2)]|J| dy_1 \, dy_2.$$

Thus, for every set B in $\mathcal{B}$,

$$Pr[(Y_1, Y_2) \epsilon B] = \iint_B \phi[w_1(y_1, y_2), w_2(y_1, y_2)]|J| dy_1 \, dy_2,$$

which implies that the joint p.d.f. $g(y_1, y_2)$ of Y_1 and Y_2 is

$$g(y_1, y_2) = \phi[w_1(y_1, y_2), w_2(y_1, y_2)]|J|, \quad (y_1, y_2) \epsilon \mathcal{B},$$
$$= 0 \text{ elsewhere.}$$

Accordingly, the marginal p.d.f. $g_1(y_1)$ of Y_1 can be obtained from the joint p.d.f. $g(y_1, y_2)$ in the usual manner by integrating on y_2. Four examples of this result will be given.

EXAMPLE 4. Let the random variable X have the p.d.f.

$$f(x) = 1, \quad 0 < x < 1,$$
$$= 0 \text{ elsewhere,}$$

and let X_1, X_2 denote a random sample from this distribution. The joint p.d.f. of X_1 and X_2 is then

$$\phi(x_1, x_2) = f(x_1)f(x_2) = 1, \quad 0 < x_1 < 1, 0 < x_2 < 1,$$
$$= 0 \text{ elsewhere.}$$

Consider the two random variables $Y_1 = X_1 + X_2$ and $Y_2 = X_1 - X_2$. We wish to find the joint p.d.f. of Y_1 and Y_2. Here the two-dimensional space A in the $x_1 x_2$ plane is that of Example 3 of this section. The one-to-one transformation $y_1 = x_1 + x_2$, $y_2 = x_1 - x_2$ maps A into the space $\mathcal{B}$ of that example. Moreover, the Jacobian of that transformation has been shown to be $J = -\frac{1}{2}$. Thus

$$g(y_1, y_2) = \phi\left[\frac{1}{2}(y_1 + y_2), \frac{1}{2}(y_1 - y_2)\right]|J|$$

$$= f\left[\frac{1}{2}(y_1 + y_2)\right]f\left[\frac{1}{2}(y_1 - y_2)\right]|J| = \frac{1}{2}, \quad (y_1, y_2) \epsilon \mathcal{B},$$
$$= 0 \text{ elsewhere.}$$

The marginal p.d.f. of Y_1 is given by

$$g_1(y_1) = \int_{-\infty}^{\infty} g(y_1, y_2) \, dy_2.$$

If we refer to Figure 4–2, it is seen that

$$g_1(y_1) = \int_{-y_1}^{y_1} \left(\frac{1}{2}\right) dy_2 = y_1, \quad 0 < y_1 \leq 1,$$

$$= \int_{y_1-2}^{2-y_1} \left(\frac{1}{2}\right) dy_2 = 2 - y_1, \quad 1 < y_1 < 2,$$

$$= 0 \text{ elsewhere.}$$

In a similar manner, the marginal p.d.f. $g_2(y_2)$ is given by

$$g_2(y_2) = \int_{-y_2}^{y_2+2} \left(\frac{1}{2}\right) dy_1 = y_2 + 1, \quad -1 < y_2 \leq 0,$$

$$= \int_{y_2}^{2-y_2} \left(\frac{1}{2}\right) dy_1 = 1 - y_2, \quad 0 < y_2 < 1,$$

$$= 0 \text{ elsewhere.}$$

Since $g(y_1, y_2) \not\equiv g_1(y_1)g_2(y_2)$, it is seen that Y_1 and Y_2 are stochastically dependent.

EXAMPLE 5. Let X_1, X_2 be a random sample of size 2 from the distribution having p.d.f.

$$f(x) = e^{-x}, \quad 0 < x < \infty,$$

$$= 0 \text{ elsewhere.}$$

Let $Y_1 = X_1 + X_2$ and $Y_2 = X_1/(X_1 + X_2)$. We shall show that Y_1 and Y_2 are stochastically independent.

Since the joint p.d.f. of X_1 and X_2 is

$$\phi(x_1, x_2) = f(x_1)f(x_2) = e^{-x_1-x_2}, \quad 0 < x_1 < \infty, \quad 0 < x_2 < \infty,$$

$$= 0 \text{ elsewhere,}$$

the space $\mathcal{A}$ is, exclusive of the points on the coordinate axes, the first quadrant of the x_1x_2 plane. Now

$$y_1 = u_1(x_1, x_2) = x_1 + x_2$$

$$y_2 = u_2(x_1, x_2) = \frac{x_1}{x_1 + x_2}$$

may be written $x_1 = y_1y_2$, $x_2 = y_1(1 - y_2)$ so that

$$J = \begin{vmatrix} y_2 & y_1 \\ 1 - y_2 & -y_1 \end{vmatrix} = -y_1 \not\equiv 0.$$

The transformation is one-to-one, and it maps $\mathcal{A}$ into $\mathcal{B} = \{(y_1, y_2); 0 < y_1 < \infty, 0 < y_2 < 1\}$ in the y_1y_2 plane. The joint p.d.f. of Y_1 and Y_2 is then

$$g(y_1, y_2) = y_1 e^{-y_1}, \quad 0 < y_1 < \infty, \quad 0 < y_2 < 1,$$

$$= 0 \text{ elsewhere.}$$

The marginal probability density functions of Y_1 and Y_2 are respectively given by

$$g_1(y_1) = \int_0^1 y_1 e^{-y_1} \, dy_2 = y_1 e^{-y_1}, \quad 0 < y_1 < \infty,$$
$$= 0 \text{ elsewhere},$$

and

$$g_2(y_2) = \int_0^\infty y_1 e^{-y_1} \, dy_1 = \Gamma(2) = 1, \quad 0 < y_2 < 1,$$
$$= 0 \text{ elsewhere}.$$

Since it is evident that $g(y_1, y_2) \equiv g_1(y_1)g_2(y_2)$ for all values of y_1 and y_2, then $Y_1 = X_1 + X_2$ and $Y_2 = X_1/(X_1 + X_2)$ are stochastically independent.

EXAMPLE 6. We now solve the problem suggested in the introductory remarks of this chapter. There $Y_1 = (\frac{1}{2})(X_1 - X_2)$, where X_1 and X_2 are stochastically independent random variables, each having the p.d.f.

$$f(x) = \frac{1}{2} e^{-\frac{x}{2}}, \quad 0 < x < \infty,$$
$$= 0 \text{ elsewhere}.$$

The joint p.d.f. of X_1 and X_2 is

$$f(x_1)f(x_2) = \frac{1}{4} e^{-\frac{x_1 + x_2}{2}}, \quad 0 < x_1 < \infty, \quad 0 < x_2 < \infty,$$
$$= 0 \text{ elsewhere}.$$

Let $Y_2 = X_2$ so that $y_1 = (\frac{1}{2})(x_1 - x_2)$, $y_2 = x_2$, or $x_1 = 2y_1 + y_2$, $x_2 = y_2$ define a one-to-one transformation from $\mathcal{A} = \{(x_1, x_2); 0 < x_1 < \infty, 0 < x_2 < \infty\}$ to $\mathcal{B} = \{(y_1, y_2); -2y_1 < y_2 \text{ and } 0 < y_2, -\infty < y_1 < \infty\}$. The Jacobian of the transformation is

$$J = \begin{vmatrix} 2 & 1 \\ 0 & 1 \end{vmatrix} = 2;$$

hence the joint p.d.f. of Y_1 and Y_2 is

$$g(y_1, y_2) = \frac{1}{4} e^{-(y_1 + y_2)} |2|, \quad (y_1, y_2) \epsilon \mathcal{B},$$
$$= 0 \text{ elsewhere}.$$

Thus the p.d.f. of Y_1 is given by

$$g_1(y_1) = \int_{-2y_1}^\infty \left(\frac{1}{2}\right) e^{-(y_1 + y_2)} \, dy_2 = \frac{1}{2} e^{y_1}, \quad -\infty < y_1 < 0,$$

$$= \int_0^\infty \left(\frac{1}{2}\right) e^{-(y_1 + y_2)} \, dy_2 = \frac{1}{2} e^{-y_1}, \quad 0 \leq y_1 < \infty,$$

or

$$g_1(y_1) = \frac{1}{2} e^{-|y_1|}, \quad -\infty < y_1 < \infty,$$

as stated in the introductory remarks of this chapter.

EXAMPLE 7.   In this example, a rather important result is established.   Let X_1 and X_2 be stochastically independent random variables with joint p.d.f. $f_1(x_1)f_2(x_2)$ that is positive on the two-dimensional space A.   Let $Y_1 = u_1(X_1)$, a function of X_1 alone, and $Y_2 = u_2(X_2)$, a function of X_2 alone.   We assume for the present that $y_1 = u_1(x_1)$, $y_2 = u_2(x_2)$ define a one-to-one transformation from A to a two-dimensional set B in the y_1y_2 plane.   Thus, solving for x_1 and x_2 in terms of y_1 and y_2, we have $x_1 = w_1(y_1)$ and $x_2 = w_2(y_2)$ so that

$$J = \begin{vmatrix} w'_1(y_1) & 0 \\ 0 & w'_2(y_2) \end{vmatrix} = w'_1(y_1)w'_2(y_2) \neq 0.$$

Hence the joint p.d.f. of Y_1 and Y_2 is

$$g(y_1, y_2) = f_1[w_1(y_1)]f_2[w_2(y_2)] \, |w'_1(y_1)w'_2(y_2)|, \ (y_1, y_2) \, \epsilon B,$$
$$= 0 \text{ elsewhere.}$$

However, from the procedure for changing variables in the case of one random variable, we see that the marginal probability density functions of Y_1 and Y_2 are respectively $g_1(y_1) = f_1[w_1(y_1)] \, |w'_1(y_1)|$ and $g_2(y_2) = f_2[w_2(y_2)] \, |w'_2(y_2)|$ for y_1 and y_2 in some appropriate sets.   Consequently,

$$g(y_1, y_2) \equiv g_1(y_1)g_2(y_2).$$

Thus, summarizing, we note that if X_1 and X_2 are stochastically independent random variables, then $Y_1 = u_1(X_1)$ and $Y_2 = u_2(X_2)$ are also stochastically independent random variables.   This is the fact alluded to in the Comment, page 61.

Exercises

4.5.   Let X have the p.d.f. $f(x) = x^2/9$, $0 < x < 3$, zero elsewhere.   Find the p.d.f. of $Y = X^3$.

4.6.   If the p.d.f. of X is $f(x) = 2xe^{-x^2}$, $0 < x < \infty$, zero elsewhere, determine the p.d.f. of $Y = X^2$.

4.7.   Let X_1, X_2 be a random sample from the distribution having p.d.f. $f(x) = 1$, $0 < x < 1$, zero elsewhere.   Find first the joint p.d.f. of $Y_1 = X_1X_2$ and $Y_2 = X_2$, and then find the marginal p.d.f. of Y_1.

4.8.   Let X_1, X_2 be a random sample from the normal distribution $n(x; 0, 1)$. Show that the marginal p.d.f. of $Y_1 = X_1/X_2$ is the *Cauchy* p.d.f.

$$g_1(y_1) = \frac{1}{\pi(1 + y_1^2)}, \quad -\infty < y_1 < \infty.$$

Hint: Let $Y_2 = X_2$ and first determine the joint p.d.f. of Y_1 and Y_2.   Be sure to multiply by the absolute value of the Jacobian.

4.9.   Let X_1 and X_2 be two stochastically independent random variables having gamma distributions and joint p.d.f.

$$f(x_1, x_2) = \frac{1}{\Gamma(\alpha)\Gamma(\beta)}x_1^{\alpha-1}x_2^{\beta-1}e^{-x_1-x_2}, \quad 0 < x_1 < \infty, \ \ 0 < x_2 < \infty,$$

zero elsewhere, where $\alpha > 0$, $\beta > 0$. Show that the marginal p.d.f. of $Y_1 = X_1/(X_1 + X_2)$ is the *beta* p.d.f.

$$g_1(y_1) = \frac{\Gamma(\alpha + \beta)}{\Gamma(\alpha)\Gamma(\beta)}y_1^{\alpha-1}(1 - y_1)^{\beta-1}, \quad 0 < y_1 < 1,$$

zero elsewhere.   Hint: Let $Y_2 = X_1 + X_2$ and find first the joint p.d.f. of Y_1 and Y_2.

4.10. Find the mean and variance of the beta distribution considered in Exercise 4.9.   Hint: From that exercise, we know

$$\int_0^1 y^{\alpha-1}(1 - y)^{\beta-1} \, dy = \frac{\Gamma(\alpha)\Gamma(\beta)}{\Gamma(\alpha + \beta)}$$

for all $\alpha > 0$, $\beta > 0$.

4.11.   Determine the constant c in each of the following so that each $f(x)$ is a beta p.d.f.

(a) $f(x) = cx(1 - x)^3$, $0 < x < 1$, zero elsewhere.
(b) $f(x) = cx^4(1 - x)^5$, $0 < x < 1$, zero elsewhere.
(c) $f(x) = cx^2(1 - x)^8$, $0 < x < 1$, zero elsewhere.

4.3.   The t and F Distributions.   Four special distributions (the binomial, the Poisson, the normal, and the chi-square) were introduced in Chapter Two and some of their properties were noted. It is the purpose of this section to define two additional distributions which are quite useful in certain problems of statistical inference that are considered in Chapters Six, Nine, and Ten.

Let W denote a random variable which is $n(w; 0, 1)$; let V denote a random variable which has a chi-square distribution with r degrees of freedom; and let W and V be stochastically independent.   Then the joint p.d.f. of W and V, say, $\phi(w, v)$, is the product of the p.d.f. of W and that of V or

$$\phi(w, v) = \frac{1}{\sqrt{2\pi}} e^{-\frac{w^2}{2}} \frac{1}{\Gamma\left(\frac{r}{2}\right)2^{\frac{r}{2}}} v^{\frac{r}{2}-1} e^{-\frac{v}{2}}, \quad -\infty < w < \infty, \ 0 < v < \infty$$

$$= 0 \text{ elsewhere.}$$

Define a new random variable T by writing

$$T = \frac{W}{\sqrt{\dfrac{V}{r}}}.$$

The change of variable technique will be used to obtain the p.d.f. $g_1(t)$ of T.   The equations

$$t = \frac{w}{\sqrt{\dfrac{v}{r}}} \quad \text{and} \quad u = v$$

define a one-to-one transformation which maps $A = \{(w, v); -\infty < w < \infty, 0 < v < \infty\}$ into $B = \{(t, u); -\infty < t < \infty, 0 < u < \infty\}$. Since $w = t\sqrt{u}/\sqrt{r}$, $v = u$, the absolute value of the Jacobian of the transformation is $|J| = \sqrt{u}/\sqrt{r}$. Accordingly, the joint p.d.f. of T and $U = V$ is given by

$$g(t, u) = \phi\left(\frac{t\sqrt{u}}{\sqrt{r}}, u\right)|J|$$

$$= \frac{1}{\sqrt{2\pi}\Gamma\left(\frac{r}{2}\right)2^{\frac{r}{2}}} u^{\frac{r}{2}-1} e^{-\frac{u}{2}\left(1 + \frac{t^2}{r}\right)} \left(\frac{\sqrt{u}}{\sqrt{r}}\right), \quad \begin{array}{l} -\infty < t < \infty, \\ 0 < u < \infty, \end{array}$$

$= 0$ elsewhere.

The marginal p.d.f. of T is then

$$g_1(t) = \int_{-\infty}^{\infty} g(t, u)\, du \qquad \text{general form of eq.}$$

$$= \int_{0}^{\infty} \frac{1}{\sqrt{2\pi r}\Gamma\left(\frac{r}{2}\right)2^{\frac{r}{2}}} u^{\frac{r+1}{2}-1} e^{-\frac{u}{2}\left(1 + \frac{t^2}{r}\right)}\, du. \qquad \text{specific form}$$

In this integral let $z = u[1 + (t^2/r)]/2$, and it is seen that

$$g_1(t) = \int_{0}^{\infty} \frac{1}{\sqrt{2\pi r}\Gamma\left(\frac{r}{2}\right)2^{\frac{r}{2}}}\left(\frac{2z}{1 + \frac{t^2}{r}}\right)^{\frac{r+1}{2}-1} e^{-z}\left(\frac{2}{1 + \frac{t^2}{r}}\right) dz$$

$$= \frac{\Gamma\left(\frac{r+1}{2}\right)}{\sqrt{\pi r}\,\Gamma\left(\frac{r}{2}\right)} \frac{1}{\left(1 + \frac{t^2}{r}\right)^{\frac{r+1}{2}}}, \quad -\infty < t < \infty.$$

Thus, if W is $n(w; 0, 1)$, if V has a chi-square distribution with r degrees of freedom, and if W and V are stochastically independent, then

$$T = \frac{W}{\sqrt{\dfrac{V}{r}}}$$

has the immediately preceding p.d.f. $g_1(t)$. The distribution of the random variable T is usually called a t distribution. It should be observed that a t distribution is completely determined by the parameter r, the number of degrees of freedom of the random variable that has the chi-square distribution. Some approximate values of

$$Pr(T \le t) = \int_{-\infty}^{t} g_1(w) \, dw$$

for selected values of r and t, can be found in Table III, in the appendix.

Next consider two stochastically independent chi-square random variables U and V having r_1 and r_2 degrees of freedom, respectively. The joint p.d.f. $\phi(u, v)$ of U and V is then

$$\phi(u, v) = \frac{1}{\Gamma\!\left(\frac{r_1}{2}\right)\Gamma\!\left(\frac{r_2}{2}\right)2^{\frac{r_1+r_2}{2}}} u^{\frac{r_1}{2}-1} v^{\frac{r_2}{2}-1} e^{-\frac{u+v}{2}}, \quad \begin{array}{l} 0 < u < \infty \\ 0 < v < \infty, \end{array}$$

$= 0$ elsewhere.

We define the new random variable

$$F = \frac{\dfrac{U}{r_1}}{\dfrac{V}{r_2}}$$

and we propose finding the p.d.f. $g_1(f)$ of F. The equations

$$f = \frac{\dfrac{u}{r_1}}{\dfrac{v}{r_2}}, \quad z = v,$$

define a one-to-one transformation which maps the set $A = \{(u, v);$ $0 < u < \infty, 0 < v < \infty\}$ into the set $B = \{(f, z); 0 < f < \infty, 0 < z < \infty\}$. Since $u = (r_1/r_2)zf$, $v = z$, the absolute value of the Jacobian of the transformation is $|J| = (r_1/r_2)z$. The joint p.d.f. $g(f, z)$ of the random variables F and $Z = V$ is then

$$g(f, z) = \frac{1}{\Gamma\!\left(\frac{r_1}{2}\right)\Gamma\!\left(\frac{r_2}{2}\right)2^{\frac{r_1+r_2}{2}}}\left(\frac{r_1 z f}{r_2}\right)^{\frac{r_1}{2}-1} z^{\frac{r_2}{2}-1} e^{-\frac{z}{2}\left(\frac{r_1 f}{r_2}+1\right)}\left(\frac{r_1 z}{r_2}\right),$$

provided $(f, z)\epsilon B$, and zero elsewhere. The marginal p.d.f. $g_1(f)$ of F is then

$$g_1(f) = \int_{-\infty}^{\infty} g(f, z) \, dz \qquad \text{general form}$$

$$= \int_{0}^{\infty} \frac{\left(\frac{r_1}{r_2}\right)^{\frac{r_1}{2}} (f)^{\frac{r_1}{2}-1}}{\Gamma\!\left(\frac{r_1}{2}\right)\Gamma\!\left(\frac{r_2}{2}\right)2^{\frac{r_1+r_2}{2}}} z^{\frac{r_1+r_2}{2}-1} e^{-\frac{z}{2}\left(\frac{r_1 f}{r_2}+1\right)} \, dz. \qquad \text{specific}$$

If we change the variable of integration by writing

$$y = \frac{z}{2}\left(\frac{r_1 f}{r_2} + 1\right),$$

it can be seen that

$$g_1(f) = \int_0^\infty \frac{\left(\frac{r_1}{r_2}\right)^{\frac{r_1}{2}}(f)^{\frac{r_1}{2}-1}}{\Gamma\left(\frac{r_1}{2}\right)\Gamma\left(\frac{r_2}{2}\right)2^{\frac{r_1+r_2}{2}}}\left(\frac{2y}{\frac{r_1 f}{r_2}+1}\right)^{\frac{r_1+r_2}{2}-1} e^{-y}\left(\frac{2}{\frac{r_1 f}{r_2}+1}\right) dy$$

$$= \frac{\Gamma\left(\frac{r_1+r_2}{2}\right)\left(\frac{r_1}{r_2}\right)^{\frac{r_1}{2}}}{\Gamma\left(\frac{r_1}{2}\right)\Gamma\left(\frac{r_2}{2}\right)}\frac{(f)^{\frac{r_1}{2}-1}}{\left(1+\frac{r_1 f}{r_2}\right)^{\frac{r_1+r_2}{2}}}, \quad 0 < f < \infty$$

$$= 0 \text{ elsewhere.}$$

Accordingly, if U and V are stochastically independent chi-square variables with r_1 and r_2 degrees of freedom, respectively, then

$$F = \frac{\dfrac{U}{r_1}}{\dfrac{V}{r_2}}$$

has the immediately preceding p.d.f. $g_1(f)$. The distribution of this random variable is usually called an F distribution. It should be observed that an F distribution is completely determined by the two parameters r_1 and r_2. Table IV, in the appendix, gives some approximate values of

$$Pr(F \leq f) = \int_0^f g_1(w)\,dw$$

for selected values of r_1, r_2, and f.

Exercises

4.12. Let T have a t distribution with ten degrees of freedom. Find $Pr(|T| > 2.228)$ from Table III.

4.13. Let T have a t distribution with 14 degrees of freedom. Determine b so that $Pr(-b < T < b) = 0.90$.

4.14. Let F have an F distribution with parameters r_1 and r_2. Prove that $1/F$ has an F distribution with parameters r_2 and r_1.

4.15. If F has an F distribution with parameters $r_1 = 5$ and $r_2 = 10$, find a and b so that $Pr(F \leq a) = 0.05$ and $Pr(F \leq b) = 0.95$, and accordingly, $Pr(a$

$<F<b) = 0.90$.   Hint: Write $Pr(F \leq a) = Pr(1/F \geq 1/a) = 1 - Pr(1/F \leq 1/a)$, and use the result of Exercise 4.14 and Table IV.

4.16. Find the mean of the F distribution with parameters r_1 and $r_2 > 2$.

4.17. Let $T = W/\sqrt{V/r}$, where the stochastically independent variables W and V are respectively normal with mean zero and variance one and chi-square with r degrees of freedom. Show that T^2 has an F distribution with parameters $r_1 = 1$ and $r_2 = r$.   Hint: What is the distribution of the numerator of T^2?

4.18. Show that

$$Y = \frac{1}{1 + \dfrac{r_1}{r_2}F},$$

where F has an F distribution with parameters r_1 and r_2, has a beta distribution (Exercise 4.9, page 73).

4.19. Let X_1, X_2 be a random sample from a distribution having the p.d.f. $f(x) = e^{-x}$, $0 < x < \infty$, zero elsewhere.   Show that $Z = X_1/X_2$ has an F distribution.

4.4. Transformations of Several Variables.   In Section 4.2 it was seen that the determination of the joint p.d.f. of two functions of two random variables of the continuous type was essentially a corollary to a theorem in analysis having to do with the change of variables in a twofold integral. This theorem has a natural extension to n-fold integrals.   This extension is as follows: Consider an integral of the form

$$\int_A \cdots \int \phi(x_1, x_2, \cdots, x_n)\, dx_1\, dx_2 \cdots dx_n$$

taken over a subset A of an n dimensional space $\mathcal{A}$.   Let

$$y_1 = u_1(x_1, x_2, \cdots, x_n),\ y_2 = u_2(x_1, x_2, \cdots, x_n),\ \cdots,\ y_n = u_n(x_1, \cdots, x_n),$$

together with the inverse functions

$$x_1 = w_1(y_1, y_2, \cdots, y_n),\ x_2 = w_2(y_1, y_2, \cdots, y_n),\ \cdots,\ x_n = w_n(y_1, y_2, \cdots, y_n)$$

define a one-to-one transformation which maps $\mathcal{A}$ into $\mathcal{B}$ in the $y_1, y_2, \cdots, y_n$ space (and hence maps the subset A of $\mathcal{A}$ into a subset B of $\mathcal{B}$).   Let the first partial derivatives of the inverse functions be continuous and let the n by n determinant (called the Jacobian)

$$J = \begin{vmatrix} \dfrac{\partial x_1}{\partial y_1} & \dfrac{\partial x_1}{\partial y_2} & \cdots & \dfrac{\partial x_1}{\partial y_n} \\[2mm] \dfrac{\partial x_2}{\partial y_1} & \dfrac{\partial x_2}{\partial y_2} & \cdots & \dfrac{\partial x_2}{\partial y_n} \\[2mm] \vdots & \vdots & & \vdots \\[2mm] \dfrac{\partial x_n}{\partial y_1} & \dfrac{\partial x_n}{\partial y_2} & \cdots & \dfrac{\partial x_n}{\partial y_n} \end{vmatrix}$$

not vanish identically in $\mathcal{B}$.   Then

$$\int \cdots \int_A \phi(x_1, x_2, \cdots, x_n)\, dx_1\, dx_2 \cdots dx_n$$

$$= \int \cdots \int_B \phi[w_1(y_1, \cdots, y_n), w_2(y_1, \cdots, y_n), \cdots, w_n(y_1, \cdots, y_n)]|J|\, dy_1\, dy_2 \cdots dy_n.$$

Whenever the conditions of this theorem are satisfied, we can determine the joint p.d.f. of n functions of n random variables.   Appropriate changes of notation in Section 4.2 (to indicate n-space as opposed to two-space) is all that is needed to show that the joint p.d.f. of the random variables $Y_1 = u_1(X_1, X_2, \cdots, X_n)$, $Y_2 = u_2(X_1, X_2, \cdots, X_n)$, $\cdots$, $Y_n = u_n(X_1, X_2, \cdots, X_n)$ —where the joint p.d.f. of $X_1, X_2, \cdots, X_n$ is $\phi(x_1, \cdots, x_n)$—is given by

$$g(y_1, y_2, \cdots, y_n) = |J|\, \phi[w_1(y_1, \cdots, y_n), \cdots, w_n(y_1, \cdots, y_n)],$$

when $(y_1, y_2, \cdots, y_n)\epsilon\mathcal{B}$, and is zero elsewhere.

The result of the following illustrative example will have an important role in subsequent chapters.   Let the random variable X have a p.d.f. $f(x)$, which can be written in the form

$$(1) \qquad f(x) = e^{p(\theta)K(x)+S(x)+q(\theta)}, \quad a < x < b,$$
$$= 0 \text{ elsewhere},$$

and where neither a nor b depends upon θ.   For instance, the normal p.d.f.

$$f(x) = \frac{1}{\sqrt{2\pi\theta}}e^{-\frac{x^2}{2\theta}} = e^{\left(-\frac{1}{2\theta}\right)x^2 - \ln\sqrt{2\pi\theta}}, \quad -\infty < x < \infty,$$

where θ is the variance σ^2, is of this form.   The chi-square p.d.f., with θ the number of degrees of freedom,

$$f(x) = \frac{1}{\Gamma\left(\frac{\theta}{2}\right)2^{\frac{\theta}{2}}}x^{\frac{\theta}{2}-1}e^{-\frac{x}{2}} = e^{\left(\frac{\theta}{2}\right)\ln x - \left(\frac{x}{2} + \ln x\right) - \ln\left(\Gamma\left(\frac{\theta}{2}\right)2^{\theta/2}\right)}, \quad 0 < x < \infty,$$
$$= 0 \text{ elsewhere},$$

is of the form (1).   However

$$f(x) = \frac{1}{\theta} = e^{-\ln\theta}, \quad 0 < x < \theta,$$
$$= 0 \text{ elsewhere},$$

is not of this form, for $b = \theta$.

Let $X_1, X_2, \cdots, X_n$ denote a random sample from a distribution having a p.d.f. of the form (1).   The statistic

$$Y_1 = K(X_1) + K(X_2) + \cdots + K(X_n)$$

turns out to be a very important one. We shall obtain, under one restriction yet to be stated, the form of the p.d.f. of Y_1 by using the change of variable technique. The joint p.d.f. of $X_1, X_2, \cdots, X_n$ is

$$f(x_1)f(x_2) \cdots f(x_n) = e^{p(\theta)\sum\limits_{1}^{n}K(x_i)+\sum\limits_{1}^{n}S(x_i)+nq(\theta)}, \quad a < x_i < b,$$
$$= 0 \text{ elsewhere.}$$

Our interest is in the p.d.f. of Y_1, but our method requires that we first obtain the joint p.d.f. of Y_1 and $(n-1)$ other random variables, say, $Y_2, Y_3, \cdots, Y_n$. To avoid tedious computations, we should define $Y_2, Y_3, \cdots, Y_n$ with some care. Let us take $Y_2 = X_2$, $Y_3 = X_3$, $\cdots$, $Y_n = X_n$. Consider the transformation

$$y_1 = K(x_1) + K(x_2) + \cdots + K(x_n)$$
$$y_2 = \qquad\qquad x_2$$
$$\vdots \qquad\qquad\qquad \vdots$$
$$y_n = \qquad\qquad\qquad\qquad x_n$$

We now impose our restriction. It is that $K(x)$ shall be of such a nature that the transformation is one-to-one and that the inverse functions

$$x_1 = w_1(y_1, y_2, \cdots, y_n)$$
$$x_2 = \qquad y_2$$
$$\vdots \qquad\quad \vdots$$
$$x_n = \qquad\qquad y_n$$

yield the Jacobian

$$J = \begin{vmatrix} \dfrac{\partial x_1}{\partial y_1} & \dfrac{\partial x_1}{\partial y_2} & \cdots & \dfrac{\partial x_1}{\partial y_n} \\ 0 & 1 & \cdots & 0 \\ \vdots & \vdots & & \vdots \\ 0 & 0 & & 1 \end{vmatrix} = \dfrac{\partial x_1}{\partial y_1}$$

which is continuous and does not vanish identically. Hence, the joint p.d.f. of $Y_1, Y_2, \cdots, Y_n$ is given by

$$g(y_1, y_2, \cdots, y_n) = |J|e^{y_1 p(\theta)+S[w_1(y_1,y_2,\cdots,y_n)]+\sum\limits_{2}^{n}S(y_i)+nq(\theta)},$$

provided $(y_1, y_2, \cdots, y_n)\epsilon\mathcal{B}$, and is equal to zero elsewhere, where $\mathcal{B}$ is the mapping of $A = \{(x_1, x_2, \cdots, x_n); a < x_i < b, i = 1, 2, \cdots, n\}$ under the given transformation. Since θ does not enter the transformation, it is obvious that neither $\mathcal{B}$ nor J depends upon θ. The p.d.f. of Y_1 is obtained by integrating $g(y_1, y_2, \cdots, y_n)$ over a set B of all values of $(y_1, y_2, \cdots, y_n)\epsilon\mathcal{B}$, with y_1 held fast. That is,

$$g_1(y_1) = \int \cdots \int\limits_{B} |J|e^{y_1 p(\theta)+S(w_1)+\sum\limits_{2}^{n}S(y_i)+nq(\theta)} \, dy_2 \, dy_3 \cdots dy_n$$

$$= e^{y_1 p(\theta) + n q(\theta)} \int_B \cdots \int |J| e^{S(w_1) + \overset{n}{\underset{2}{\sum}} S(y_i)} dy_2 \, dy_3 \cdots dy_n.$$

Since $\mathscr{B}$ does not depend upon θ, neither does B, and the integral

$$\int_B \cdots \int |J| e^{S[w_1(y_1,\cdots,y_n)] + \overset{n}{\underset{2}{\sum}} S(y_i)} dy_2 \, dy_3 \cdots dy_n$$

is at most a function of y_1 alone, say, $R(y_1)$. This means that the p.d.f. of Y_1 has the form

(2)
$$g_1(y_1) = R(y_1) e^{y_1 p(\theta) + n q(\theta)}, \quad c < y_1 < d,$$
$$= 0 \text{ elsewhere,}$$

where $R(y_1)$ and the constants c and d do not depend upon θ. This is the result that has an important role in subsequent chapters.

Here we took $X_1, X_2, \cdots, X_n$ to be a random sample from a continuous type of distribution and showed that $Y_1 = K(X_1) + K(X_2) + \cdots + K(X_n)$ has a p.d.f. having the form (2). This same form (2) holds if the random sample is from a discrete type of distribution having p.d.f. with functional form (1) on a discrete set that does not depend upon θ. In each step of the argument we merely omit the Jacobian and replace integration by summation.

Exercises

4.20. Let X_1, X_2, X_3 denote a random sample from a normal distribution $n(x; 0, 1)$. Let the random variables Y_1, Y_2, Y_3 be defined by

$$X_1 = Y_1 \cos Y_2 \sin Y_3, \; X_2 = Y_1 \sin Y_2 \sin Y_3, \text{ and } X_3 = Y_1 \cos Y_3,$$

where $0 \le Y_1 < \infty, 0 \le Y_2 < 2\pi, 0 \le Y_3 \le \pi$. Find the joint p.d.f. of Y_1, Y_2, Y_3.

4.21. Let the p.d.f. of X be $f(x) = (\ln \theta)\theta^{-x}, \; 0 < x < \infty, \; 1 < \theta < \infty$, zero elsewhere. Show that this p.d.f. is of the form (1) of this section. If X_1, X_2 is a random sample from this distribution, find the joint p.d.f. of $Y_1 = K(X_1) + K(X_2) = X_1 + X_2$ and $Y_2 = X_2$. Show that the marginal p.d.f. of Y_1 is of the form (2) with

$$g_1(y_1) = y_1 e^{(-\ln \theta)y_1 + 2 \ln [\ln \theta]}, \quad 0 < y_1 < \infty,$$

zero elsewhere.

4.22. Show that the gamma p.d.f.

$$f(x) = \frac{1}{\theta^2} x e^{-\frac{x}{\theta}}, \quad 0 < x < \infty, \quad 0 < \theta,$$

zero elsewhere, is of the form (1) of this section. If X_1, X_2, X_3 is a random sample from this distribution, then $Y_1 = X_1 + X_2 + X_3$, since $K(x) = x$. Let $Y_2 = X_2$

and $Y_3 = X_3$, and find the joint p.d.f. of Y_1, Y_2, Y_3 and then the marginal p.d.f. of Y_1.

4.23. Let X_1, X_2, X_3 denote a random sample from the distribution having p.d.f. $f(x) = e^{-x}$, $0 < x < \infty$, zero elsewhere. Show that

$$Y_1 = \frac{X_1}{X_1 + X_2}, \quad Y_2 = \frac{X_1 + X_2}{X_1 + X_2 + X_3}, \quad Y_3 = X_1 + X_2 + X_3$$

are mutually stochastically independent.

4.5. Transformations Not One-to-One. Let $\phi(x_1, x_2, \cdots, x_n)$ be the joint p.d.f. of $X_1, X_2, \cdots, X_n$ which are random variables of the continuous type. Let A be the n–dimensional space where $\phi(x_1, x_2, \cdots, x_n) > 0$, and consider the transformation $y_1 = u_1(x_1, x_2, \cdots, x_n)$, $y_2 = u_2(x_1, x_2, \cdots, x_n)$, $\cdots, y_n = u_n(x_1, x_2, \cdots, x_n)$ which maps A into B in the $y_1, y_2, \cdots, y_n$ space. To each point of A there will correspond, of course, but one point in B; but to a point in B there may correspond more than one point in A. That is, the transformation may not be one-to-one. Suppose, however, that we can represent A as the union of a finite number, say, k, of mutually exclusive sets $A_1, A_2, \cdots, A_k$ so that

$$y_1 = u_1(x_1, x_2, \cdots, x_n), \cdots, y_n = u_n(x_1, x_2, \cdots, x_n)$$

define a one-to-one transformation of each A_i into B. Thus, to each point in B, there will correspond exactly one point in each of $A_1, A_2, \cdots, A_k$. Let

$$\begin{aligned} x_1 &= w_{1i}(y_1, y_2, \cdots, y_n), \\ x_2 &= w_{2i}(y_1, y_2, \cdots, y_n), \qquad i = 1, 2, \cdots, k, \\ &\ \vdots \\ x_n &= w_{ni}(y_1, y_2, \cdots, y_n), \end{aligned}$$

denote the k groups of n inverse functions, one group for each of these k transformations. Let the first partial derivatives be continuous and let each

$$J_i = \begin{vmatrix} \dfrac{\partial w_{1i}}{\partial y_1} & \dfrac{\partial w_{1i}}{\partial y_2} & \cdots & \dfrac{\partial w_{1i}}{\partial y_n} \\[2ex] \dfrac{\partial w_{2i}}{\partial y_1} & \dfrac{\partial w_{2i}}{\partial y_2} & \cdots & \dfrac{\partial w_{2i}}{\partial y_n} \\[1ex] \vdots & \vdots & & \vdots \\[1ex] \dfrac{\partial w_{ni}}{\partial y_1} & \dfrac{\partial w_{ni}}{\partial y_2} & \cdots & \dfrac{\partial w_{ni}}{\partial y_n} \end{vmatrix}, \quad i = 1, 2, \cdots, k,$$

be not identically equal to zero in B. From a consideration of the probability of the union of k mutually exclusive events and by applying the change of variable technique to the probability of each of these events, it can be seen that the joint p.d.f. of $Y_1 = u_1(X_1, X_2, \cdots, X_n)$, $Y_2 =$

$u_2(X_1, X_2, \cdots, X_n), \cdots, Y_n = u_n(X_1, X_2, \cdots, X_n)$, is given by

$$g(y_1, y_2, \cdots, y_n) = \sum_{i=1}^{k} |J_i| \phi[w_{1i}(y_1, \cdots, y_n), \cdots, w_{ni}(y_1, \cdots, y_n)],$$

provided $(y_1, y_2, \cdots, y_n)\epsilon\mathcal{B}$, and equals zero elsewhere. The p.d.f. of any Y_i, say, Y_1, is then

$$g_1(y_1) = \int_{-\infty}^{\infty} \cdots \int_{-\infty}^{\infty} g(y_1, y_2, \cdots, y_n) \, dy_2 \cdots dy_n.$$

To illustrate this result, take $n = 1$ and let X have the normal p.d.f. $n(x; 0, 1)$. As on page 38, consider the random variable $Y = X^2$. The transformation $y = x^2$ maps the set $\{x; -\infty < x < \infty\}$ into the set $\{y; 0 \le y < \infty\}$, but the transformation is not one-to-one, since to each point $y \ne 0$ in the set $\{y; 0 \le y < \infty\}$, there correspond two points $-\sqrt{y}$ and $\sqrt{y}$ in the set $\{x; -\infty < x < \infty\}$. Moreover, the set $\{x; -\infty < x < \infty\}$ cannot be represented as the union of two mutually exclusive sets each of which under $y = x^2$ maps into $\{y; 0 \le y < \infty\}$. However, there is a way out of our difficulty. On page 15, we tried to emphasize that with a continuous type of random variable X, we have $Pr(X = b) = 0$, so that we can change the definition of the p.d.f. at any point b without in any manner affecting the distribution of X. In fact, we may, without altering the distribution of X, redefine the p.d.f. on an entire set of points C as long as $Pr(X\epsilon C) = 0$. Fortunately we can also do this kind of thing with a p.d.f. in any finite number of random variables of the continuous type. Accordingly, for the purpose of this proof, let us redefine our normal p.d.f. as follows:

$$f(x) = \frac{1}{\sqrt{2\pi}} e^{-\frac{x^2}{2}}, \quad x \ne 0$$
$$= 0, \quad x = 0.$$

The set $\mathcal{A}$ on which $f(x) > 0$ is $\mathcal{A} = \{x; -\infty < x < 0, 0 < x < \infty\}$, which is the union of the two mutually exclusive sets

$$A_1 = \{x; -\infty < x < 0\} \text{ and } A_2 = \{x; 0 < x < \infty\}.$$

Moreover, $y = x^2$ defines a one-to-one transformation which maps each of A_1 and A_2 into $\mathcal{B} = \{y; 0 < y < \infty\}$. The two inverses of $y = x^2$ are respectively $x = -\sqrt{y}$ and $x = \sqrt{y}$, so $J_1 = -1/(2\sqrt{y})$ and $J_2 = 1/(2\sqrt{y})$. Thus the p.d.f. of $Y = X^2$ is the previously found chi-square p.d.f. with one degree of freedom, namely,

$$g(y) = \left|\frac{-1}{2\sqrt{y}}\right|\frac{1}{\sqrt{2\pi}}e^{-\frac{y}{2}} + \left|\frac{1}{2\sqrt{y}}\right|\frac{1}{\sqrt{2\pi}}e^{-\frac{y}{2}}, \quad 0 < y < \infty,$$

$$= \frac{1}{\sqrt{\pi}2^{\frac{1}{2}}}y^{\frac{1}{2}-1}e^{-\frac{y}{2}}, \quad 0 < y < \infty,$$

$$= 0 \text{ elsewhere.}$$

Incidentally, it must be that $\Gamma(\frac{1}{2}) = \sqrt{\pi}$. Finally, having obtained the solution to the problem of the p.d.f. of $Y = X^2$, most of us would doubtless prefer to go back and take our normal p.d.f. $f(x)$ to be defined as usual, namely,

$$f(x) = \frac{1}{\sqrt{2\pi}}e^{-\frac{x^2}{2}}, \quad -\infty < x < \infty.$$

We should like to emphasize to the student that we do these somewhat artificial things only for the purpose of making a relatively simple proof.

Exercises

4.24. If $f(x) = \frac{1}{2}$, $-1 < x < 1$, zero elsewhere, is the p.d.f. of the random variable X, find the p.d.f. of $Y = X^2$.

4.25. Show that the normal p.d.f.

$$n(x; 0, \theta) = \frac{1}{\sqrt{2\pi\theta}}e^{-\frac{x^2}{2\theta}}, \quad -\infty < x < \infty, \quad 0 < \theta,$$

is of the form (1), page 79. If X_1, X_2 is a random sample from this distribution, then $Y_1 = K(X_1) + K(X_2) = X_1{}^2 + X_2{}^2$ in the notation of that section. Let $Y_2 = X_2$. Find the joint p.d.f. of Y_1 and Y_2 and then the marginal p.d.f. of Y_1.

4.6. Order Statistics. In this section the notion of an order statistic will be defined and we shall investigate some of the simpler properties of such a statistic. These statistics have in recent times come to play an important role in statistical inference partly because some of their properties do not depend upon the distribution from which the random sample is obtained.

Let X_1, X_2, $\cdots$, X_n denote a random sample from a distribution of the continuous type having p.d.f. $f(x)$ that is positive, provided $a < x < b$. Let Y_1 be the smallest of these X_i, Y_2 the next X_i in order of magnitude, $\cdots$, and Y_n the largest X_i. That is, $Y_1 < Y_2 < \cdots < Y_n$ represent X_1, X_2, $\cdots$, X_n when the latter are arranged in ascending order of magnitude. Then Y_i, $i = 1, 2, \cdots, n$, is called the ith order statistic of the random sample X_1, X_2, $\cdots$, X_n. It will be shown that the joint p.d.f. of Y_1, Y_2,

$\cdots$, Y_n is given by

(1) $\quad g(y_1, y_2, \cdots, y_n) = (n!)f(y_1)f(y_2) \cdots f(y_n), \quad a < y_1 < y_2 < \cdots < y_n < b,$
$\qquad\qquad = 0$ elsewhere.

We shall prove this only for the case $n = 3$, but the argument is seen to be entirely general. With $n = 3$, the joint p.d.f. of X_1, X_2, X_3 is $f(x_1)f(x_2)f(x_3)$. Consider a probability such as $Pr(a < X_1 = X_2 < b, a < X_3 < b)$. This probability is given by

$$\int_a^b \int_a^b \int_{x_2}^{x_2} f(x_1)f(x_2)f(x_3) \, dx_1 \, dx_2 \, dx_3 = 0,$$

since

$$\int_{x_2}^{x_2} f(x_1) \, dx_1$$

is defined in calculus to be zero. As in the latter part of the preceding section we may, without altering the distribution of X_1, X_2, X_3, define the joint p.d.f. $f(x_1)f(x_2)f(x_3)$ to be zero at all points (x_1, x_2, x_3) which have at least two of their coordinates equal. Then the set A where $f(x_1)f(x_2)f(x_3) > 0$ is the union of the six mutually exclusive sets:

$$A_1 = \{(x_1, x_2, x_3); \quad a < x_1 < x_2 < x_3 < b\},$$
$$A_2 = \{(x_1, x_2, x_3); \quad a < x_2 < x_1 < x_3 < b\},$$
$$A_3 = \{(x_1, x_2, x_3); \quad a < x_1 < x_3 < x_2 < b\},$$
$$A_4 = \{(x_1, x_2, x_3); \quad a < x_2 < x_3 < x_1 < b\},$$
$$A_5 = \{(x_1, x_2, x_3); \quad a < x_3 < x_1 < x_2 < b\},$$
$$A_6 = \{(x_1, x_2, x_3); \quad a < x_3 < x_2 < x_1 < b\}.$$

There are six of these sets because we can arrange x_1, x_2, x_3 in precisely $3! = 6$ ways. Consider the functions $y_1 = $ minimum of x_1, x_2, x_3; $y_2 = $ middle in magnitude of x_1, x_2, x_3; and $y_3 = $ maximum of x_1, x_2, x_3. These functions define one-to-one transformations which map each of A_1, A_2, $\cdots$, A_6 into the same set $\mathcal{B} = \{(y_1, y_2, y_3); a < y_1 < y_2 < y_3 < b\}$. The inverse functions are, for points in A_1, $x_1 = y_1, x_2 = y_2, x_3 = y_3$; for points in A_2, they are $x_1 = y_2, x_2 = y_1, x_3 = y_3$; and so on for each of the remaining four sets. Then we have that

$$J_1 = \begin{vmatrix} 1 & 0 & 0 \\ 0 & 1 & 0 \\ 0 & 0 & 1 \end{vmatrix} = 1$$

and

$$J_2 = \begin{vmatrix} 0 & 1 & 0 \\ 1 & 0 & 0 \\ 0 & 0 & 1 \end{vmatrix} = -1.$$

It is easily verified that the absolute value of each of the $3! = 6$ Jacobians is $+1$. Thus the joint p.d.f. of the three order statistics $Y_1 = $ minimum of X_1, X_2, X_3; $Y_2 = $ middle in magnitude of X_1, X_2, X_3; $Y_3 = $ maximum of X_1, X_2, X_3 is

$$g(y_1, y_2, y_3) = |J_1|f(y_1)f(y_2)f(y_3) + |J_2|f(y_2)f(y_1)f(y_3)$$
$$+ \cdots + |J_6|f(y_3)f(y_2)f(y_1), \quad a < y_1 < y_2 < y_3 < b,$$
$$= (3!)f(y_1)f(y_2)f(y_3), \quad a < y_1 < y_2 < y_3 < b,$$
$$= 0 \text{ elsewhere.}$$

This is form (1) with $n = 3$.

EXAMPLE 1. Let X_1, X_2 be a random sample from a distribution having p.d.f.

$$f(x) = 1, \quad 0 < x < 1,$$
$$= 0 \text{ elsewhere.}$$

Although X_1 and X_2 are stochastically independent, show that the order statistics Y_1 and Y_2 are stochastically dependent.   The joint p.d.f. of Y_1 and Y_2 is

$$g(y_1, y_2) = (2!)f(y_1)f(y_2) = 2, \quad 0 < y_1 < y_2 < 1,$$
$$= 0 \text{ elsewhere.}$$

Accordingly, the marginal probability density functions are respectively

$$g_1(y_1) = \int_{-\infty}^{\infty} g(y_1, y_2) \, dy_2 = \int_{y_1}^{1} 2dy_2 = 2(1 - y_1), \quad 0 < y_1 < 1,$$
$$= 0 \text{ elsewhere,}$$

and

$$g_2(y_2) = \int_{-\infty}^{\infty} g(y_1, y_2) \, dy_1 = \int_{0}^{y_2} 2dy_1 = 2y_2, \quad 0 < y_2 < 1,$$
$$= 0 \text{ elsewhere.}$$

Since $g(y_1, y_2) \not\equiv g_1(y_1)g_2(y_2)$, the order statistics are stochastically dependent.

EXAMPLE 2. Let X_1, X_2, X_3, X_4 be a random sample from a distribution having p.d.f.

$$f(x) = \frac{1}{\theta}, \quad 0 < x < \theta, \quad 0 < \theta,$$
$$= 0 \text{ elsewhere.}$$

A 95 per cent confidence interval for the unknown parameter θ is to be found by using the order statistic Y_4.   The joint p.d.f. of the four order statistics Y_1, Y_2, Y_3, Y_4 is

$$g(y_1, y_2, y_3, y_4) = \frac{4!}{\theta^4}, \quad 0 < y_1 < y_2 < y_3 < y_4 < \theta,$$
$$= 0 \text{ elsewhere.}$$

Accordingly, the marginal p.d.f. of Y_4 is

$$g_4(y_4) = \int_0^{y_4} \int_0^{y_3} \int_0^{y_2} \frac{4!}{\theta^4} \, dy_1 \, dy_2 \, dy_3$$

$$= \frac{4y_4^3}{\theta^4}, \quad 0 < y_4 < \theta,$$

$$= 0 \text{ elsewhere.}$$

Now, if we select $0 < c_1 < c_2 \leq 1$ so that

$$Pr(c_1\theta < Y_4 < c_2\theta) = \int_{c_1\theta}^{c_2\theta} \frac{4y_4^3}{\theta^4} \, dy_4 = 0.95,$$

then

$$Pr\left(\frac{Y_4}{c_2} < \theta < \frac{Y_4}{c_1}\right) = 0.95;$$

and, if Y_4 is observed to be y_4, the interval $(y_4/c_2, y_4/c_1)$ serves as a 95 per cent confidence interval for θ. It can be verified that $c_1 = \sqrt[4]{0.05}$ and $c_2 = 1$ satisfy the above conditions. Hence $(y_4, y_4/\sqrt[4]{0.05})$ is one 95 per cent confidence interval for θ.

Exercises

4.26. Let $Y_1 < Y_2 < Y_3 < Y_4$ be the order statistics of a random sample of size 4 from the distribution having p.d.f. $f(x) = e^{-x}$, $0 < x < \infty$, zero elsewhere. Find $Pr(3 \leq Y_4)$.

4.27. Let X_1, X_2, X_3 be a random sample from a distribution of the continuous type having p.d.f. $f(x) = 2x$, $0 < x < 1$, zero elsewhere. Compute the probability that the smallest of these X_i exceeds the median of the distribution.

4.28. Let $Y_1 < Y_2 < Y_3$ be the order statistics of a random sample of size 3 from the distribution having p.d.f. $f(x) = e^{-(x-\theta)}$, $\theta < x < \infty$, zero elsewhere, where $-\infty < \theta < \infty$. Determine the function $c(\theta)$ of θ so that $Pr[\theta < Y_1 < c(\theta)] = 0.95$. From this result show how to construct a 95 per cent confidence interval for θ.

4.29. In Example 2 of this section, we selected $c_1 = \sqrt[4]{0.05}$ and $c_2 = 1$ in order to obtain a 95 per cent confidence interval for θ. However, there are many ways of selecting $0 < c_1 < c_2 \leq 1$ so that

$$\int_{c_1\theta}^{c_2\theta} \frac{4y_4^3}{\theta^4} \, dy_4 = 0.95,$$

and each of these ways leads to a 95 per cent confidence interval $(y_4/c_2, y_4/c_1)$ for θ. Show that for a given y_4 the particular choice of c_1 and c_2 yields the shortest 95 per cent confidence interval of this type for θ.

4.30. Let $f(x) = 1/6$, $x = 1, 2, 3, 4, 5, 6$, zero elsewhere, be the p.d.f. of a distribution of the discrete type. Show that the p.d.f. of the smallest item of a random sample of size 5 from this distribution is

$$g_1(y_1) = \left(\frac{7 - y_1}{6}\right)^5 - \left(\frac{6 - y_1}{6}\right)^5, \quad y_1 = 1, 2, \cdots, 6,$$

zero elsewhere. Note that in this exercise the random sample is from a distribution of the discrete type. All formulas in the text were derived under the assumption that the random sample is from a distribution of the continuous type and are not applicable. Why?

4.7. Functions of Order Statistics. Certain functions of the order statistics $Y_1, Y_2, \cdots, Y_n$ are important statistics themselves. A few of these are (a) $Y_n - Y_1$, which is called the range of the random sample; (b) $(Y_1 + Y_n)/2$, which is called the mid-range of the random sample; and (c) if n is odd, $Y_{(n+1)/2}$, which is called the median of the random sample.

EXAMPLE 1. Let $Y_1, Y_2, \cdots, Y_5$ denote the order statistics of a random sample of size 5 from a distribution having p.d.f.

$$f(x) = e^{-x}, \quad 0 < x < \infty,$$
$$= 0 \text{ elsewhere.}$$

We are to find the p.d.f. of the median Y_3 of the random sample. The joint p.d.f. of $Y_1, Y_2, \cdots, Y_5$ is

$$g(y_1, y_2, \cdots, y_5) = (5!)e^{-y_1-y_2-y_3-y_4-y_5}, \quad 0 < y_1 < y_2 < y_3 < y_4 < y_5 < \infty,$$
$$= 0 \text{ elsewhere.}$$

Accordingly, the p.d.f. of Y_3 is

$$g_3(y_3) = \int_{y_3}^{\infty} \int_{y_4}^{\infty} \int_{0}^{y_3} \int_{0}^{y_2} (5!)e^{-y_1-y_2-y_3-y_4-y_5} dy_1\, dy_2\, dy_5\, dy_4$$

$$= \frac{5!}{(2!)(2!)} e^{-3y_3}(1 - e^{-y_3})^2, \quad 0 < y_3 < \infty,$$

$$= 0 \text{ elsewhere.}$$

EXAMPLE 2. Let Y_1, Y_2, Y_3 be the order statistics of a random sample of size 3 from a distribution having p.d.f.

$$f(x) = 1, \quad 0 < x < 1,$$
$$= 0 \text{ elsewhere.}$$

We seek the p.d.f. of the sample range $Z_1 = Y_3 - Y_1$. The joint p.d.f. of Y_1, Y_2, Y_3 is

$$g(y_1, y_2, y_3) = 3!, \quad 0 < y_1 < y_2 < y_3 < 1,$$
$$= 0 \text{ elsewhere.}$$

Consequently the joint p.d.f. of Y_1 and Y_3 is

$$g_{13}(y_1, y_3) = \int_{y_1}^{y_3} 3!\, dy_2 = 6(y_3 - y_1), \quad 0 < y_1 < y_3 < 1,$$

$$= 0 \text{ elsewhere.}$$

In addition to $Z_1 = Y_3 - Y_1$, let $Z_2 = Y_3$. Consider the functions $z_1 = y_3 - y_1$, $z_2 = y_3$, and their inverses $y_1 = z_2 - z_1$, $y_3 = z_2$, so that the corresponding Jacobian of the one-to-one transformation is

$$J = \begin{vmatrix} \dfrac{\partial y_1}{\partial z_1} & \dfrac{\partial y_1}{\partial z_2} \\[2ex] \dfrac{\partial y_3}{\partial z_1} & \dfrac{\partial y_3}{\partial z_2} \end{vmatrix} = \begin{vmatrix} -1 & 1 \\ 0 & 1 \end{vmatrix} = -1.$$

Thus the joint p.d.f. of Z_1 and Z_2 is

$$h(z_1, z_2) = |-1| \, 6z_1 = 6z_1, \quad 0 < z_1 < z_2 < 1,$$
$$= 0 \text{ elsewhere.}$$

Accordingly, the p.d.f. of the range $Z_1 = Y_3 - Y_1$ of the random sample of size 3 is

$$h_1(z_1) = \int_{z_1}^{1} 6z_1 \, dz_2 = 6z_1(1 - z_1), \quad 0 < z_1 < 1,$$

$$= 0 \text{ elsewhere.}$$

Exercises

4.31. Find the probability that the range of a random sample of size 4 from the uniform distribution having the p.d.f. $f(x) = 1, 0 < x < 1$, zero elsewhere, is less than $\frac{1}{2}$.

4.32. Let $Y_1 < Y_2 < Y_3$ be the order statistics of a random sample of size 3 from a distribution having the p.d.f. $f(x) = 2x, 0 < x < 1$, zero elsewhere. Show that $Z_1 = Y_1/Y_2$, $Z_2 = Y_2/Y_3$, and $Z_3 = Y_3$ are mutually stochastically independent.

4.33. If $Y_1 < Y_2 < Y_3$ are the order statistics of a random sample of size 3 from the distribution having p.d.f. $f(x) = 1, \theta - \frac{1}{2} < x < \theta + \frac{1}{2}$, zero elsewhere, show that $Pr(\theta - 0.4 < Y_2 < \theta + 0.4) = 0.944$. Describe, from this result, how to construct a 94.4 per cent confidence interval for θ.

CHAPTER FIVE

POINT ESTIMATION

In some of the preceding chapters we have considered the problem of estimating certain parameters of distributions by means of a collection of sample values. In each instance, we first determined a random interval such that prior to the performance of the random experiment there is a predetermined probability, say, 0.95, that the random interval includes the unknown parameter. The outcome of the random experiment provides an interval with numerically determined end points; we call this interval a 95 per cent confidence interval for the unknown parameter. This method of estimation of a parameter is called *interval estimation*.

However, in certain instances, it may not be adequate for the purpose at hand to say that we are 95 per cent confident that an unknown parameter of a certain distribution is between, say, 2 and 3; the problem may require a specific number or point as an estimate of the parameter. This method of estimation of a parameter will be called *point estimation*.

Before we go into this problem, we shall introduce the notion of conditional probability density. These conditional probability densities will play an important part in our development of point estimation.

5.1. Conditional Distributions. Let X_1 and X_2 denote random variables of either the continuous or discrete type, having joint p.d.f. $f(x_1, x_2)$ and marginal probability density functions $f_1(x_1)$ and $f_2(x_2)$, respectively. We now introduce a new function to be called a conditional p.d.f. When $f_1(x_1) > 0$, we define the symbol $f(x_2|x_1)$ by the relation

$$f(x_2|x_1) = \frac{f(x_1, x_2)}{f_1(x_1)}.$$

In this relation x_1 is to be thought of as having a fixed (but any fixed) value for which $f_1(x_1) > 0$. It is evident that $f(x_2|x_1)$ is non-negative, and if X_2 is a continuous type of random variable, that

$$\int_{-\infty}^{\infty} f(x_2|x_1) \, dx_2 = \int_{-\infty}^{\infty} \frac{f(x_1, \, x_2)}{f_1(x_1)} \, dx_2$$

$$= \frac{1}{f_1(x_1)} \int_{-\infty}^{\infty} f(x_1, \, x_2) \, dx_2$$

$$= \frac{1}{f_1(x_1)} f_1(x_1) = 1.$$

If X_2 is a discrete type of random variable, summation on x_2 would replace integration on x_2 with the same result. That is, $f(x_2|x_1)$ has the properties of a p.d.f. of one random variable. It is called the *conditional* p.d.f. of X_2, given $X_1 = x_1$. In a similar manner, when $f_2(x_2) > 0$, the conditional p.d.f. of X_1, given $X_2 = x_2$, is defined by

$$f(x_1|x_2) = \frac{f(x_1, \, x_2)}{f_2(x_2)}.$$

The notation $Pr(a < X_2 < b|X_1 = x_1)$ may be read "the conditional probability that $a < X_2 < b$, given that $X_1 = x_1$." It is defined, if X_2 is of the continuous type, by

$$Pr(a < X_2 < b|X_1 = x_1) = \int_{a}^{b} f(x_2|x_1) \, dx_2$$

$$= \frac{\int_{a}^{b} f(x_1, \, x_2) \, dx_2}{f_1(x_1)},$$

provided $f_1(x_1) > 0$. If there is no ambiguity, this may be seen in the form $Pr(a < X_2 < b|x_1)$. In like manner, with X_1 a continuous type of random variable, we define the conditional probability that $c < X_1 < d$, given $X_2 = x_2$, by

$$Pr(c < X_1 < d|X_2 = x_2) = \int_{c}^{d} f(x_1|x_2) \, dx_1$$

$$= \frac{\int_{c}^{d} f(x_1, \, x_2) \, dx_1}{f_2(x_2)},$$

provided $f_2(x_2) > 0$. With random variables of the discrete type, these definitions of conditional probability make use of summation instead of integration.

The notion of mathematical expectation is extended to conditional distributions. Let $f(x_2|x_1)$ be the conditional p.d.f. of a continuous type of random variable X_2, given $X_1 = x_1$, and let $u(X_2)$ be a function of X_2.

The conditional expectation of $u(X_2)$, given $X_1 = x_1$, is denoted by $E[u(X_2)|x_1]$ and (if it exists) is defined by

$$E[u(X_2)|x_1] = \int_{-\infty}^{\infty} u(x_2)f(x_2|x_1)\ dx_2$$

$$= \frac{\int_{-\infty}^{\infty} u(x_2)f(x_1, x_2)\ dx_2}{f_1(x_1)},$$

provided $f_1(x_1) > 0$. In particular we have the conditional mean value of $u(X_2) = X_2$, given $X_1 = x_1$, to be

$$E(X_2|x_1) = \int_{-\infty}^{\infty} x_2 f(x_2|x_1)\ dx_2 = \frac{\int_{-\infty}^{\infty} x_2 f(x_1, x_2)\ dx_2}{f_1(x_1)}.$$

If $u(X_2) = [X_2 - E(X_2|x_1)]^2$, the conditional variance of X_2, given $X_1 = x_1$, is

$$E\{[X_2 - E(X_2|x_1)]^2|x_1\} = \frac{\int_{-\infty}^{\infty} [x_2 - E(X_2|x_1)]^2 f(x_1, x_2)\ dx_2}{f_1(x_1)}.$$

In like manner, we define

$$E[u(X_1)|x_2] = \int_{-\infty}^{\infty} u(x_1)f(x_1|x_2)\ dx_1,$$

provided $f_2(x_2) > 0$ and X_1 is of the continuous type. The usual modification is made when the random variables are of the discrete type.

From the point of view of future work, it is important to observe that $E[u(X_2)|x_1]$ is a function of x_1 alone, say, $\phi(x_1)$. Then $\phi(X_1)$ itself is a random variable and has its own p.d.f.

Before we extend these definitions to distributions of n random variables, we shall give some illustrative examples.

EXAMPLE 1. Let X_1 and X_2 have the joint p.d.f.

$$f(x_1, x_2) = 2, \quad 0 < x_1 < x_2 < 1,$$

$$= 0 \text{ elsewhere.}$$

Then the marginal probability density functions are respectively

$$f_1(x_1) = \int_{x_1}^{1} 2dx_2 = 2(1 - x_1), \quad 0 < x_1 < 1,$$

$$= 0 \text{ elsewhere,}$$

and

$$f_2(x_2) = \int_{0}^{x_2} 2dx_1 = 2x_2, \quad 0 < x_2 < 1,$$

$$= 0 \text{ elsewhere.}$$

The conditional p.d.f. of X_1, given $X_2 = x_2$, is

$$f(x_1|x_2) = \frac{2}{2x_2} = \frac{1}{x_2}, \quad 0 < x_1 < x_2, \quad 0 < x_2 < 1,$$

$$= 0 \text{ elsewhere.}$$

Here the conditional mean and conditional variance of X_1, given $X_2 = x_2$, are respectively

$$E(X_1|x_2) = \int_{-\infty}^{\infty} x_1 f(x_1|x_2) \, dx_1$$

$$= \int_0^{x_2} x_1 \left(\frac{1}{x_2}\right) dx_1$$

$$= \frac{x_2}{2}, \quad 0 < x_2 < 1,$$

and

$$E\{[X_1 - E(X_1|x_2)]^2|x_2\} = \int_0^{x_2} \left(x_1 - \frac{x_2}{2}\right)^2 \left(\frac{1}{x_2}\right) dx_1$$

$$= \frac{x_2^2}{12}, \quad 0 < x_2 < 1.$$

Finally we shall compare the values of $Pr(0 < X_1 < \frac{1}{2}|X_2 = \frac{3}{4})$ and $Pr(0 < X_1 < \frac{1}{2})$. We have

$$Pr\left(0 < X_1 < \frac{1}{2}\middle|X_2 = \frac{3}{4}\right) = \int_0^{1/2} f\left(x_1\middle|\frac{3}{4}\right) dx_1 = \int_0^{1/2} \left(\frac{4}{3}\right) dx_1 = \frac{2}{3},$$

but

$$Pr\left(0 < X_1 < \frac{1}{2}\right) = \int_0^{1/2} f_1(x_1) \, dx_1 = \int_0^{1/2} 2(1 - x_1) \, dx_1 = \frac{3}{4}.$$

EXAMPLE 2.   By definition of $f(x_1|x_2)$, we may write any joint p.d.f. $f(x_1, x_2)$ as

$$f(x_1, x_2) = f(x_1|x_2)f_2(x_2).$$

Suppose we have an instance where $f(x_1|x_2)$ does not depend upon x_2. Then

$$\int_{-\infty}^{\infty} f(x_1, x_2) \, dx_2 = \int_{-\infty}^{\infty} f(x_1|x_2)f_2(x_2) \, dx_2$$

$$= f(x_1|x_2) \int_{-\infty}^{\infty} f_2(x_2) \, dx_2$$

$$= f(x_1|x_2).$$

However,

$$\int_{-\infty}^{\infty} f(x_1, x_2) \, dx_2 = f_1(x_1) ,$$

the marginal p.d.f. of X_1; so

$$f_1(x_1) = f(x_1|x_2) \quad \text{and} \quad f(x_1, x_2) = f_1(x_1)f_2(x_2)$$

when $f(x_1|x_2)$ does not depend upon x_2. That is, if the conditional distribution of X_1, given $X_2 = x_2$, is independent of any assumption about x_2, then $f(x_1, x_2)$

$= f_1(x_1)f_2(x_2)$. These considerations actually motivate the definition of stochastic independence of X_1 and X_2, page 42.

We now proceed to generalize the definitions of a conditional p.d.f. and a conditional expectation. Let $f(x_1, x_2, \cdots, x_n)$ be the joint p.d.f. of the n random variables $X_1, X_2, \cdots, X_n$. Let $f_1(x_1), f_2(x_2), \cdots, f_n(x_n)$ be respectively the (one variable) marginal probability density functions. If $f_1(x_1) > 0$, the symbol $f(x_2, \cdots, x_n | x_1)$ is defined by the relation

$$f(x_2, \cdots, x_n | x_1) = \frac{f(x_1, x_2, \cdots, x_n)}{f_1(x_1)},$$

and $f(x_2, \cdots, x_n | x_1)$ is called the *joint conditional* p.d.f. of $X_2, \cdots, X_n$, given $X_1 = x_1$. More generally, the joint conditional p.d.f. of any $n - 1$ random variables, say, $X_1, \cdots, X_{i-1}, X_{i+1}, \cdots, X_n$, given $X_i = x_i$, is defined as the joint p.d.f. of $X_1, X_2, \cdots, X_n$ divided by the marginal p.d.f. $f_i(x_i)$, provided $f_i(x_i) > 0$. We remark that there are many other conditional probability density functions, but these are adequate for our present purposes.

The conditional mathematical expectation of a function of $n - 1$ of the n random variables $X_1, X_2, \cdots, X_n$, given the other, is defined in a natural way. For instance, the conditional expectation of $u(X_2, \cdots, X_n)$, given $X_1 = x_1$, is defined, for random variables of the continuous type, by

$$E[u(X_2, \cdots, X_n) | x_1] = \int_{-\infty}^{\infty} \cdots \int_{-\infty}^{\infty} u(x_2, \cdots, x_n) f(x_2, \cdots, x_n | x_1) \, dx_2 \cdots dx_n$$

$$= \frac{\displaystyle\int_{-\infty}^{\infty} \cdots \int_{-\infty}^{\infty} u(x_2, \cdots, x_n) f(x_1, x_2, \cdots, x_n) \, dx_2 \cdots dx_n}{f_1(x_1)},$$

provided $f_1(x_1) > 0$. This conditional expectation is a function of x_1 alone, say, $\phi(x_1)$, so that $\phi(X_1)$ is itself a random variable and has its own distribution.

Exercises

5.1. Let X_1 and X_2 have the joint p.d.f. $f(x_1, x_2) = x_1 + x_2$, $0 < x_1 < 1$, $0 < x_2 < 1$, zero elsewhere. Find the conditional mean and variance of X_2, given $X_1 = x_1$, $0 < x_1 < 1$.

5.2. Let $f(x_1 | x_2) = c_1 x_1 / x_2^2$, $0 < x_1 < x_2$, $0 < x_2 < 1$, zero elsewhere, and $f_2(x_2) = c_2 x_2^4$, $0 < x_2 < 1$, zero elsewhere, denote respectively the conditional p.d.f. of X_1, given $X_2 = x_2$, and the marginal p.d.f. of X_2. Determine (a) the constants c_1 and c_2, (b) the joint p.d.f. of X_1 and X_2 (c) $Pr(\frac{1}{4} < X_1 < \frac{1}{2} | X_2 = \frac{5}{8})$, and (d) $Pr(\frac{1}{4} < X_1 < \frac{1}{2})$.

5.3. Let $f(x_1, x_2) = 21 x_1^2 x_2^3$, $0 < x_1 < x_2 < 1$, zero elsewhere, be the joint p.d.f.

of X_1 and X_2. Find the conditional mean and variance of X_1, given $X_2 = x_2$, $0 < x_2 < 1$.

5.4. If X_1 and X_2 are random variables of the discrete type having p.d.f. $f(x_1, x_2) = (x_1 + 2x_2)/18$, $(x_1, x_2) = (1, 1)$, $(1, 2)$, $(2, 1)$, $(2, 2)$, zero elsewhere, determine the conditional mean and variance of X_2, given $X_1 = x_1$, $x_1 = 1$ or 2.

5.5. Let $Y_1 < Y_2 < Y_3$ be the order statistics of a random sample of size 3 from the distribution having p.d.f. $f(x) = 2x$, $0 < x < 1$, zero elsewhere. Find the conditional p.d.f. of Y_1 and Y_2, given $Y_3 = y_3$, $0 < y_3 < 1$. Then compute $E(Y_1Y_2|y_3)$.

5.2. The Problem of Point Estimation. Suppose a distribution has a p.d.f. of known functional form, but it involves a certain unknown parameter θ that may have any value in an interval of values. This will be indicated by writing the p.d.f. in the form $f(x; \theta)$, $\gamma < \theta < \delta$, where γ and δ are known. We may, for instance, have

$$f(x; \theta) = \frac{1}{\sqrt{2\pi}}e^{-\frac{(x-\theta)^2}{2}}, \quad -\infty < x < \infty, \quad -\infty < \theta < \infty,$$

or

$$f(x; \theta) = \frac{1}{\theta}, \quad 0 < x < \theta, \quad 0 < \theta < \infty,$$

$$= 0 \text{ elsewhere.}$$

Let $X_1, X_2, \cdots, X_n$ denote a random sample from a distribution having p.d.f. $f(x; \theta)$, $\gamma < \theta < \delta$. The problem is how to define a statistic $Y_1 = u_1(X_1, X_2, \cdots, X_n)$ so that if $x_1, x_2, \cdots, x_n$ are the observed experimental values of $X_1, X_2, \cdots, X_n$, then the number $y_1 = u_1(x_1, x_2, \cdots, x_n)$ will be a good point estimate of θ. In this connection, we need the following definition.

Definition 1.   Any statistic whose mathematical expectation is equal to a parameter θ is called an *unbiased* statistic for the parameter θ.

Now it would seem that if $y_1 = u_1(x_1, x_2, \cdots, x_n)$ is to qualify as a good point estimate of θ, there should be a great probability that the statistic $Y_1 = u_1(X_1, X_2, \cdots, X_n)$ will be close to θ; that is, θ should be a sort of rallying point for the numbers $y_1 = u_1(x_1, x_2, \cdots, x_n)$. This can be achieved in one way by requiring that $Y_1 = u_1(X_1, X_2, \cdots, X_n)$ be an unbiased statistic for θ and that the variance of Y_1 be smaller than the variance of every other unbiased statistic for θ. We do this because the variance of Y_1 is a measure of the intensity of the concentration of the probability for Y_1 in the neighborhood of the point $\theta = E(Y_1)$. Accordingly we define a "best" statistic for the parameter θ in the following manner.

Definition 2. For a given positive integer n, $Y_1 = u_1(X_1, X_2, \cdots, X_n)$ will be called the *best* statistic for the parameter θ if Y_1 is unbiased, $E(Y_1) = \theta$, and if the variance of Y_1 is less than the variance of every other unbiased statistic for θ.

For example, let $X_1, X_2, \cdots, X_9$ denote a random sample from a normal distribution $n(x; \theta, 1)$. In accordance with the theorem of Section 3.3, page 56, the statistic $\bar{X} = (X_1 + X_2 + \cdots + X_9)/9$ is normal with mean θ and variance $\sigma_{\bar{X}}^2 = 1/9$. Thus $\bar{X}$ is an unbiased statistic for θ. The statistic X_1 is also normal with mean θ and variance $\sigma_{X_1}^2 = 1$; so X_1 is also an unbiased statistic for θ. Although $\sigma_{\bar{X}}^2 < \sigma_{X_1}^2$, we cannot say, with $n = 9$, that $\bar{X}$ is the best statistic for θ; the definition of a best statistic requires that the comparison be made with every unbiased statistic for θ. To be sure, it is quite impossible to tabulate all other unbiased statistics for this parameter θ; so, other methods must be developed for making the comparisons of the variances. A beginning on this problem will be made in Section 5.3.

Exercises

5.6. Show that the mean $\bar{X}$ of a random sample of size n from a distribution having p.d.f. $f(x; \theta) = (1/\theta)e^{-(x/\theta)}, 0 < x < \infty, 0 < \theta < \infty$, zero elsewhere, is an unbiased statistic for θ and has variance θ^2/n.

5.7. Let $X_1, X_2, \cdots, X_n$ denote a random sample from a normal distribution with mean zero and variance $\theta, 0 < \theta < \infty$. Show that $\sum_{1}^{n} X_i^2/n$ is an unbiased statistic for θ and has variance $2\theta^2/n$.

5.8. Let $Y_1 < Y_2 < Y_3$ be the order statistics of a random sample of size 3 from the uniform distribution having p.d.f. $f(x; \theta) = 1/\theta, 0 < x < \theta, 0 < \theta < \infty$, zero elsewhere. Show that $4Y_1, 2Y_2$, and $(4/3)Y_3$ are all unbiased statistics for θ. Find the variance of each of these unbiased statistics.

5.9. Let Y_1 and Y_2 be two stochastically independent unbiased statistics for θ. Say the variance of Y_1 is twice the variance of Y_2. Find the constants k_1 and k_2 so that $k_1 Y_1 + k_2 Y_2$ is an unbiased statistic with smallest possible variance for such a linear combination.

5.3. A Sufficient Statistic for a Parameter.

Let $X_1, X_2, \cdots, X_n$, for a fixed positive integer n, denote a random sample from a distribution having p.d.f. $f(x; \theta), \gamma < \theta < \delta$. The joint p.d.f. of $X_1, X_2, \cdots, X_n$ is then

$$f(x_1; \theta)f(x_2; \theta) \cdots f(x_n; \theta).$$

Let $Y_1 = u_1(X_1, \cdots, X_n)$, $Y_2 = u_2(X_1, \cdots, X_n)$, $\cdots$, $Y_n = u_n(X_1, \cdots, X_n)$ be n statistics such that the change of variable technique of Chapter Four is applicable. In the notation of that chapter (with the exception of indicating θ explicitly), the joint p.d.f. of $Y_1, Y_2, \cdots, Y_n$ is, if the transformation is one-to-one,

$$g(y_1, y_2, \cdots, y_n; \theta) = |J|f[w_1(y_1, \cdots, y_n); \theta]$$
$$f[w_2(y_1, \cdots, y_n); \theta] \cdots f[w_n(y_1, \cdots, y_n); \theta]$$

for random variables of the continuous type, and

$$g(y_1, y_2, \cdots, y_n; \theta) = f[w_1(y_1, \cdots, y_n); \theta]$$
$$f[w_2(y_1, \cdots, y_n); \theta] \cdots f[w_n(y_1, \cdots, y_n); \theta]$$

for random variables of the discrete type. If the transformation is not one-to-one, the right-hand member in each case is the sum of, say, k terms of this form. Whether or not the transformation is one-to-one, the marginal p.d.f. of Y_1 is given by

$$g_1(y_1; \theta) = \int_{-\infty}^{\infty} \cdots \int_{-\infty}^{\infty} g(y_1, y_2, \cdots, y_n; \theta) \, dy_2 \cdots dy_n$$

in the continuous case and by

$$g_1(y_1; \theta) = \sum_{y_n} \cdots \sum_{y_2} g(y_1, y_2, \cdots, y_n; \theta)$$

in the discrete case. For either the continuous or discrete case, the conditional p.d.f. of $Y_2, \cdots, Y_n$, given $Y_1 = y_1$, is

$$h(y_2, \cdots, y_n | y_1; \theta) = \frac{g(y_1, y_2, \cdots, y_n; \theta)}{g_1(y_1; \theta)}$$

provided $g_1(y_1; \theta) > 0$. In the interest of conservation of space, it will be tacitly assumed in the future that if a transformation is not one-to-one but is such as can be treated by the method of Section 4.5, the joint p.d.f. $g(y_1, y_2, \cdots, y_n; \theta)$ would be given by a sum of k terms.

In general the conditional p.d.f. $h(y_2, \cdots, y_n | y_1; \theta)$ will depend upon θ, as is indicated by the notation. In certain cases, however, as will be seen presently, the conditional p.d.f. will not depend upon θ, and these cases will be very important to us. The following definition is made.

Definition. Let $X_1, X_2, \cdots, X_n$, for a fixed positive integer n, denote a random sample from a distribution having p.d.f. $f(x; \theta)$, $\gamma < \theta < \delta$. The statistic $Y_1 = u_1(X_1, X_2, \cdots, X_n)$ is called a _sufficient statistic_ for θ if, and only if, for any other statistics $Y_2 = u_2(X_1, X_2, \cdots, X_n), \cdots, Y_n = u_n(X_1, X_2, \cdots, X_n)$, (for which the Jacobian is not identically vanishing), the conditional p.d.f. $h(y_2, \cdots, y_n | y_1)$ of $Y_2, \cdots, Y_n$, given $Y_1 = y_1$, _does not depend upon the parameter_ θ.

Perhaps it should be emphasized that when we say a function does not depend upon θ, we mean not only that θ does not appear in the "formula" but also that the domain of the function does not involve θ. For example, the function

$$f(x) = \tfrac{1}{2}, \quad \theta - 1 < x < \theta + 1, \quad -\infty < \theta < \infty,$$
$$= 0 \text{ elsewhere,}$$

does depend upon θ.

Comment. Why we use the terminology "sufficient statistic" can be explained as follows: If a statistic Y_1 satisfies the preceding definition, then the conditional p.d.f. of Y_2, say, given $Y_1 = y_1$, does not depend upon the parameter θ. As a consequence, once given $Y_1 = y_1$, it is impossible to use Y_2 to make a statistical inference about θ; for example, we could not find a confidence interval for θ based on Y_2. In a sense, Y_1 exhausts all the information about θ that is contained in the sample. It is in this sense that we call Y_1 a sufficient statistic for θ.

When a sufficient statistic Y_1 for a parameter θ exists, we shall see later that it may serve as the basis for a best statistic for θ. At the moment however, let us give some simple examples of sufficient statistics.

EXAMPLE 1. Let X_1 and X_2 denote a random sample from the normal distribution $n(x; \theta, 1)$, $-\infty < \theta < \infty$. We shall show that $Y_1 = X_1 + X_2$ is a sufficient statistic for θ. Let $Y_2 = X_2$. Consider the functions $y_1 = x_1 + x_2$, $y_2 = x_2$. The inverse functions are $x_1 = y_1 - y_2$, $x_2 = y_2$, so that the Jacobian $J = 1$. The joint p.d.f. of X_1 and X_2 is

$$\frac{1}{2\pi} e^{-\frac{(x_1-\theta)^2+(x_2-\theta)^2}{2}}, \quad -\infty < x_1 < \infty, \quad -\infty < x_2 < \infty;$$

consequently the joint p.d.f. of Y_1 and Y_2 is

$$g(y_1, y_2; \theta) = \frac{1}{2\pi} e^{-\frac{(y_1-y_2-\theta)^2+(y_2-\theta)^2}{2}}, \quad -\infty < y_1 < \infty, \quad -\infty < y_2 < \infty.$$

But we know from other considerations that $Y_1 = X_1 + X_2$ is $n(y_1; 2\theta, 2)$. Hence the conditional p.d.f. of Y_2, given $Y_1 = y_1$, is

$$h(y_2|y_1; \theta) = \frac{\dfrac{1}{2\pi} e^{-\frac{(y_1-y_2-\theta)^2+(y_2-\theta)^2}{2}}}{\dfrac{1}{\sqrt{2}\sqrt{2\pi}} e^{-\frac{(y_1-2\theta)^2}{2\cdot 2}}}$$

$$= \frac{e^{-\frac{1}{2}(y_1{}^2+y_2{}^2+\theta^2-2y_1y_2-2y_1\theta+2y_2\theta+y_2{}^2-2y_2\theta+\theta^2)}}{\sqrt{\pi}\, e^{-\frac{1}{4}(y_1{}^2-4y_1\theta+4\theta^2)}}$$

$$= \frac{1}{\sqrt{\pi}} e^{-\frac{1}{4}(y_1{}^2-4y_1y_2+4y_2{}^2)}$$

$$= \frac{1}{\sqrt{\frac{1}{2}}\sqrt{2\pi}} e^{-\frac{(y_2-y_1/2)^2}{2(\frac{1}{2})}}$$

Thus $h(y_2|y_1; \theta) = h(y_2|y_1)$ does not depend upon θ, and $Y_1 = X_1 + X_2$ is a sufficient statistic for the parameter θ.

The reader may question whether or not it is possible to show that $Y_1 = X_1 + X_2$ of Example 1 is a sufficient statistic for θ if Y_2 is selected to be some function other than X_2, say, $Y_2 = X_1 - X_2$ or $Y_2 = X_1 + 2X_2$.

As a partial answer we can take one of these suggested expressions for Y_2 and proceed as before. However, if we let $Y_2 = u_2(X_1, X_2)$, a general function for which the conditions of the definitions are satisfied, we could answer the question once and for all. It is easy to verify that the joint p.d.f. of X_1 and X_2 can be written

$$\frac{1}{2\pi}e^{-\frac{[(x_1+x_2)-2\theta]^2}{2\cdot2} - \frac{(x_1+x_2)^2-4x_1x_2}{2\cdot2}}, \quad -\infty < x_1 < \infty, \quad -\infty < x_2 < \infty.$$

The transformation $y_1 = x_1 + x_2$, $y_2 = u_2(x_1, x_2)$, with the inverse functions $x_1 = w_1(y_1, y_2)$, $x_2 = w_2(y_1, y_2)$, say, and the nonvanishing Jacobian J yields the joint p.d.f. of Y_1 and Y_2 as being

$$g(y_1, y_2; \theta) = \frac{|J|}{2\pi}e^{-\frac{(y_1-2\theta)^2}{2\cdot2} - \frac{y_1^2-4w_1(y_1,y_2)w_2(y_1,y_2)}{2\cdot2}}$$

Do we it and haven't time to

Since the Jacobian J does not depend upon θ, the quotient of $g(y_1, y_2; \theta)$ and $n(y_1; 2\theta, 2)$, that is $h(y_2|y_1; \theta)$, cannot depend upon θ. Accordingly $Y_1 = X_1 + X_2$ is a sufficient statistic for θ, and this result in no way depends upon the manner in which Y_2 is selected. That is, if it is possible to find one statistic Y_2 satisfying the conditions of the definition so that the conditional p.d.f. of Y_2, given $Y_1 = y_1$, does not depend upon θ, then the conditional p.d.f. of every statistic Y_2, given $Y_1 = y_1$, does not depend upon θ. This is not only true in this example but is also true in every case in which there exists a sufficient statistic for the parameter under consideration.

In Example 1, we also took, for simplicity, a random sample of size $n = 2$. Later (and much more easily) it will be seen that if $X_1, X_2, \cdots, X_n$, is a random sample from $n(x; \theta, \sigma^2)$, then $Y_1 = X_1 + X_2 + \cdots + X_n$ is, for a given positive integer n and for every given value of $\sigma^2 > 0$, a sufficient statistic for the mean θ of the normal distribution.

EXAMPLE 2. Let X_1, X_2 denote a random sample of size 2 from a binomial distribution having p.d.f.

Later!

$$f(x; \theta) = \frac{2!}{x!(2-x)!}\theta^x(1-\theta)^{2-x}, \quad x = 0, 1, 2,$$

$$= 0 \text{ elsewhere,}$$

where $0 < \theta < 1$. Recall, page 50, that $Y_1 = X_1 + X_2$ has the p.d.f.

$$g_1(y_1; \theta) = \frac{4!}{y_1!(4-y_1)!}\theta^{y_1}(1-\theta)^{4-y_1}, \quad y_1 = 0, 1, 2, 3, 4,$$

$$= 0 \text{ elsewhere.}$$

We shall show that Y_1 is a sufficient statistic for θ. The joint p.d.f. of X_1 and X_2 is

$$\frac{2!}{x_1!(2-x_1)!}\theta^{x_1}(1-\theta)^{2-x_1}\frac{2!}{x_2!(2-x_2)!}\theta^{x_2}(1-\theta)^{2-x_2}$$

$$= \frac{2!\,2!}{x_1!x_2!(2-x_1)!(2-x_2)!}\theta^{x_1+x_2}(1-\theta)^{4-(x_1+x_2)}$$

for the nine points $(x_1, x_2) = (0, 0), (0, 1), \cdots, (2, 2)$, and is equal to zero elsewhere. Let $Y_2 = X_2$. The transformation $y_1 = x_1 + x_2$, $y_2 = x_2$ implies that $x_1 = y_1 - y_2$, $x_2 = y_2$. Since we are dealing with random variables of the discrete type, no Jacobian is involved, and at points of nonzero probability the joint p.d.f. of Y_1 and Y_2 is

$$\frac{4\theta^{y_1}(1 - \theta)^{4-y_1}}{(y_1 - y_2)! \, y_2! \, (2 - y_1 + y_2)! \, (2 - y_2)!}.$$

If this joint p.d.f. of Y_1 and Y_2 is divided by $g_1(y_1; \theta)$, it is seen that the quotient, which is the conditional p.d.f. of Y_2, given $Y_1 = y_1$, does not depend upon θ. Thus $Y_1 = X_1 + X_2$ is a sufficient statistic for θ in the given binomial p.d.f.

EXAMPLE 3.   Let X_1, X_2, X_3, X_4, denote a random sample from a distribution having p.d.f.

$$f(x; \theta) = \frac{1}{\theta}, \quad 0 < x < \theta, \quad 0 < \theta < \infty,$$

$$= 0 \text{ elsewhere.}$$

Let $Y_1 < Y_2 < Y_3 < Y_4$ denote the order statistics of this random sample. We shall show that Y_4 is a sufficient statistic for θ. From Section 4.6, page 85, the joint p.d.f. of Y_1, Y_2, Y_3, Y_4 is

$$g(y_1, y_2, y_3, y_4; \theta) = \frac{4!}{\theta^4}, \quad 0 < y_1 < y_2 < y_3 < y_4 < \theta,$$

$$= 0 \text{ elsewhere.}$$

Consequently, the p.d.f. of Y_4 is

$$g_4(y_4; \theta) = \int_0^{y_4} \int_0^{y_3} \int_0^{y_2} \frac{4!}{\theta^4} \, dy_1 \, dy_2 \, dy_3$$

$$= \frac{4y_4{}^3}{\theta^4}, \quad 0 < y_4 < \theta,$$

$$= 0 \text{ elsewhere.}$$

Accordingly, the conditional p.d.f. of Y_1, Y_2, Y_3, given $Y_4 = y_4$, is

$$h(y_1, y_2, y_3 | y_4; \theta) = \frac{3!}{y_4{}^3}, \quad 0 < y_1 < y_2 < y_3 < y_4,$$

$$= 0 \text{ elsewhere,}$$

for every fixed y_4, $0 < y_4 < \theta$. Since $h(y_1, y_2, y_3 | y_4; \theta)$ does not depend upon θ, then Y_4, the largest item of the random sample of size 4, is a sufficient statistic for θ. In a later exercise, the student is asked to show that the largest item in a random sample X_1, X_2, $\cdots$, X_n is a sufficient statistic for θ in every p.d.f. of the form

$$f(x; \theta) = Q(\theta)M(x), \quad 0 < x < \theta, \quad 0 < \theta < \infty,$$

$$= 0 \text{ elsewhere.}$$

Exercises

5.10. Let X_1, X_2, X_3 denote a random sample of size 3 from the distribution having p.d.f. $f(x; \theta) = (1/\theta)e^{-x/\theta}$, $0 < x < \infty$, $0 < \theta < \infty$, zero elsewhere. Show that $Y_1 = X_1 + X_2 + X_3$ is a sufficient statistic for θ. For convenience, let $Y_2 = X_2 + X_3$ and $Y_3 = X_3$, so by the corresponding transformation the space $\{(x_1, x_2, x_3), \ 0 < x_i < \infty\}$ is mapped into the space $\{(y_1, y_2, y_3); \ 0 < y_3 < y_2 < y_1 < \infty\}$.

5.11. Let $Y_1 < Y_2 < Y_3 < Y_4$ be the order statistics of a random sample of size 4 from the distribution having p.d.f. $f(x; \theta) = e^{-(x-\theta)}$, $\theta < x < \infty$, $-\infty < \theta < \infty$, zero elsewhere. Show that the conditional p.d.f. of Y_2, Y_3, Y_4, given $Y_1 = y_1$, does not depend upon θ so that Y_1 is a sufficient statistic for θ.

⑤.12. If X_1, X_2 is a random sample of size 2 from the normal distribution $n(x; 0, \theta)$, $0 < \theta < \infty$, and if $Y_1 = X_1{}^2 + X_2{}^2$ and $Y_2 = X_2$, show that Y_1 is a sufficient statistic for θ. *Double Jacobian idea 4.5*

5.4. The Fisher–Neyman Criterion.

It may be quite tedious to verify that a statistic $Y_1 = u_1(X_1, X_2, \cdots, X_n)$ satisfies the definition of being a sufficient statistic for a parameter. We shall establish a rule, called the *Fisher-Neyman criterion*, which considerably reduces the computation.

THEOREM. Let X_1, X_2, $\cdots$, X_n denote a random sample from a distribution having p.d.f. $f(x; \theta)$, $\gamma < \theta < \delta$. Let $Y_1 = u_1(X_1, X_2, \cdots, X_n)$ be a statistic whose p.d.f. is $g_1(y_1; \theta)$. Then $Y_1 = u_1(X_1, X_2, \cdots, X_n)$ is a sufficient statistic for θ if, and only if,

$$f(x_1; \theta)f(x_2; \theta) \cdots f(x_n; \theta) = g_1[u_1(x_1, x_2, \cdots, x_n); \theta]H(x_1, x_2, \cdots, x_n),$$

where $H(x_1, x_2, \cdots, x_n)$ does not depend upon θ.

PROOF. To prove the Fisher-Neyman criterion for random variables of the continuous type, suppose first that

$$f(x_1; \theta)f(x_2; \theta) \cdots f(x_n; \theta) = g_1[u_1(x_1, x_2, \cdots, x_n); \theta]H(x_1, x_2, \cdots, x_n).$$

We shall make the transformation $y_1 = u_1(x_1, \cdots, x_n)$, $y_2 = u_2(x_1, \cdots, x_n)$, $\cdots$, $y_n = u_n(x_1, \cdots, x_n)$ having the inverse functions $x_1 = w_1(y_1, \cdots, y_n)$, $x_2 = w_2(y_1, \cdots, y_n)$, $\cdots$, $x_n = w_n(y_1, \cdots, y_n)$ and Jacobian J. Thus

$$f[w_1(y_1, \cdots, y_n); \theta] \cdots f[w_n(y_1, \cdots, y_n); \theta]|J|$$
$$= g_1(y_1; \theta)H[w_1(y_1, \cdots, y_n), \cdots, w_n(y_1, \cdots, y_n)]|J|.$$

(31 on both sides)

The left-hand member is the joint p.d.f. $g(y_1, y_2, \cdots, y_n; \theta)$ of $Y_1 = u_1(X_1, \cdots, X_n)$, $Y_2 = u_2(X_1, \cdots, X_n)$, $\cdots$, $Y_n = u_n(X_1, \cdots, X_n)$. In the right-hand member, $g_1(y_1; \theta)$ is the p.d.f. of Y_1, so that $H(w_1, w_2, \cdots, w_n)|J|$ is the quotient of $g(y_1, y_2, \cdots, y_n; \theta)$ and $g_1(y_1; \theta)$; that is, it is the conditional p.d.f. $h(y_2, \cdots, y_n|y_1; \theta)$ of $Y_2, \cdots, Y_n$, given $Y_1 = y_1$. But $H(x_1, x_2, \cdots, x_n)$, and thus $H[w_1(y_1, \cdots, y_n), w_2(y_1, \cdots, y_n), \cdots, w_n(y_1, \cdots, y_n)]$, was given not to depend upon θ. Since θ was not introduced in the transformation and accordingly not in the Jacobian J, it follows that $h(y_2, \cdots, y_n | y_1; \theta)$ does not depend upon θ and that Y_1 is a sufficient statistic for θ.

The converse is proved by taking

$$g(y_1, y_2, \cdots, y_n; \theta) = g_1(y_1; \theta)h(y_2, \cdots, y_n | y_1),$$

where $h(y_2, \cdots, y_n | y_1)$ does not depend upon θ. Now divide both members by the absolute value of the nonvanishing Jacobian J, and replace $y_1, y_2, \cdots, y_n$ by the functions $u_1(x_1, \cdots, x_n), u_2(x_1, \cdots, x_n), \cdots, u_n(x_1, \cdots, x_n)$ in $x_1, x_2, \cdots, x_n$. This yields

$$\frac{g[u_1(x_1, \cdots, x_n), \cdots, u_n(x_1, \cdots, x_n); \theta]}{|J^*|} = g_1[u_1(x_1, \cdots, x_n); \theta]\frac{h(u_2, \cdots, u_n | u_1)}{|J^*|}$$

where J^* is the Jacobian J with $y_1, y_2, \cdots, y_n$ replaced by their values in terms of $x_1, x_2, \cdots, x_n$. The left-hand member is necessarily the joint p.d.f. $f(x_1; \theta)f(x_2; \theta) \cdots f(x_n; \theta)$ of $X_1, X_2, \cdots, X_n$. Since $h(y_2, \cdots, y_n | y_1)$, and thus $h(u_2, \cdots, u_n | u_1)$, does not depend upon θ, then

$$H(x_1, x_2, \cdots, x_n) = \frac{h(u_2, \cdots, u_n | u_1)}{|J^*|}$$

is a function that does not depend upon θ and the proof is complete.

If the random variables are of the discrete type, of course no Jacobian is involved; but otherwise, the proof is identical with the one given.

EXAMPLE 1. Let $X_1, X_2, \cdots, X_n$ denote a random sample from the distribution having p.d.f.

$$f(x; \theta) = \theta^x(1 - \theta)^{1-x}, \quad x = 0, 1, \quad 0 < \theta < 1,$$
$$= 0 \text{ elsewhere.}$$

The statistic $Y_1 = X_1 + X_2 + \cdots + X_n$ has, page 50, the p.d.f.

$$g_1(y_1; \theta) = \frac{n!}{y_1!(n - y_1)!}\theta^{y_1}(1 - \theta)^{n-y_1}, \quad y_1 = 0, 1, \cdots, n,$$
$$= 0 \text{ elsewhere.}$$

Accordingly, the joint p.d.f. of $X_1, X_2, \cdots, X_n$ may be written

$$\theta^{x_1}(1 - \theta)^{1-x_1}\theta^{x_2}(1 - \theta)^{1-x_2}\cdots \theta^{x_n}(1 - \theta)^{1-x_n}$$

$$= \theta^{x_1+x_2+\cdots+x_n}(1 - \theta)^{n-(x_1+x_2+\cdots+x_n)}$$

$$= g_1[(x_1 + x_2 + \cdots + x_n); \theta]\left\{\frac{(x_1 + x_2 + \cdots + x_n)![n - (x_1 + x_2 + \cdots + x_n)]!}{n!}\right\}$$

In accordance with the Fisher–Neyman criterion, $Y_1 = X_1 + X_2 + \cdots + X_n$ is a sufficient statistic for θ.

EXAMPLE 2. Let $Y_1 < Y_2 < \cdots < Y_n$ denote the order statistics of a random sample $X_1, X_2, \cdots, X_n$ from the distribution having p.d.f.

$$f(x; \theta) = e^{-(x-\theta)}, \quad \theta < x < \infty, \quad -\infty < \theta < \infty,$$
$$= 0 \text{ elsewhere.}$$

The p.d.f. of the statistic Y_1 is

$$g_1(y_1; \theta) = \int_{y_1}^{\infty} \int_{y_2}^{\infty} \cdots \int_{y_{n-1}}^{\infty} n! e^{-(y_1-\theta)-(y_2-\theta)-\cdots-(y_n-\theta)} \, dy_n \, dy_{n-1} \cdots dy_2$$

$$= n e^{-n(y_1-\theta)}, \quad \theta < y_1 < \infty,$$

$$= 0 \text{ elsewhere.}$$

Thus the joint p.d.f of $X_1, X_2, \cdots, X_n$ may be written

$$e^{-(x_1-\theta)} e^{-(x_2-\theta)} \cdots e^{-(x_n-\theta)} = g_1[\min x_i; \theta] \left\{ \frac{e^{-x_1-x_2-\cdots-x_n}}{n e^{-n[\min x_i]}} \right\}.$$

By the Fisher–Neyman criterion, the first order statistic Y_1 is a sufficient statistic for θ.

Before taking the next step in our search for a best statistic for a parameter θ, let us consider an important property possessed by a sufficient statistic $Y_1 = u_1(X_1, X_2, \cdots, X_n)$ for θ. The conditional p.d.f. of another statistic, say, $Y_2 = u_2(X_1, X_2, \cdots, X_n)$, given $Y_1 = y_1$, does not depend upon θ. On intuitive grounds, we might surmise that the conditional p.d.f. of Y_2, given some linear function $aY_1 + b$, $a \neq 0$, of Y_1, does not depend upon θ. That is, it seems as though the random variable $aY_1 + b$ is also a sufficient statistic for θ. This conjecture is correct. In fact every single-valued function $Z = u(Y_1)$, or $Z = u[u_1(X_1, X_2, \cdots, X_n)]$, not involving θ, with a single-valued inverse $Y_1 = w(Z)$ is also a sufficient statistic for θ. To prove this, it is seen in the continuous case that the p.d.f. of Z, assuming that the derivative $w'(z)$ is continuous and not identically equal to zero, is

$$g(z; \theta) = g_1[w(z); \theta] \, |w'(z)|.$$

Accordingly, replacing z by $u(y_1)$ in this identity, we have

$$g[u(y_1); \theta] = g_1(y_1; \theta) \, |w'[u(y_1)]|,$$

since $y_1 = w[u(y_1)]$. If $u_1(x_1, x_2, \cdots, x_n)$ is substituted for y_1 in the preceding identity, it follows that

$$g\{u[u_1(x_1, x_2, \cdots, x_n)]; \theta\} = g_1[u_1(x_1, \cdots, x_n); \theta] \, |w'\{u[u_1(x_1, \cdots, x_n)]\}|.$$

If we solve this last identity for $g_1[u_1(x_1, \cdots, x_n); \theta]$ and substitute the result in

$$f(x_1; \theta)f(x_2; \theta) \cdots f(x_n; \theta) = g_1[u_1(x_1, \cdots, x_n); \theta]H(x_1, x_2, \cdots, x_n),$$

we have

$$f(x_1; \theta)f(x_2; \theta) \cdots f(x_n; \theta) = g\{u[u_1(x_1, x_2, \cdots, x_n)]; \theta\} \left[\frac{H(x_1, x_2, \cdots, x_n)}{|w'\{u[u_1(x_1, \cdots, x_n)]\}|} \right]$$

Because the second factor of the right-hand member does not depend upon θ, the Fisher-Neyman criterion implies that $Z = u(Y_1)$ is also a sufficient statistic for θ.

Exercises

5.13 Show that the mean $\bar{X}$ of a random sample of size n from a normal distribution with mean θ, $-\infty < \theta < \infty$, and known variance σ^2 is a sufficient statistic for θ.

5.14. Let $X_1, X_2, \cdots, X_n$ be a random sample from the normal distribution $n(x; 0, \theta)$, $0 < \theta < \infty$. Show that $\sum_1^n X_i^2$ is a sufficient statistic for θ.

5.15 Prove that the sum of the items of a random sample of size n from a Poisson distribution having parameter θ, $0 < \theta < \infty$, is a sufficient statistic for θ.

5.16. Show that the nth order statistic of a random sample of size n from the uniform distribution having p.d.f. $f(x; \theta) = 1/\theta$, $0 < x < \theta$, $0 < \theta < \infty$, zero elsewhere, is a sufficient statistic for θ. Generalize this result by considering the p.d.f. $f(x; \theta) = Q(\theta)M(x)$, $0 < x < \theta$, $0 < \theta < \infty$, zero elsewhere. Here, of course, $M(x) > 0$ and $\int_0^\theta M(x)\, dx = \dfrac{1}{Q(\theta)}$.

5.5. The Rao–Blackwell Theorem. Let $X_1, X_2, \cdots, X_n$ denote a random sample from a distribution having p.d.f. $f(x; \theta)$, $\gamma < \theta < \delta$, where it is known that $Y_1 = u_1(X_1, X_2, \cdots, X_n)$ is a sufficient statistic for θ. Let $Y_2 = u_2(X_1, X_2, \cdots, X_n)$ be another statistic (but not a function of Y_1 alone) which is an unbiased statistic for θ; that is, $E(Y_2) = \theta$. Let the joint p.d.f. $g(y_1, y_2; \theta)$ be that of the sufficient statistic Y_1 and the unbiased statistic Y_2; let $g_1(y_1; \theta)$ and $g_2(y_2; \theta)$ be respectively the marginal probability density functions of Y_1 and Y_2; and let $h(y_2|y_1)$ be the conditional p.d.f. of Y_2, given $Y_1 = y_1$. Because Y_1 is a sufficient statistic for θ, $h(y_2|y_1)$ does not depend upon θ. Hence, $E(Y_2|y_1) = \phi(y_1)$, say, does not depend upon θ. Accordingly, $\phi(Y_1)$ is itself a statistic and is a function of the sufficient statistic Y_1 alone. We shall at present show two facts about this statistic $\phi(Y_1)$:

(i)   The statistic $\phi(Y_1)$ is an unbiased statistic for θ.

(ii) The variance of the unbiased statistic $\phi(Y_1)$ is less than the variance of the unbiased statistic Y_2.

Let us consider fact (i). We have, in the continuous case,

$$E(Y_2|y_1) = \int_{-\infty}^{\infty} y_2 h(y_2|y_1)\, dy_2 = \frac{\displaystyle\int_{-\infty}^{\infty} y_2 g(y_1, y_2; \theta)\, dy_2}{g_1(y_1; \theta)} = \phi(y_1)$$

where $\phi(y_1)$ does not depend upon θ because $h(y_2|y_1)$ does not. We are to show that $E[\phi(Y_1)] = \theta$. Now

$$E[\phi(Y_1)] = \int_{-\infty}^{\infty} \phi(y_1) g_1(y_1; \theta)\, dy_1.$$

If in this integral we replace $\phi(y_1)$ by that which defines it, we have

$$E[\phi(Y_1)] = \int_{-\infty}^{\infty} \left\{ \frac{\displaystyle\int_{-\infty}^{\infty} y_2 g(y_1, y_2; \theta)\, dy_2}{g_1(y_1; \theta)} \right\} g_1(y_1; \theta)\, dy_1$$

$$= \int_{-\infty}^{\infty} \int_{-\infty}^{\infty} y_2 g(y_1, y_2; \theta)\, dy_2\, dy_1$$

$$= \int_{-\infty}^{\infty} y_2 g_2(y_2; \theta)\, dy_2 = \theta$$

[handwritten: $g_1(y_1; \theta)$'s cancel]

since $E(Y_2) = \theta$. Thus $E[\phi(Y_1)] = \theta$, which completes the proof of fact (i).

To prove fact (ii), consider   *[handwritten: math trick?]*

$$\sigma_{Y_2}{}^2 = E[(Y_2 - \theta)^2] = E\{[Y_2 - \phi(Y_1) + \phi(Y_1) - \theta]^2\}$$

$$= E\{[Y_2 - \phi(Y_1)]^2\} + E\{[\phi(Y_1) - \theta]^2\} + 2E\{[Y_2 - \phi(Y_1)][\phi(Y_1) - \theta]\}.$$

We shall show that the last term of the right-hand member of the immediately preceding equation is zero.   In the continuous case,

$$E\{[Y_2 - \phi(Y_1)][\phi(Y_1) - \theta]\} = \int_{-\infty}^{\infty} \int_{-\infty}^{\infty} [y_2 - \phi(y_1)][\phi(y_1) - \theta] g(y_1, y_2; \theta)\, dy_2\, dy_1.$$

Now $g(y_1, y_2; \theta) = h(y_2|y_1) g_1(y_1; \theta)$. Hence, if we integrate first on y_2, we have

$$E\{[Y_2 - \phi(Y_1)][\phi(Y_1) - \theta]\}$$

$$= \int_{-\infty}^{\infty} [\phi(y_1) - \theta] \left\{ \int_{-\infty}^{\infty} [y_2 - \phi(y_1)] h(y_2|y_1)\, dy_2 \right\} g_1(y_1; \theta)\, dy_1.$$

But $\phi(y_1)$ is the mean of the conditional p.d.f. $h(y_2|y_1)$.   Hence

$$\int_{-\infty}^{\infty} [y_2 - \phi(y_1)] h(y_2|y_1)\, dy_2 = 0$$

and accordingly

$$E\{[Y_2 - \phi(Y_1)][\phi(Y_1) - \theta]\} = 0.$$

Moreover

$$\sigma_{\phi(Y_1)}{}^2 = E\{[\phi(Y_1) - \theta]^2\}$$

so that the variance of the unbiased statistic Y_2 may be written

$$\sigma_{Y_2}{}^2 = E\{[Y_2 - \phi(Y_1)]^2\} + \sigma_{\phi(Y_1)}{}^2.$$

Now Y_2 is not a function of Y_1 alone, so $E\{[Y_2 - \phi(Y_1)]^2\} > 0$.   Thus

$$\sigma_{Y_2}{}^2 > \sigma_{\phi(Y_1)}{}^2$$

and fact (ii) is proved.   The proof in the discrete case is identical to the one given here with the exception that summations replace the integrations.

Facts (i) and (ii) together constitute a remarkable theorem known as the *Rao-Blackwell theorem*. It may be stated as follows:

THEOREM. Let $f(x; \theta)$, $\gamma < \theta < \delta$, be a p.d.f. of a random variable X of either the continuous or discrete type. Let $X_1, X_2, \cdots, X_n$, where n is a fixed positive integer, denote a random sample from a distribution having the p.d.f. $f(x; \theta)$. Let $Y_1 = u_1(X_1, X_2, \cdots, X_n)$ be a sufficient statistic for θ, and let $Y_2 = u_2(X_1, X_2, \cdots, X_n)$, not a function of Y_1 alone, be an unbiased statistic for θ. Then $E(Y_2|y_1) = \phi(y_1)$ defines a statistic $\phi(Y_1)$. This statistic $\phi(Y_1)$ is a function of the sufficient statistic for θ; it is an unbiased statistic for θ; and its variance is less than that of Y_2.

This theorem tells us that in our search for a best statistic for a parameter, we may, if a sufficient statistic for the parameter exists, restrict that search to functions of the sufficient statistic. For if we begin with an unbiased statistic Y_2 that is not a function of the sufficient statistic Y_1 alone, then we can always improve on this by computing $E(Y_2|y_1) = \phi(y_1)$ so that $\phi(Y_1)$ is an unbiased statistic with smaller variance than that of Y_2.

In Section 5.6 an additional concept, called "completeness," will be introduced. Completeness, in conjunction with sufficiency, will lead us to the best statistic for a parameter.

$$Y_2 \to \phi(Y_1) \quad via \quad E\left(Y_2 / y_1\right)$$

Exercises

5.17. Let $Y_1 < Y_2 < Y_3 < Y_4 < Y_5$ be the order statistics of a random sample of size 5 from the uniform distribution having p.d.f. $f(x; \theta) = 1/\theta$, $0 < x < \theta$, $0 < \theta < \infty$, zero elsewhere. Show that $2Y_3$ is an unbiased statistic for θ. Determine the joint p.d.f. of Y_3 and the sufficient statistic Y_5 for θ. Find the conditional expectation $E(2Y_3|y_5) = \phi(y_5)$. Compare the variances of $2Y_3$ and $\phi(Y_5)$.

5.18. If X_1, X_2 is a random sample of size 2 from a distribution having p.d.f. $f(x; \theta) = (1/\theta)e^{-x/\theta}$, $0 < x < \infty$, $0 < \theta < \infty$, zero elsewhere, find the joint p.d.f. of the sufficient statistic $Y_1 = X_1 + X_2$ for θ and $Y_2 = X_2$. Show that Y_2 is an unbiased statistic for θ with variance θ^2. Find $E(Y_2|y_1) = \phi(y_1)$ and the variance of $\phi(Y_1)$.

5.6. Completeness. Consider the p.d.f.

$$f(x; \theta) = \frac{1}{\theta}, \quad 0 < x < \theta, \quad 0 < \theta < \infty,$$

$$= 0 \text{ elsewhere.}$$

Let $u(x)$ be a continuous function of x (but not a function of θ), and suppose that we are told that $E[u(X)] = 0$ for every $\theta > 0$. We shall show that this requires $u(x) = 0$ for every $x > 0$. Now every $x > 0$ is here precisely the values of x that, for some θ, make $f(x; \theta) > 0$. So we could say that we shall show that $E[u(X)] = 0$ for every $\theta > 0$ requires $u(x) = 0$

at every x for which there is some θ that makes $f(x;\theta) > 0$.   Our assumption is that

$$E[u(X)] = \int_{-\infty}^{\infty} u(x)f(x;\theta)\ dx = \int_{0}^{\theta} u(x)\frac{1}{\theta}\ dx = 0, \quad \text{for } \theta > 0.$$

Thus

$$\int_{0}^{\theta} u(x)\ dx = 0, \quad \text{for } \theta > 0.$$

If we take the derivative of both members with respect to θ, we have, by the fundamental theorem of calculus, that

$$u(\theta) = 0, \quad \text{for } \theta > 0.$$

That is,

$$u(x) = 0, \quad \text{for } x > 0,$$

as we proposed to show.

Next consider the p.d.f.

$$f(x;\theta) = \theta^x(1-\theta)^{1-x}, \quad x = 0, 1, \quad 0 < \theta < 1,$$
$$= 0 \text{ elsewhere.}$$

Again, let $u(x)$ be a continuous function of x (but not a function of θ), and suppose $E[u(X)] = 0$ for every $\theta, 0 < \theta < 1$. We shall show that this requires $u(x)$ to be zero at every x for which there is some θ that makes $f(x;\theta) > 0$. In this example, every θ, $0 < \theta < 1$, makes $f(x;\theta) > 0$ at the same points, namely, at $x = 0$ and $x = 1$. Hence we shall actually show that $E[u(X)] = 0$, $0 < \theta < 1$, requires $u(0) = u(1) = 0$. We have

$$E[u(X)] = \sum_x u(x)f(x;\theta)$$

$$= \sum_{x=0}^{1} u(x)\theta^x(1-\theta)^{1-x}$$

$$= u(0)(1-\theta) + u(1)\theta$$

$$= \theta[u(1) - u(0)] + u(0) = 0, \quad 0 < \theta < 1.$$

If a linear function of z, say, $az + b$, is equal to zero for more than one value of z, then $a = b = 0$. But we have a linear function of θ, namely, $\theta[u(1) - u(0)] + u(0)$, which vanishes for every θ, $0 < \theta < 1$. Accordingly,

$$u(1) - u(0) = 0 \quad \text{and} \quad u(0) = 0$$

or

$$u(0) = u(1) = 0,$$

as we wanted to show.

We now define the concept of completeness.

Definition.   Let $f(x;\theta)$, $\gamma < \theta < \delta$, be a p.d.f. of a random variable X of either the continuous or the discrete type where, as indicated, θ belongs to some interval, $\gamma < \theta < \delta$, of values. Let $u(x)$ be a continuous function of x (but not a function of θ). If

$$E[u(X)] = 0$$

for every θ, $\gamma < \theta < \delta$, requires $u(x)$ to be zero at every point x for which there is some θ, $\gamma < \theta < \delta$, that makes $f(x; \theta) > 0$, the p.d.f. $f(x; \theta)$, $\gamma < \theta < \delta$, is called a *complete* p.d.f.

It is often helpful to express the same thought in a different way. We shall try to do this with our definition of completeness. In the first place, to say that $f(x; \theta)$, $\gamma < \theta < \delta$, is a complete p.d.f. really means that we are not talking about one p.d.f. but instead about a whole family of probability density functions. For each fixed number θ, $\gamma < \theta < \delta$, there corresponds one member of the family. In this terminology, to say that $f(x; \theta)$, $\gamma < \theta < \delta$, is complete means that if

$$E[u(X)] = 0$$

for every θ, $\gamma < \theta < \delta$, then the continuous function $u(x)$ vanishes for all values of x for which at least one member of the family $f(x; \theta)$, $\gamma < \theta < \delta$, is positive.

Comments. Two remarks should be made. On page 18 it was noted that the existence of $E[u(X)]$ requires that the integral (or sum) converge absolutely. This condition was tacitly assumed in the definition of completeness and is necessary to prove that certain families of probability density functions are complete. The second remark concerns the continuity of $u(x)$. This assumption would never be made in a more advanced textbook. The assumption does permit us to show by elementary methods that certain families of probability density functions are complete. However, the primary purpose of the assumption of continuity is to make it unnecessary to discuss certain aspects of measure theory.

We were able to show by elementary methods that the two simple probability density functions

$$f(x; \theta) = \frac{1}{\theta}, \quad 0 < x < \theta, \quad 0 < \theta < \infty,$$
$$= 0 \text{ elsewhere,}$$

and

$$f(x; \theta) = \theta^x(1 - \theta)^{1-x}, \quad x = 0, 1, \quad 0 < \theta < 1,$$
$$= 0 \text{ elsewhere,}$$

are complete. In general, however, elementary methods are not adequate. Since a proof that a p.d.f. $f(x; \theta)$, $\gamma < \theta < \delta$, is complete is a problem in analysis rather than one in probability or statistics, we shall not press the point in this book. Instead, as is our practice, we shall assert theorems from other branches of mathematics whenever they are needed.

Exercises

5.19. If $az^2 + bz + c = 0$ for more than two values of z, then $a = b = c = 0$. Use this result to show that the binomial p.d.f.

$$f(x; \theta) = \frac{2!}{x!(2-x)!}\theta^x(1-\theta)^{2-x}, \quad x = 0, 1, 2, \quad 0 < \theta < 1,$$

$$= 0 \text{ elsewhere},$$

is complete.

5.20. If the infinite series $a_0 + a_1z + a_2z^2 + a_3z^3 + \cdots$ converges to zero for all z in a given interval, then $a_0 = a_1 = a_2 = a_3 = \cdots = 0$. Use this to prove that the Poisson p.d.f. $f(x; \theta) = \theta^x e^{-\theta}/x!$, $x = 0, 1, 2, \cdots, 0 < \theta < \infty$, zero elsewhere, is complete.

5.21. Let $Y_1 < Y_2 < \cdots < Y_n$ be the order statistics of a random sample of size n from the uniform distribution having p.d.f. $f(x; \theta) = 1/\theta$, $0 < x < \theta$, $0 < \theta < \infty$, zero elsewhere. Show that the p.d.f. of Y_n, the sufficient statistic for θ, is complete.

5.22. Let the p.d.f. of X be $f(x; \theta) = Q(\theta) M(x)$, $0 < x < \theta, 0 < \theta < \infty$, zero elsewhere, where $M(x) > 0$ is a continuous function of x. Let $Y_1 < Y_2 < \cdots < Y_n$ be the order statistics of a random sample of size n from this distribution. Show that the p.d.f. of Y_n, the sufficient statistic for θ, is complete.

5.23. Show that each of the following probability density functions is not complete by finding at least one nonzero continuous function $u(x)$ such that $E[u(X)] = 0$.

(a)
$$f(x; \theta) = \frac{1}{2\theta}, \quad -\theta < x < \theta, \quad 0 < \theta < \infty,$$

$$= 0 \text{ elsewhere}.$$

(b)
$$n(x; 0, \theta), \quad 0 < \theta < \infty.$$

5.7. Uniqueness. Let the parameter θ in the p.d.f. $f(x; \theta)$, $\gamma < \theta < \delta$, have a sufficient statistic $Y_1 = u_1(X_1, X_2, \cdots, X_n)$, where $X_1, X_2, \cdots, X_n$ is a random sample from this distribution. Let the p.d.f. of Y_1 be $g_1(y_1; \theta)$, $\gamma < \theta < \delta$. It has been seen that if there is any unbiased statistic Y_2 (not a function of Y_1 alone) for θ, then there is at least one function of Y_1 that is an unbiased statistic for θ, and our search for a best statistic for θ may be restricted to functions of Y_1. Suppose it has been verified that a certain continuous function $\phi(Y_1)$, not a function of θ, is such that $E[\phi(Y_1)] = \theta$ for all values of θ, $\gamma < \theta < \delta$. Let $\psi(Y_1)$ be another continuous function of the sufficient statistic Y_1 alone so that also we have $E[\psi(Y_1)] = \theta$ for all values of θ, $\gamma < \theta < \delta$. Hence

$$E[\phi(Y_1) - \psi(Y_1)] = 0, \quad \gamma < \theta < \delta.$$

If the p.d.f. $g_1(y_1; \theta)$, $\gamma < \theta < \delta$, is complete, the continuous function $\phi(y_1) - \psi(y_1) = 0$ at all points y_1 for which there is a θ, $\gamma < \theta < \delta$, that makes $g_1(y_1; \theta) > 0$.   That is, at all points of nonzero probability density we have, for every continuous unbiased statistic $\psi(Y_1)$,

$$\phi(y_1) = \psi(y_1).$$

In this sense [that is, $\phi(y_1) = \psi(y_1)$, at all points of nonzero probability density], $\phi(Y_1)$ is the unique continuous function of Y_1 that is an unbiased statistic for θ.   In accordance with the *Rao-Blackwell theorem*, $\phi(Y_1)$ has a smaller variance than every other unbiased statistic for θ.   That is, the statistic $\phi(Y_1)$ is the best statistic for θ.   This fact is stated in the following theorem.

THEOREM.   Let $X_1, X_2, \cdots, X_n$ denote a random sample from a distribution having p.d.f. $f(x; \theta)$, $\gamma < \theta < \delta$, let $Y_1 = u_1(X_1, X_2, \cdots, X_n)$ be a sufficient statistic for θ, and let Y_1 have a complete p.d.f. $g_1(y_1; \theta)$, $\gamma < \theta < \delta$.   If there is a continuous function of Y_1 that is an unbiased statistic for θ, then this function of Y_1 is the unique best statistic for θ.   Here "unique" is used in the sense described in the preceding paragraph.

This theorem is a special case of a very general theorem due to Lehmann and Scheffé.   Our assumption of continuity is unnecessarily restrictive, but it seems undesirable to try to relax it here.   Such an attempt only creates problems, called measure theoretic problems, which we wish to avoid.

In the next section we shall study a fairly large class of probability density functions, for which a sufficient statistic Y_1 for θ can be determined by inspection and whose p.d.f. $g_1(y_1; \theta)$, $\gamma < \theta < \delta$, is complete.

Exercises

5.24.   Let $X_1, X_2, \cdots, X_n$ represent a random sample from each of the discrete distributions having the following probability density functions:

(a) $f(x; \theta) = \theta^x(1 - \theta)^{1-x}$, $x = 0, 1$, $0 < \theta < 1$,   zero elsewhere.

(b) $f(x; \theta) = \dfrac{\theta^x e^{-\theta}}{x!}$, $x = 0, 1, 2, \cdots$, $0 < \theta < \infty$,   zero elsewhere.

Show in each case that $Y_1 = \sum_1^n X_i$ is a sufficient statistic for θ and that the p.d.f. of Y_1 is complete.   Find, for each distribution, the unique continuous function of Y_1 that is the best statistic for θ.

5.25.   Show that the first order statistic Y_1 of a random sample of size n from the distribution having p.d.f. $f(x; \theta) = e^{-(x-\theta)}$, $\theta < x < \infty$, $-\infty < \theta < \infty$, zero elsewhere, is a sufficient statistic for θ and that Y_1 has a complete p.d.f.   Find the unique continuous function of this statistic that is the best statistic for θ.

5.8. The Koopman–Pitman Class of Probability Density Functions.
Consider a p.d.f. which can be written in the form (see illustrative example on page 79)

$$(1) \qquad f(x; \theta) = e^{p(\theta)K(x)+S(x)+q(\theta)}, \quad a < x < b, \quad \gamma < \theta < \delta,$$

$$= 0 \text{ elsewhere,}$$

where $p(\theta)$ is a nontrivial continuous function of θ, $\gamma < \theta < \delta$, and $S(x)$ and $K'(x) \not\equiv 0$ are continuous functions of x.   A p.d.f. of the form (1) will be said to belong to the Koopman-Pitman class of probability density functions; and if a and b do not depend upon θ, we shall say that we have a regular case.   For example,

$$f(x; \theta) = \frac{1}{\sqrt{2\pi\theta}} e^{-\frac{x^2}{2\theta}} = e^{\left(-\frac{1}{2\theta}\right)x^2 - \ln \sqrt{2\pi\theta}}, \quad -\infty < x < \infty, \quad 0 < \theta < \infty,$$

is a regular case of the Koopman-Pitman class.

Let $X_1, X_2, \cdots, X_n$ denote a random sample from a distribution having a p.d.f. of the regular case of form (1).   As an illustration of the change of variable technique, we found, page 81, that the statistic $Y_1 = K(X_1) + K(X_2) + \cdots + K(X_n)$ has the p.d.f. of the form

$$(2) \qquad g_1(y_1; \theta) = R(y_1)e^{p(\theta)y_1+nq(\theta)}, \quad c < y_1 < d, \quad \gamma < \theta < \delta,$$

$$= 0 \text{ elsewhere.}$$

At the time it was emphasized that the function $R(y_1)$ does not depend upon θ.   It is true, in obtaining form (2), that we did assume the transformation $y_1 = K(x_1) + K(x_2) + \cdots + K(x_n), y_2 = x_2, y_3 = x_3, \cdots, y_n = x_n$ to be one-to-one.   But if the methods of Section 4.5, page 82, are used, $g_1(y_1; \theta)$ as given above in form (2) remains valid even if the transformation is not one-to-one and without distinction as to whether X is of the continuous or the discrete type.

We show next that $Y_1 = \sum_1^n K(X_i)$ is a sufficient statistic for the parameter θ in a regular case.   The Fisher–Neyman criterion will be used. The joint p.d.f. of $X_1, X_2, \cdots, X_n$ is, at points of positive probability density,

$$e^{p(\theta)\sum_1^n K(x_i)+\sum_1^n S(x_i)+nq(\theta)} = R\left[\sum_1^n K(x_i)\right]e^{p(\theta)\sum_1^n K(x_i)+nq(\theta)} \left\{ \frac{e^{\sum_1^n S(x_i)}}{R\left[\sum_1^n K(x_i)\right]} \right\}.$$

Consequently, since the last factor of the right-hand member clearly does not depend upon θ, $Y_1 = \sum_1^n K(X_i)$ is a sufficient statistic for θ in a regular case of the Koopman-Pitman class.

At this point we shall use a theorem in analysis to assert that the p.d.f. $g_1(y_1; \theta)$, $\gamma < \theta < \delta$, is complete. This is the same theorem we used when we maintained that a moment-generating function (if it exists) uniquely determines a distribution. In the present context it can be stated as this theorem.

THEOREM. Let $f(x; \theta)$, $\gamma < \theta < \delta$, be a p.d.f. which represents a regular case of the Koopman-Pitman class, form (1). Then if $X_1, X_2, \cdots, X_n$ (where n is a fixed positive integer) is a random sample from a distribution with p.d.f. $f(x; \theta)$, the statistic $Y_1 = K(X_1) + K(X_2) + \cdots + K(X_n)$ is a sufficient statistic for θ and the p.d.f. $g_1(y_1; \theta)$, $\gamma < \theta < \delta$, of Y_1 is complete.

This theorem has useful implications. In a regular case of form (1), we can see by inspection that the sufficient statistic is $Y_1 = \sum_1^n K(X_i)$. If we can see how to form a continuous function of Y_1, say, $\phi(Y_1)$, so that $E[\phi(Y_1)] = \theta$, then the statistic $\phi(Y_1)$ is unique and is the best statistic for θ.

EXAMPLE 1. Let $X_1, X_2, \cdots, X_n$ denote a random sample from a normal distribution having p.d.f.

$$f(x; \theta) = \frac{1}{\sigma\sqrt{2\pi}}e^{-\frac{(x-\theta)^2}{2\sigma^2}}, \quad -\infty < x < \infty, \quad -\infty < \theta < \infty,$$

or

$$f(x; \theta) = e^{\left(\frac{\theta}{\sigma^2}\right)x - \frac{x^2}{2\sigma^2} - \ln\sqrt{2\pi\sigma^2} - \frac{\theta^2}{2\sigma^2}}.$$

Here σ^2 is any given positive number. This is a regular case of the Koopman-Pitman class with

$$p(\theta) = \frac{\theta}{\sigma^2}, \quad K(x) = x, \quad S(x) = -\frac{x^2}{2\sigma^2} - \ln\sqrt{2\pi\sigma^2}, \quad q(\theta) = -\frac{\theta^2}{2\sigma^2}.$$

Accordingly, $Y_1 = X_1 + X_2 + \cdots + X_n = n\bar{X}$ is a sufficient statistic for the mean θ of a normal distribution for every given value of the variance σ^2. Now Y_1 has the complete p.d.f. $n(y_1; n\theta, n\sigma^2)$. Since $E(Y_1) = n\theta$, then $\phi(Y_1) = Y_1/n = \bar{X}$ is the only continuous function of Y_1 that is an unbiased statistic for θ; and being a function of the sufficient statistic Y_1, it has minimum variance. That is, $\bar{X}$ is the unique best statistic for θ. Incidentally, since Y_1 is a single-valued function of $\bar{X}$, $\bar{X}$ itself is also a sufficient statistic for θ and $\bar{X}$ has a complete p.d.f.

EXAMPLE 2. Let $X_1, X_2, \cdots, X_n$ denote a random sample from the normal distribution having p.d.f.

$$f(x; \theta) = \frac{1}{\sqrt{2\pi\theta}}e^{-\frac{x^2}{2\theta}}, \quad -\infty < x < \infty, \quad 0 < \theta < \infty,$$

or

$$f(x; \theta) = e^{\left(-\frac{1}{2\theta}\right)x^2 - \ln\sqrt{2\pi\theta}}.$$

Hence $Y_1 = \sum_1^n X_i^2$ is a sufficient statistic for θ, and the p.d.f. of Y_1 is complete. Since

$$E(Y_1) = E\left(\sum_1^n X_i^2\right) = \sum_1^n E(X_i^2) = n\theta,$$

the statistic $\phi(Y_1) = Y_1/n = \sum_1^n X_i^2/n$, which is also a sufficient statistic for θ, is the unique best statistic for θ.

Exercises

5.26. Write the p.d.f.

$$f(x; \theta) = \frac{1}{6\theta^4}x^3 e^{-\frac{x}{\theta}}, \quad 0 < x < \infty, \quad 0 < \theta < \infty,$$

zero elsewhere, in the Koopman-Pitman form. If $X_1, X_2, \cdots, X_n$ is a random sample from this distribution, find a sufficient statistic Y_1 for θ and the unique continuous function $\phi(Y_1)$ of this statistic that is the best statistic for θ. Is $\phi(Y_1)$ itself a sufficient statistic?

5.27. Let $X_1, X_2, \cdots, X_n$ be a random sample from the distribution having the p.d.f. $f(x; \theta) = \theta x^{\theta-1}$, $0 < x < 1$, $0 < \theta < \infty$, zero elsewhere. Find a sufficient statistic for θ.

5.28. Let X be a random variable with a p.d.f. of a regular case of the Koopman-Pitman class. Show that $E[K(X)] = -q'(\theta)/p'(\theta)$, provided these derivatives exist, by differentiating both members of the equality

$$\int_a^b e^{p(\theta)K(x)+S(x)+q(\theta)} dx = 1$$

with respect to θ. By a second differentiation, find the variance of $K(X)$.

5.9. The Case of Several Parameters. On page 97 we defined a sufficient statistic Y_1 for a single parameter θ in a p.d.f. $f(x; \theta)$, $\gamma < \theta < \delta$. In many interesting problems we encounter, the p.d.f. may not contain just one parameter θ but perhaps two (or more) parameters, say, θ_1 and θ_2. In such cases we define, if they exist, joint sufficient statistics for the parameters.

As before, the notion of a conditional p.d.f. forms the basis of the definition of sufficiency; so, we first define some additional conditional probability density functions. These are natural extensions of the definition of $f(x_2, \cdots, x_n|x_1)$, as given on page 94. Let $f(x_1, x_2, \cdots, x_n)$ be the joint p.d.f. of the random variables $X_1, X_2, \cdots, X_n$, and let $f_{12}(x_1, x_2)$ be the joint p.d.f. of X_1 and X_2. If $f_{12}(x_1, x_2) > 0$, the function $f(x_3, \cdots, x_n|x_1, x_2)$ is defined by the relation

$$f(x_3, \cdots, x_n|x_1, x_2) = \frac{f(x_1, x_2, \cdots, x_n)}{f_{12}(x_1, x_2)}, \quad n > 2,$$

and $f(x_3, \cdots, x_n|x_1, x_2)$ is called the conditional p.d.f. of $X_3, \cdots, X_n$, given $X_1 = x_1$ and $X_2 = x_2$. Further, the function $f(x_4, \cdots, x_n|x_1^{\cdot}, x_2, x_3)$, defined by the relation

$$f(x_4, \cdots, x_n|x_1, x_2, x_3) = \frac{f(x_1, x_2, \cdots, x_n)}{f_{123}(x_1, x_2, x_3)}, \quad n > 3,$$

[where $f_{123}(x_1, x_2, x_3) > 0$ is the joint p.d.f. of X_1, X_2, X_3] is called the conditional p.d.f. of $X_4, \cdots, X_n$, given $X_1 = x_1$, $X_2 = x_2$, $X_3 = x_3$. The conditional p.d.f. of any number of the random variables $X_1, X_2, \cdots, X_n$, given values for the remaining variables, is defined as the ratio of the joint p.d.f. of all n random variables to the joint p.d.f. of those variables which have been assigned.

We now consider joint sufficient statistics for several parameters. We give the definition for two joint sufficient statistics for two parameters, but the extension to more than two parameters is a natural one.

Definition. Let $X_1, X_2, \cdots, X_n$ denote a random sample from a distribution having p.d.f. $f(x; \theta_1, \theta_2)$, where $\gamma_1 < \theta_1 < \delta_1$, $\gamma_2 < \theta_2 < \delta_2$. Let $Y_1 = u_1(X_1, X_2, \cdots, X_n)$, $Y_2 = u_2(X_1, X_2, \cdots, X_n)$, $\cdots$, $Y_n = u_n(X_1, X_2, \cdots, X_n)$ be n statistics such that the Jacobian does not vanish identically. Let $g(y_1, y_2, \cdots, y_n; \theta_1, \theta_2)$ denote the joint p.d.f. of $Y_1, Y_2, \cdots, Y_n$, and let $g_{12}(y_1, y_2; \theta_1, \theta_2)$ be the joint p.d.f. of Y_1 and Y_2. The statistics Y_1 and Y_2 are called *joint sufficient statistics* for θ_1 and θ_2 if, and only if, the conditional p.d.f.

$$h(y_3, \cdots, y_n|y_1, y_2) = \frac{g(y_1, y_2, \cdots, y_n; \theta_1, \theta_2)}{g_{12}(y_1, y_2; \theta_1, \theta_2)}$$

of $Y_3, \cdots, Y_n$, given $Y_1 = y_1$ and $Y_2 = y_2$, does not depend upon θ_1 or θ_2 or both θ_1 and θ_2.

As may be anticipated, there is a Fisher–Neyman criterion for the existence of joint sufficient statistics. In the notation of the preceding paragraph, this criterion can be stated as follows: The statistics $Y_1 = u_1(X_1, X_2, \cdots, X_n)$ and $Y_2 = u_2(X_1, X_2, \cdots, X_n)$ are joint sufficient statistics for θ_1 and θ_2 if, and only if,

$$f(x_1; \theta_1, \theta_2)f(x_2; \theta_1, \theta_2) \cdots f(x_n; \theta_1, \theta_2)$$
$$= g_{12}[u_1(x_1, x_2, \cdots, x_n), u_2(x_1, x_2, \cdots, x_n); \theta_1, \theta_2]H(x_1, x_2, \cdots, x_n)$$

where $H(x_1, x_2, \cdots, x_n)$ does not depend upon both or either of θ_1 and θ_2.

EXAMPLE 1. Let $X_1, X_2, \cdots, X_n$ be a random sample from a distribution having p.d.f.

$$f(x; \theta_1, \theta_2) = \frac{1}{2\theta_2}, \quad \theta_1 - \theta_2 < x < \theta_1 + \theta_2,$$

$$= 0 \text{ elsewhere,}$$

where $-\infty < \theta_1 < \infty, 0 < \theta_2 < \infty$. Let $Y_1 < Y_2 < \cdots < Y_n$ be the order statistics. The joint p.d.f. of Y_1 and Y_n is given by

$$g_{1n}(y_1, y_n; \theta_1, \theta_2) = \int_{y_1}^{y_n} \cdots \int_{y_1}^{y_3} \frac{n!}{(2\theta_2)^n} \, dy_2 \cdots dy_{n-1}$$

$$= \frac{n(n-1)}{(2\theta_2)^n}(y_n - y_1)^{n-2}, \quad \theta_1 - \theta_2 < y_1 < y_n < \theta_1 + \theta_2,$$

and equals zero elsewhere. Accordingly the joint p.d.f. of $X_1, X_2, \cdots, X_n$ can be written, for points of positive probability density,

$$\left(\frac{1}{2\theta_2}\right)^n = \frac{n(n-1)[\max (x_i) - \min (x_i)]^{n-2}}{(2\theta_2)^n}\left(\frac{1}{n(n-1)[\max (x_i) - \min (x_i)]^{n-2}}\right)$$

Since the last factor does not depend upon the parameters, the Fisher–Neyman criterion assures us that Y_1 and Y_n are joint sufficient statistics for θ_1 and θ_2. This result can also be established by showing that the conditional p.d.f. of $Y_2, Y_3, \cdots, Y_{n-1}$, given $Y_1 = y_1$ and $Y_n = y_n$, does not depend upon the parameters.

There is an extension of the Rao-Blackwell theorem to joint sufficient statistics for several parameters, but that extension will not be included in this book. However, the concept of completeness is generalized as follows: Let $f(v_1, v_2, \cdots, v_k; \theta_1, \theta_2, \cdots, \theta_m)$ be a p.d.f. of k random variables $V_1, V_2, \cdots, V_k$ so that f depends on m parameters $\theta_1, \theta_2, \cdots \theta_m$, where $\gamma_j < \theta_j < \delta_j, j = 1, 2, \cdots, m$. Let $u(v_1, v_2, \cdots, v_k)$ be a continuous function of $v_1, v_2, \cdots, v_k$ (but not a function of $\theta_1, \theta_2, \cdots \theta_m$). If

$$E[u(V_1, V_2, \cdots, V_k)] = 0$$

for all $\theta_j, \gamma_j < \theta_j < \delta_j, j = 1, 2, \cdots, m$ implies that $u(v_1, v_2, \cdots, v_k) = 0$ at all points $(v_1, v_2, \cdots, v_k)$ for which there is some $(\theta_1, \theta_2, \cdots, \theta_m)$ that makes the p.d.f. positive, we shall say that the p.d.f. $f(v_1, v_2, \cdots, v_k; \theta_1, \theta_2, \cdots, \theta_m)$. $\gamma_j < \theta_j < \delta_j$, is complete.

The remainder of our treatment of the case of more than one parameter will be restricted to regular cases of the Koopman-Pitman class. Let $X_1, X_2, \cdots, X_n, n \geq m$, denote a random sample from a distribution that depends on m parameters and has a p.d.f. of the form

(1) $\quad f(x; \theta_1, \theta_2, \cdots, \theta_m) = e^{\sum\limits_{1}^{m} p_j(\theta_1, \theta_2, \cdots, \theta_m)K_j(x) + S(x) + q(\theta_1, \theta_2, \cdots, \theta_m)}$

for $a < x < b$, and equals zero elsewhere, where

(i) $S(x)$ is continuous,
(ii) the $K_j'(x)$, $j = 1, 2, \cdots, m$, are continuous and no one is a linear homogeneous function of the others,
(iii) the $p_j(\theta_1, \theta_2, \cdots, \theta_m)$, $j = 1, 2, \cdots, m$, are non-trivial, functionally independent, continuous functions of θ_j, $\gamma_j < \theta_j < \delta_j, j = 1, 2, \cdots, m$,
(iv) a and b do not depend on $\theta_1, \theta_2, \cdots \theta_m$.

As in the preceding section, we refer to form (1) as a regular case of the Koopman-Pitman class of probability density functions.   It can be shown that the statistics

$$Y_1 = \sum_1^n K_1(X_i), \quad Y_2 = \sum_1^n K_2(X_i), \cdots, \quad Y_m = \sum_1^n K_m(X_i)$$

have a joint p.d.f. of the form

(2) $$R(y_1, y_2, \cdots, y_m)e^{\sum_1^m p_j(\theta_1, \theta_2, \cdots, \theta_m) y_j + n q(\theta_1, \theta_2, \cdots, \theta_m)}$$

for the points of positive probability density; here $R(y_1, y_2, \cdots, y_m)$ does not depend on the parameters.   Consequently, at points of positive probability density, the joint p.d.f. of $X_1, X_2, \cdots, X_n$, namely,

$$e^{\sum_{j=1}^m [p_j(\theta_1, \theta_2, \cdots, \theta_m) \sum_{i=1}^n K_j(x_i)] + \sum_{i=1}^n S(x_i) + n q(\theta_1, \theta_2, \cdots, \theta_m)}$$

can be written as the product of

$$R\left[\sum_{i=1}^n K_1(x_i), \cdots, \sum_{i=1}^n K_m(x_i) \right] e^{\sum_{j=1}^m \left[p_j(\theta_1, \cdots, \theta_m) \sum_{i=1}^n K_j(x_i) \right] + n q(\theta_1, \cdots, \theta_m)}$$

and

$$\frac{e^{\sum_{i=1}^n S(x_i)}}{R\left[\sum_{i=1}^n K_1(x_i), \cdots, \sum_{i=1}^n K_m(x_i) \right]}.$$

This implies, by the Fisher–Neyman criterion, that the statistics

$$Y_1 = \sum_1^n K_1(X_i), \quad Y_2 = \sum_1^n K_2(X_i), \cdots, \quad Y_m = \sum_1^n K_m(X_i)$$

are m joint sufficient statistics for the m parameters $\theta_1, \theta_2, \cdots, \theta_m$.   Moreover, according to a theorem of analysis, it can be asserted that in a regular case of the Koopman-Pitman class, form (1), with conditions (i) to (iv) satisfied, the joint p.d.f. [form (2)] of these m joint sufficient statistics $Y_1, Y_2, \cdots, Y_m$ for the m parameters $\theta_1, \theta_2, \cdots, \theta_m$ is complete when $n \geq m$.

EXAMPLE 2. Let $X_1, X_2, \cdots, X_n$, $n \geq 2$, be a random sample from the normal distribution having p.d.f.

$$f(x; \theta_1, \theta_2) = \frac{1}{\sqrt{2\pi\theta_2}}e^{-\frac{(x-\theta_1)^2}{2\theta_2}}, \quad -\infty < x < \infty,$$

where $-\infty < \theta_1 < \infty$ and $0 < \theta_2 < \infty$. This may be written as

$$f(x; \theta_1, \theta_2) = e^{\left(-\frac{1}{2\theta_2}\right)x^2 + \left(\frac{\theta_1}{\theta_2}\right)x - \frac{\theta_1^2}{2\theta_2} - \ln\sqrt{2\pi\theta_2}}.$$

Therefore we can take $K_1(x) = x^2$ and $K_2(x) = x$. Consequently the statistics

$$Y_1 = \sum_1^n X_i^2 \quad \text{and} \quad Y_2 = \sum_1^n X_i$$

are joint sufficient statistics for θ_1 and θ_2. Since the relations

$$Z_1 = \frac{Y_2}{n} = \bar{X}, \quad Z_2 = \frac{Y_1 - \dfrac{Y_2^2}{n}}{n-1} = \frac{\sum(X_i - \bar{X})^2}{n-1}$$

define a one-to-one mapping from the y_1y_2 plane to the z_1z_2 plane, Z_1 and Z_2 are also joint sufficient statistics for θ_1 and θ_2. Moreover,

$$E(Z_1) = \theta_1 \quad \text{and} \quad E(Z_2) = \theta_2.$$

From the completeness of the joint p.d.f. of Y_1 and Y_2, we have that Z_1 and Z_2 are the only continuous functions of Y_1 and Y_2 which are unbiased statistics for θ_1 and θ_2, respectively.

Not always do we sample from a distribution having a p.d.f. of one random variable X. We could, for instance, sample from a distribution of two random variables V and W with joint p.d.f. $f(v, w; \theta_1, \theta_2, \cdots, \theta_m)$. By a random sample $(V_1, W_1), (V_2, W_2), \cdots, (V_n, W_n)$ from a distribution of this sort, we would mean that the joint p.d.f. of these $2n$ random variables is given by

$$f(v_1, w_1; \theta_1, \cdots, \theta_m)f(v_2, w_2; \theta_1, \cdots, \theta_m) \cdots f(v_n, w_n; \theta_1, \cdots, \theta_m).$$

In particular suppose that the random sample is taken from a distribution having the p.d.f. of V and W of the Koopman-Pitman class

$$(3) \quad f(v, w; \theta_1, \cdots, \theta_m) = e^{\sum\limits_1^m p_j(\theta_1, \theta_2, \cdots, \theta_m)K_j(v,w) + S(v,w) + q(\theta_1, \cdots, \theta_m)}$$

for $a < v < b$, $c < w < d$, and equals zero elsewhere, where a, b, c, d do not depend on the parameters and conditions similar to (i), (ii), (iii) in form (1) are imposed. Then the m statistics

$$Y_1 = \sum_1^n K(V_i, W_i), \quad Y_2 = \sum_1^n K_2(V_i, W_i), \cdots, Y_m = \sum_1^n K_m(V_i, W_i)$$

are joint sufficient statistics for the m parameters $\theta_1, \theta_2, \cdots, \theta_m$, and the joint p.d.f. of these m joint sufficient statistics is complete.

Exercises

5.29. Let $Y_1 < Y_2 < Y_3$ be the order statistics of a random sample of size 3 from the distribution with p.d.f.

$$f(x; \theta_1, \theta_2) = \frac{1}{\theta_2} e^{-\frac{(x-\theta_1)}{\theta_2}}, \quad \theta_1 < x < \infty, \quad \begin{matrix} -\infty < \theta_1 < \infty \\ 0 < \theta_2 < \infty \end{matrix},$$

zero elsewhere. Find the joint p.d.f. of $Z_1 = Y_1$, $Z_2 = Y_2$, and $Z_3 = Y_1 + Y_2 + Y_3$. The corresponding transformation maps the space $\{(y_1, y_2, y_3), \theta_1 < y_1 < y_2 < y_3 < \infty\}$ into the space $\{(z_1, z_2, z_3); \theta_1 < z_1 < z_2 < (z_3 - z_1)/2 < \infty\}$. Show that Z_1 and Z_3 are joint sufficient statistics for θ_1 and θ_2.

5.30. If $Y_1 < Y_2 < Y_3$ are the order statistics of a random sample of size 3 from a uniform distribution having the p.d.f. $f(x; \theta) = \frac{1}{2}$, $\theta - 1 < x < \theta + 1$, $-\infty < \theta < \infty$, zero elsewhere, show that Y_1 and Y_3 are joint sufficient statistics for θ by showing that the conditional p.d.f. of Y_2, given Y_1 and Y_3, does not depend on θ. However, show that the joint p.d.f. of Y_1 and Y_3 is not complete by finding at least two functions of Y_1 and Y_3 that are unbiased statistics for θ.

5.31. Let the p.d.f. $f(x; \theta_1, \theta_2)$ be of the form

$$e^{p_1(\theta_1, \theta_2)K_1(x) + p_2(\theta_1, \theta_2)K_2(x) + S(x) + q(\theta_1, \theta_2)}, \quad a < x < b,$$

zero elsewhere. Let $K'_1(x) = cK'_2(x)$. Show that $f(x; \theta_1, \theta_2)$ can be written in the form

$$e^{p(\theta_1, \theta_2)K(x) + S(x) + q_1(\theta_1, \theta_2)}, \quad a < x < b,$$

zero elsewhere. This is the reason why it is required that no one $K'_j(x)$ be a linear homogeneous function of the others; that is, so that the number of sufficient statistics equals the number of parameters.

5.10. Maximum Likelihood Estimation of Parameters. In this section we present a brief discussion of a very general method of point estimation of parameters known as the *method of maximum likelihood*. Consider a random sample $X_1, X_2, \cdots, X_n$ from a distribution having p.d.f. $f(x; \theta)$, $\gamma < \theta < \delta$. The joint p.d.f. of $X_1, X_2, \cdots, X_n$ is $f(x_1; \theta)f(x_2; \theta) \cdots f(x_n; \theta)$. This joint p.d.f. may be regarded as a function of θ. When so regarded, it is called the likelihood function L of the random sample, and we write

$$L(\theta; x_1, x_2, \cdots, x_n) = f(x_1; \theta)f(x_2; \theta) \cdots f(x_n; \theta).$$

Suppose we can find a function of $x_1, x_2, \cdots, x_n$, say, $u(x_1, x_2, \cdots, x_n)$, such that when θ is replaced by $u(x_1, x_2, \cdots, x_n)$, the likelihood function L is a maximum. That is, $L[u(x_1, x_2, \cdots, x_n); x_1, x_2, \cdots, x_n]$ is at least as great as $L(\theta; x_1, x_2, \cdots, x_n)$ for every θ, $\gamma < \theta < \delta$. If $\gamma < u(x_1, x_2, \cdots, x_n) < \delta$ for every point $(x_1, x_2, \cdots, x_n)$ of positive probability density, then the statistic $u(X_1, X_2, \cdots, X_n)$ will be called a *maximum likelihood statistic* for θ. A maximum likelihood statistic for θ will be denoted by the symbol $\hat{\theta} = u(X_1, X_2, \cdots, X_n)$. We remark that in many instances there will be a unique maximum likelihood statistic $\hat{\theta}$ for a parameter θ, and often it may be obtained by the process of differentiation. A few examples should help clarify these definitions and statements.

EXAMPLE 1. Let $X_1, X_2, \cdots, X_n$ be a random sample from the normal distribution having p.d.f. $n(x; \theta, 1)$, $-\infty < \theta < \infty$. Here

$$L(\theta; x_1, x_2, \cdots, x_n) = \left(\frac{1}{\sqrt{2\pi}}\right)^n e^{-\frac{\sum\limits_1^n (x_i - \theta)^2}{2}}.$$

This function L can be maximized by setting the first derivative of L, with respect to θ, equal to zero and solving the resulting equation for θ. We note, however, that each of the functions L and $\ln L$ is a maximum for the same value θ. So, it may be easier to solve

$$\frac{d \ln L(\theta; x_1, x_2, \cdots, x_n)}{d\theta} = 0.$$

For this example,

$$\frac{d \ln L(\theta; x_1, x_2, \cdots, x_n)}{d\theta} = \sum_1^n (x_i - \theta).$$

If this derivative is equated to zero, the solution for θ is $u(x_1, x_2, \cdots, x_n) = \left(\sum\limits_1^n x_i\right)/n$. That $\left(\sum\limits_1^n x_i\right)/n$ actually maximizes L is easily seen. Thus the statistic

$$\hat{\theta} = u(X_1, X_2, \cdots, X_n) = \frac{1}{n}\sum_1^n X_i = \bar{X}$$

is the unique maximum likelihood statistic for the mean θ.

EXAMPLE 2. Let $X_1, X_2, \cdots, X_n$ be a random sample from the distribution having p.d.f.

$$f(x; \theta) = \theta^x(1 - \theta)^{1-x}, \quad x = 0, 1, \quad 0 \le \theta \le 1,$$

$$= 0 \text{ elsewhere},$$

where $f(0; 0) = f(1; 1) = 1$. Thus, if $0 < \theta < 1$,

$$L(\theta; x_1, x_2, \cdots, x_n) = \theta^{\sum\limits_1^n x_i}(1 - \theta)^{n-\sum\limits_1^n x_i}$$

and

$$\ln L(\theta; x_1, x_2, \cdots, x_n) = \left(\sum_1^n x_i\right)\ln \theta + \left(n - \sum_1^n x_i\right)\ln (1 - \theta).$$

Now

$$\frac{d \ln L(\theta; x_1, x_2, \cdots, x_n)}{d\theta} = \frac{\sum\limits_1^n x_i}{\theta} - \frac{n - \sum\limits_1^n x_i}{1 - \theta} = 0$$

yields the solution $\theta = \left(\sum\limits_1^n x_i\right)/n$. This value actually maximizes the likelihood function for $0 \le \theta \le 1$, and so the statistic

$$\hat{\theta} = \frac{\sum\limits_1^n X_i}{n} = \bar{X}$$

is the unique maximum likelihood statistic for θ.

EXAMPLE 3. Let

$$f(x; \theta) = \frac{1}{\theta}, \quad 0 < x \le \theta, \quad 0 < \theta < \infty,$$

$$= 0 \text{ elsewhere,}$$

and let $X_1, X_2, \cdots, X_n$ denote a random sample from this distribution. Note that we have taken $0 < x \le \theta$ instead of $0 < x < \theta$ so as to avoid a discussion of supremum versus maximum. Here

$$L(\theta; x_1, x_2, \cdots, x_n) = \frac{1}{\theta^n}, \quad 0 < x_i \le \theta,$$

which is an ever-decreasing function of θ. The maximum of such functions cannot be found by differentiation but by selecting θ as small as possible. Now $\theta \ge$ each x_i; in particular, then, $\theta \ge \max(x_i)$. Thus L can be made no larger than

$$\frac{1}{[\max (x_i)]^n}$$

and the unique maximum likelihood statistic $\hat{\theta}$ for θ in this example is the nth order statistic $\max(X_i)$.

EXAMPLE 4. Let

$$f(x; \theta) = 1, \quad \theta - \tfrac{1}{2} \le x \le \theta + \tfrac{1}{2}, \quad -\infty < \theta < \infty,$$

$$= 0 \text{ elsewhere,}$$

and let $X_1, X_2, \cdots, X_n$ denote a random sample from this distribution. Then

$$L(\theta; x_1, x_2, \cdots, x_n) = 1, \quad \theta - \tfrac{1}{2} \le x_i \le \theta + \tfrac{1}{2},$$

$$= 0 \text{ elsewhere.}$$

Thus L attains its maximum provided

$$\theta - \tfrac{1}{2} \le \min (x_i) \quad \text{and} \quad \max (x_i) \le \theta + \tfrac{1}{2},$$

or when

$$\theta \le \min (x_i) + \tfrac{1}{2} \quad \text{and} \quad \max (x_i) - \tfrac{1}{2} \le \theta.$$

So, every statistic $u(X_1, X_2, \cdots, X_n)$ such that

$$\max (X_i) - \tfrac{1}{2} \le u(X_1, X_2, \cdots, X_n) \le \min (X_i) + \tfrac{1}{2}$$

is a maximum likelihood statistic for θ. One such statistic is

$$u(X_1, X_2, \cdots, X_n) = \frac{\min(X_i) + \max(X_i)}{2}.$$

One of the important properties of the method of maximum likelihood is contained in the following theorem.

THEOREM. Let $X_1, X_2, \cdots, X_n$ denote a random sample from a distribution having p.d.f. $f(x; \theta)$, $\gamma < \theta < \delta$. If a sufficient statistic $Y_1 = u_1(X_1, X_2, \cdots, X_n)$ for θ exists, and if a maximum likelihood statistic $\hat{\theta}$ for θ also exists, then $\hat{\theta}$ is a function of $Y_1 = u_1(X_1, X_2, \cdots, X_n)$.

PROOF.   Let $g_1(y_1; \theta)$ be the p.d.f. of the sufficient statistic Y_1.   Then, by the Fisher–Neyman criterion,

$$L(\theta; x_1, x_2, \cdots, x_n) = f(x_1; \theta)f(x_2; \theta) \cdots f(x_n; \theta)$$
$$= g_1[u_1(x_1, x_2, \cdots, x_n); \theta]H(x_1, x_2, \cdots, x_n),$$

where $H(x_1, x_2, \cdots, x_n)$ does not depend on θ.   That is, in maximizing L with respect to θ, $H(x_1, x_2, \cdots, x_n)$ plays the role of a constant, so that each of the functions L and $g_1[u_1(x_1, x_2, \cdots, x_n); \theta]$ is a maximum simultaneously. Apart from trivial solutions (that is, θ a constant) any θ that maximizes $g_1[u_1(x_1, x_2, \cdots, x_n); \theta]$ will be a function of $u_1(x_1, x_2, \cdots, x_n)$.   Thus the maximum likelihood statistic $\hat{\theta}$ is a function of the sufficient statistic $Y_1 = u_1(X_1, X_2, \cdots, X_n)$.   This important fact was illustrated in Examples 1, 2, and 3 of this section.

The preceding definitions and properties are easily generalized.   If X_1, $X_2, \cdots, X_n$ is a random sample from a distribution having the p.d.f. $f(x; \theta_1, \theta_2)$, $\gamma_1 < \theta_1 < \delta_1$, $\gamma_2 < \theta_2 < \delta_2$, the likelihood function is defined by

$$L(\theta_1, \theta_2; x_1, x_2, \cdots, x_n) = f(x_1; \theta_1, \theta_2)f(x_2; \theta_1, \theta_2) \cdots f(x_n; \theta_1, \theta_2).$$

Those functions $u_1(x_1, x_2, \cdots, x_n)$ and $u_2(x_1, x_2, \cdots, x_n)$ that maximize L with respect to θ_1 and θ_2 respectively, define maximum likelihood statistics $\hat{\theta}_1 = u_1(X_1, X_2, \cdots, X_n)$ and $\hat{\theta}_2 = u_2(X_1, X_2, \cdots, X_n)$.   If two joint sufficient statistics Y_1 and Y_2 for θ_1 and θ_2 exist and if the maximum likelihood statistics $\hat{\theta}_1$ and $\hat{\theta}_2$ for θ_1 and θ_2 exist, then $\hat{\theta}_1$ and $\hat{\theta}_2$ are functions of Y_1 and Y_2.   If we have a random sample (V_1, W_1), (V_2, W_2), $\cdots$, (V_n, W_n) from a distribution of V and W which has p.d.f. $f(v, w; \theta_1, \theta_2, \theta_3)$, the likelihood function is defined by

$$L(\theta_1, \theta_2, \theta_3; v_1, w_1, \cdots, v_n, w_n) = \prod_{i=1}^{n} f(v_i, w_i; \theta_1, \theta_2, \theta_3).$$

Functions u_1, u_2, u_3 of $v_1, w_1, \cdots, v_n, w_n$ that maximize L with respect to θ_1, θ_2, θ_3, respectively, define maximum likelihood statistics $\hat{\theta}_1, \hat{\theta}_2$, and $\hat{\theta}_3$ for the parameters $\theta_1, \theta_2, \theta_3$.   Other extensions are made in ways similar to those of the two illustrations given in this paragraph.

Exercises

5.32.   Let $X_1, X_2, \cdots, X_n$ represent a random sample from each of the distributions having the following probability density functions:

(a) $f(x; \theta) = \dfrac{\theta^x e^{-\theta}}{x!}$, $x = 0, 1, 2, \cdots$, $0 \le \theta < \infty$,   zero elsewhere.

(b) $f(x; \theta) = \theta x^{\theta-1}$, $0 < x < 1$, $0 < \theta < \infty$,   zero elsewhere.

(c) $f(x; \theta) = \dfrac{1}{\theta} e^{-\frac{x}{\theta}}$, $0 < x < \infty$, $0 < \theta < \infty$,   zero elsewhere.

(d) $f(x; \theta) = \dfrac{1}{2} e^{-|x-\theta|}$, $-\infty < x < \infty$, $-\infty < \theta < \infty$.

(e) $f(x; \theta) = e^{-(x-\theta)}$, $\theta < x < \infty$, $-\infty < \theta < \infty$,   zero elsewhere.

In each case find the maximum likelihood statistic $\hat{\theta}$ for θ.   If a sufficient statistic Y_1 also exists, express $\hat{\theta}$ as a function of Y_1.

5.33.   If $X_1, X_2, \cdots, X_n$ is a random sample from a normal distribution with mean θ_1 and variance θ_2, show that $\hat{\theta}_1 = \bar{X}$ and $\hat{\theta}_2 = \sum_1^n (X_i - \bar{X})^2/n$.

5.34.   Let $X_1, X_2, \cdots, X_n$ be a random sample from the distribution having p.d.f. $f(x; \theta_1, \theta_2) = (1/\theta_2)e^{-\frac{(x-\theta_1)}{\theta_2}}$, $\theta_1 < x < \infty, -\infty < \theta_1 < \infty, 0 < \theta_2 < \infty$, zero elsewhere.   Find the maximum likelihood statistics for θ_1 and θ_2.

5.35.   (Madow)   Prove the following: Let $X_1, X_2, \cdots, X_n$ denote a random sample from a distribution having p.d.f. $f(x; \theta)$, $\gamma < \theta < \delta$.   Let the likelihood function $L(\theta) = f(x_1; \theta)\ f(x_2; \theta) \cdots f(x_n; \theta)$.   Let $Y_1 = u_1(X_1, X_2, \cdots, X_n)$ be a sufficient statistic for the parameter θ.   If $g_1(y_1; \theta_0)$ is the p.d.f. of the sufficient statistic Y_1 in the special case $\theta = \theta_0$, then the p.d.f. $g_1(y_1; \theta)$ of the sufficient statistic Y_1 for every θ, $\gamma < \theta < \delta$, is given by

$$g_1(y_1; \theta) = g_1(y_1; \theta_0)\frac{L(\theta)}{L(\theta_0)}.$$

CHAPTER SIX

SUFFICIENCY AND STOCHASTIC INDEPENDENCE

In Chapter Five it was seen that the properties of sufficiency and completeness can be combined to provide a most attractive theory of point estimation. In this chapter we shall investigate the impact of sufficiency and completeness upon the stochastic independence of certain statistics. This stochastic independence will, upon occasion, materially simplify some otherwise difficult problems in sampling distribution theory.

6.1. Sufficiency, Completeness, and Stochastic Independence. We shall prove a special case of the following theorem.

THEOREM. Let $X_1, X_2, \cdots, X_n$ denote a random sample from a distribution having a p.d.f. $f(x; \theta)$, $\gamma < \theta < \delta$. Let $Y_1 = u_1(X_1, X_2, \cdots, X_n)$ be a sufficient statistic for θ and let the p.d.f. $g_1(y_1; \theta)$, $\gamma < \theta < \delta$, of Y_1 be complete. Let $Z = u(X_1, X_2, \cdots, X_n)$ be any other statistic (not a function of Y_1 alone). If the distribution of Z does not depend upon θ, then Z is stochastically independent of the sufficient statistic Y_1.

PROOF. We shall prove the theorem under the assumptions that $f(x; \theta)$ is the p.d.f. of a random variable X of the continuous type and that the conditional p.d.f. of Z, given $Y_1 = y_1$, is a continuous function of y_1. Denote the joint p.d.f. of Y_1 and Z by $g(y_1, z; \theta)$; the conditional p.d.f. of Z, given $Y_1 = y_1$, by $h(z|y_1)$; and the p.d.f. of Z by $g_2(z)$. The integral

$$(1) \qquad \int_{-\infty}^{\infty} [g_2(z) - h(z|y_1)]g_1(y_1; \theta)dy_1 = 0$$

for all θ, $\gamma < \theta < \delta$, because

$$\int_{-\infty}^{\infty} g_2(z)g_1(y_1; \theta) \, dy_1 = g_2(z)$$

and

$$\int_{-\infty}^{\infty} h(z|y_1)g_1(y_1; \theta) \, dy_1 = \int_{-\infty}^{\infty} \frac{g(y_1, z; \theta)}{g_1(y_1; \theta)}g_1(y_1; \theta) \, dy_1 = g_2(z).$$

Since Y_1 is a sufficient statistic for θ, $h(z|y_1)$ does not depend upon θ. From the hypothesis, $g_2(z)$ does not depend upon θ; thus $g_2(z) - h(z|y_1)$ does not depend upon θ. Moreover $h(z|y_1)$, thus $g_2(z) - h(z|y_1)$, is a continuous function of y_1 by assumption. Since $g_1(y_1; \theta)$, $\gamma < \theta < \delta$, is complete, the expression (1) requires that

$$g_2(z) - h(z|y_1) = 0 \qquad \text{or} \qquad g_2(z) = h(z|y_1)$$

at all points y_1 where, for some θ, $g_1(y_1; \theta) > 0$. However,

$$g(y_1, z; \theta) = g_1(y_1; \theta)h(z|y_1), \quad g_1(y_1; \theta) > 0,$$

so that

$$g(y_1, z; \theta) = g_1(y_1; \theta)g_2(z), \quad g_1(y_1; \theta) > 0.$$

That is, Z is stochastically independent of the sufficient statistic Y_1, as was to be proved.

If it is assumed that a statistic Z is stochastically independent of a statistic Y_1, then, of course, $g_2(z) = h(z|y_1)$. It is interesting to observe that if Y_1 is a sufficient statistic for θ, then $h(z|y_1)$, and hence $g_2(z)$, does not depend upon θ whether $g_1(y_1; \theta)$, $\gamma < \theta < \delta$, is or is not complete. That is, the theorem may not be stated as an "if, and only if," condition for the stochastic independence of the statistic Z and the sufficient statistic Y_1. However, if we restrict $f(x; \theta)$ to represent a regular case (continuous or discrete) of the Koopman–Pitman class [form (1), page 111], and if $X_1, X_2, \cdots, X_n$ is a random sample from this distribution, then the p.d.f. $g_1(y_1; \theta)$, $\gamma < \theta < \delta$, of the sufficient statistic $Y_1 = \sum_1^n K(X_i)$ is complete. In those cases the statistic Z is stochastically independent of the sufficient statistic Y_1 if, and only if, the distribution of Z does not depend upon θ.

It should be remarked that the theorem (including the special formulation of it for regular cases of the Koopman-Pitman class) extends immediately to probability density functions which involve m parameters for which there exist m joint sufficient statistics. For example, let $X_1, X_2, \cdots, X_n$ be a random sample from a distribution having the p.d.f. $f(x; \theta_1, \theta_2)$ that represents a regular case of the Koopman-Pitman class such that there are two joint sufficient statistics for θ_1 and θ_2. Then any other statistic $Z = u(X_1, X_2, \cdots, X_n)$ is stochastically independent of the joint sufficient statistics if, and only if, the distribution of Z does not depend upon θ_1 or θ_2.

We shall give some examples illustrative of the theorem.

EXAMPLE 1. Let the random variable X be $n(x; \mu, \sigma^2)$, and let $X_1, X_2, \cdots, X_n$ denote a random sample from this distribution. The mean of the random sample is $\bar{X} = \sum_1^n X_i/n$, and the variance is $S^2 = \sum_1^n (X_i - \bar{X})^2/n$. We shall show that the statistic S^2 is stochastically independent of the statistic $\bar{X}$. The stochastic independence of $\bar{X}$ and S^2, when the random sample is from a normal distribution, is one of the more important results in elementary sampling distribution theory. It has been seen, page 112, that $\bar{X}$ is, for every given $\sigma^2 > 0$, a sufficient statistic for μ, $-\infty < \mu < \infty$, and that the p.d.f. of the sufficient statistic $\bar{X}$ is complete. If the distribution of S^2 does not depend upon μ, then, in accordance with the theorem, S^2 is stochastically independent of $\bar{X}$. Now the distribution of S^2 is uniquely determined by its moment-generating function $M_{S^2}(t)$. Our problem will be solved if we can show that $M_{S^2}(t)$ does not depend upon μ. Now

$$M_{S^2}(t) = E\left[e^{t\sum_{1}^{n}\frac{(X_i-\bar{X})^2}{n}}\right]$$

$$= \int_{-\infty}^{\infty}\cdots\int_{-\infty}^{\infty}e^{\frac{t}{n}\sum_{1}^{n}(x_i-\bar{x})^2}\left(\frac{1}{\sigma\sqrt{2\pi}}\right)^{n}e^{-\sum_{1}^{n}\frac{(x_i-\mu)^2}{2\sigma^2}}\,dx_1\,dx_2\cdots dx_n.$$

This is a fairly complicated integral, and we shall make no effort to evaluate it. But by the following argument it is easy to see that $M_{S^2}(t)$ does not depend upon μ. Consider the one-to-one transformation $w_1 = x_1 - \mu$, $\cdots$, $w_n = x_n - \mu$ which maps the entire $x_1 x_2 \cdots x_n$ space into the entire $w_1 w_2 \cdots w_n$ space. The Jacobian $J = 1$. Under this transformation

$$\sum_{1}^{n}(x_i - \mu)^2 = \sum_{1}^{n}w_i^2$$

and

$$\sum_{1}^{n}(x_i - \bar{x})^2 = \sum_{1}^{n}(w_i - \bar{w})^2$$

where $\bar{w} = (w_1 + w_2 + \cdots + w_n)/n$. Thus

$$M_{S^2}(t) = \int_{-\infty}^{\infty}\cdots\int_{-\infty}^{\infty}e^{\frac{t}{n}\sum_{1}^{n}(w_i-\bar{w})^2}\left(\frac{1}{\sigma\sqrt{2\pi}}\right)^{n}e^{-\frac{\sum_{1}^{n}w_i^2}{2\sigma^2}}\,dw_1\cdots dw_n,$$

and $M_{S^2}(t)$ obviously does not depend upon μ. Accordingly, the variance S^2 of the random sample from the distribution $n(x; \mu, \sigma^2)$ is stochastically independent of the mean $\bar{X}$ of the sample. Of course then $\bar{X}$ is stochastically independent of S, and each of $\sqrt{n}(\bar{X} - \mu)/\sigma$ and $n(\bar{X} - \mu)^2/\sigma^2$ is stochastically independent of nS^2/σ^2 and so on.

EXAMPLE 2. Let X_1, X_2, X_3, X_4 denote a random sample from a distribution having p.d.f.

$$f(x; \theta) = \frac{1}{\theta}, \quad 0 < x < \theta, \quad 0 < \theta < \infty,$$

$$= 0 \text{ elsewhere.}$$

Let $Y_1 < Y_2 < Y_3 < Y_4$ denote the order statistics of this random sample. In Example 3, page 100, it was shown that the fourth order statistic $Y_4 = \max(X_i)$ is a sufficient statistic for θ and that the p.d.f. of Y_4 is given by

$$g_4(y_4; \theta) = \frac{4y_4^3}{\theta^4}, \quad 0 < y_4 < \theta, \quad 0 < \theta < \infty,$$

$$= 0 \text{ elsewhere.}$$

By Exercise 5.21, page 109, this p.d.f. is complete. It will now be shown that the statistic $Z = (Y_1 + Y_2 + Y_3 + Y_4)/Y_4$ is stochastically independent of the sufficient statistic Y_4. For

$$M_Z(t) = E\left(e^{t\frac{Y_1+Y_2+Y_3+Y_4}{Y_4}}\right)$$

$$= \int_0^\theta \int_0^{y_4} \int_0^{y_3} \int_0^{y_2} e^{t\frac{y_1+y_2+y_3+y_4}{y_4}} \left(\frac{4!}{\theta^4}\right) dy_1\, dy_2\, dy_3\, dy_4.$$

The one-to-one transformation $w_1 = y_1/\theta$, $w_2 = y_2/\theta$, $w_3 = y_3/\theta$, $w_4 = y_4/\theta$ has $|J| = \theta^4$, and it maps $0 < y_1 < y_2 < y_3 < y_4 < \theta$ into $0 < w_1 < w_2 < w_3 < w_4 < 1$. Consequently

$$M_Z(t) = \int_0^1 \int_0^{w_4} \int_0^{w_3} \int_0^{w_2} e^{t\frac{w_1+w_2+w_3+w_4}{w_4}} (4!)\, dw_1\, dw_2\, dw_3\, dw_4,$$

which clearly does not depend upon θ. Thus the distribution of Z does not depend upon θ, and so Z is stochastically independent of Y_4, the sufficient statistic for θ, since the p.d.f. of Y_4 is complete.

EXAMPLE 3. Let

$$f(x; \theta_1, \theta_2) = \frac{1}{\sqrt{2\pi\theta_2}} e^{-\frac{(x-\theta_1)^2}{2\theta_2}}, \quad -\infty < x < \infty, \quad \begin{array}{l} -\infty < \theta_1 < \infty \\ 0 < \theta_2 < \infty, \end{array}$$

$$= e^{\left(-\frac{1}{2\theta_2}\right)x^2 + \left(\frac{\theta_1}{\theta_2}\right)x - \frac{\theta_1^2}{2\theta_2} - \ln\sqrt{2\pi\theta_2}}$$

$$= e^{p_1(\theta_1,\theta_2)x^2 + p_2(\theta_1,\theta_2)x + q(\theta_1,\theta_2)}$$

so that we have a regular case of the Koopman-Pitman class. If $X_1, X_2, \cdots, X_n$ is a random sample from a distribution with this p.d.f., then $\sum_1^n X_i^2$ and $\sum_1^n X_i$ are joint sufficient statistics for θ_1 and θ_2, so that likewise are $\bar{X} = \sum_1^n X_i/n$ and $S^2 = \sum_1^n (X_i - \bar{X})^2/n$. Consider the statistic

$$Z = \frac{\sum_1^{n-1}(X_{i+1} - X_i)^2}{\sum_1^n (X_i - \bar{X})^2}.$$

The one-to-one transformation $y_i = (x_i - \theta_1)/\sqrt{\theta_2}$, $i = 1, 2, \cdots, n$, may be used to show that $M_Z(t)$ does not depend upon θ_1, θ_2. That is, Z is stochastically independent of both $\bar{X}$ and S^2.

Exercises

6.1. Let X_1, X_2 be a random sample of size 2 from a distribution having the p.d.f. $f(x; \theta) = (1/\theta)e^{-x/\theta}$, $0 < x < \infty$, $0 < \theta < \infty$, zero elsewhere. Show that $Z = X_1/(X_1 + X_2)$ has a moment-generating function that does not depend upon

θ. Thus $Y_1 = X_1 + X_2$, the sufficient statistic for θ, is stochastically independent of Z.

6.2. Let $Y_1 < Y_2 < \cdots < Y_n$ be the order statistics of a random sample from the normal distribution $n(x; \theta, \sigma^2)$, $-\infty < \theta < \infty$. Show that the moment-generating function of $Z = Y_n - \bar{Y}$ does not depend upon θ. Thus the sufficient statistic $\bar{Y} = \sum_1^n Y_i/n$ for θ is stochastically independent of Z.

6.3. Let $X_1, X_2, \cdots, X_n$ be a random sample from the normal distribution $n(x; \theta, \sigma^2)$, $-\infty < \theta < \infty$. Prove that a necessary and sufficient condition that the statistics $Z = \sum_1^n a_i X_i$ and $Y_1 = \sum_1^n X_i$, a sufficient statistic for θ, be stochastically independent[1] is that $\sum_1 a_i = 0$.[1]

6.4. Let $Y_1 < Y_2 < \cdots < Y_n$ be the order statistics of a random sample of size n from the distribution having p.d.f. $f(x; \theta) = e^{-(x-\theta)}$, $\theta < x < \infty$, $-\infty < \theta < \infty$, zero elsewhere. Show that $Z = \sum_1^n (Y_i - Y_1)$ and the sufficient statistic Y_1 for θ are stochastically independent.

6.2. The Distribution of nS^2/σ^2. In this section we shall find the distribution of the random variable $W = nS^2/\sigma^2 = \sum_1^n (X_i - \bar{X})^2/\sigma^2$ where $X_1, X_2, \cdots, X_n$ denote a random sample of size n from a distribution which is $n(x; \mu, \sigma^2)$. Specifically it will be shown that $W = nS^2/\sigma^2$ has a chi-square distribution with $n - 1$ degrees of freedom. This can be done easily if we use the following preliminary proposition:

Let U, V, W denote three random variables where

(i) $U = V + W$,

(ii) U and V have chi-square distributions with r and r_1 degrees of freedom, respectively, where $r > r_1$,

(iii) V and W are stochastically independent.

We shall show that conditions (i), (ii), and (iii) imply that W has a chi-square distribution with $r - r_1$ degrees of freedom. By conditions (i) and (iii) we have

$$M_U(t) = E[e^{t(V+W)}] = E(e^{tV})E(e^{tW})$$
$$= M_V(t)M_W(t).$$

By condition (ii),

$$M_U(t) = \frac{1}{(1 - 2t)^{\frac{r}{2}}} \quad \text{and} \quad M_V(t) = \frac{1}{(1 - 2t)^{\frac{r_1}{2}}}, \quad t < \frac{1}{2}.$$

Thus

$$\frac{1}{(1 - 2t)^{\frac{r}{2}}} = \frac{1}{(1 - 2t)^{\frac{r_1}{2}}} M_W(t),$$

or

$$M_W(t) = \frac{1}{(1 - 2t)^{\frac{r-r_1}{2}}}, \quad t < \frac{1}{2}.$$

Accordingly W has a chi-square distribution with $r - r_1$ degrees of freedom.

Consider the random variable $\sum_{1}^{n}(X_i - \mu)^2/\sigma^2$, where $X_1, X_2, \cdots, X_n$ denote a random sample from the distribution $n(x; \mu, \sigma^2)$. Now

$$\frac{\sum_{1}^{n}(X_i - \mu)^2}{\sigma^2} = \frac{\sum_{1}^{n}(X_i - \bar{X} + \bar{X} - \mu)^2}{\sigma^2}$$

$$= \frac{\sum_{1}^{n}(X_i - \bar{X})^2}{\sigma^2} + \frac{n(\bar{X} - \mu)^2}{\sigma^2}$$

since $2(\bar{X} - \mu)\sum_{1}^{n}(X_i - \bar{X}) = 0$. That is,

$$\frac{\sum_{1}^{n}(X_i - \mu)^2}{\sigma^2} = \frac{n(\bar{X} - \mu)^2}{\sigma^2} + \frac{nS^2}{\sigma^2}.$$

In the preliminary proposition, take

$$U = \frac{\sum_{1}^{n}(X_i - \mu)^2}{\sigma^2}, \qquad V = \frac{n(\bar{X} - \mu)^2}{\sigma^2}, \qquad W = \frac{nS^2}{\sigma^2}$$

so that condition (i) is satisfied. On page 60, it was proved that $U = \sum_{1}^{n}(X_i - \mu)^2/\sigma^2$ has a chi-square distribution with $r = n$ degrees of freedom. Since $\sqrt{n}(\bar{X} - \mu)/\sigma$ is normally distributed with mean zero and variance one, then (as proved on page 38) $V = n(\bar{X} - \mu)^2/\sigma^2$ has a chi-square distribution with $r_1 = 1$ degree of freedom; and condition (ii) is satisfied. Condition (iii), the stochastic independence of $n(\bar{X} - \mu)^2/\sigma^2$ and nS^2/σ^2, was established on page 125. Accordingly, when sampling from a normal distribution, $W = nS^2/\sigma^2$ has a chi-square distribution with $r - r_1 = n - 1$ degrees of freedom, as asserted at the outset of this section.

The fact that nS^2/σ^2 has a chi-square distribution with $n - 1$ degrees of freedom, whatever the value of μ, when the random sample $X_1, X_2, \cdots, X_n$ is from the normal distribution $n(x; \mu, \sigma^2)$, has important implications from the point of view of statistical inference. Some of these implications will be considered in the subsequent section, while others will be deferred to Chapter Nine.

Exercises

6.5. Find the mean and variance of $S^2 = \sum_{1}^{n}(X_i - \bar{X})^2/n$, where $X_1, X_2, \cdots, X_n$ is a random sample from $n(x; \mu, \sigma^2)$. Hint: Find the mean and variance of nS^2/σ^2.

6.6. Let S^2 be the variance of a random sample of size 6 from the normal distribution $n(x; \mu, 12)$. Find $Pr(2.30 < S^2 < 22.2)$.

6.7. Let $Y_1 < Y_2 < \cdots < Y_n$ be the order statistics of a random sample of size n from a distribution having the p.d.f. $f(x; \theta) = e^{-(x-\theta)}, \theta < x < \infty, -\infty < \theta < \infty$, zero elsewhere. Find the p.d.f. of $Z = \sum_1^n (Y_i - Y_1)$. Hint: Write $\sum_1^n (Y_i - \theta)$ $= n(Y_1 - \theta) + \sum_1^n (Y_i - Y_1)$. Find the moment-generating functions of $\sum_1^n (Y_i - \theta)$ and $n(Y_1 - \theta)$. Use the facts that Y_1 is a sufficient statistic for θ and that Y_1 and $\sum_1^n (Y_i - Y_1)$ are stochastically independent, to find the moment-generating function of $\sum_1^n (Y_i - Y_1)$.

6.3. Confidence Intervals for Variances. In Section 3.4, page 61, we were able to make a statistical inference about the unknown variance σ^2 of a distribution which is $n(x; \mu, \sigma^2)$ when μ was a known number. This inference was of the nature of finding a confidence interval (with prescribed confidence coefficient) for σ^2. The fact that nS^2/σ^2 has a chi-square distribution with $n - 1$ degrees of freedom, whatever the value of μ, implies that we can make this kind of inference about the unknown variance σ^2 even though μ itself is unknown. In the notation of Section 3.4, we can, with some preassigned probability, say, 0.95, find numbers a and b, $0 < a < b$, such that

$$Pr\left(a < \frac{nS^2}{\sigma^2} < b\right) = 0.95.$$

Here, of course, we would find a and b by using a chi-square distribution with $n - 1$ degrees of freedom. In accordance with the convention adopted in Section 3.4, we would select a and b so that

$$Pr\left(\frac{nS^2}{\sigma^2} < a\right) = 0.025 \quad \text{and} \quad Pr\left(\frac{nS^2}{\sigma^2} > b\right) = 0.025.$$

We then have

$$Pr\left(\frac{nS^2}{b} < \sigma^2 < \frac{nS^2}{a}\right) = 0.95,$$

so that $(nS^2/b, nS^2/a)$ is a random interval having probability 0.95 of including the fixed but unknown point (parameter) σ^2. After the random experiment has been performed and we find, say, $X_1 = x_1, X_2 = x_2, \cdots,$ $X_n = x_n$, with $s^2 = \sum_1^n (x_i - \bar{x})^2/n$, we have, as a 95 per cent confidence interval for σ^2, the interval $(ns^2/b, ns^2/a)$.

EXAMPLE 1. If, in the preceding discussion, we have $n = 9, s^2 = 7.63$, then the interval $\left[\dfrac{9(7.63)}{17.5}, \dfrac{9(7.63)}{2.18}\right]$ or $(3.92, 31.50)$ is a 95 per cent confidence interval for the variance σ^2.

Next let X and Y denote stochastically independent random variables having normal distributions $n(x; \mu_1, \sigma_1^2)$ and $n(y; \mu_2, \sigma_2^2)$, respectively. The four parameters μ_1, μ_2, σ_1^2, σ_2^2 are unknown, but at the moment we have no concern with μ_1 and μ_2. (Statistical inferences about μ_1 and μ_2 will be considered in the subsequent section). At this time we shall determine a confidence interval for the ratio σ_2^2/σ_1^2.

Comment. Consider a situation in which a random variable X has a normal distribution with variance σ_1^2. Although σ_1^2 is not known, it is found that the experimental values of X are quite widely dispersed, so that σ_1^2 must be fairly large. It is believed that a certain modification in conducting the experiment may reduce the variance. After the modification has been effected, let the random variable be denoted by Y, and let Y have a normal distribution with variance σ_2^2. Naturally it is hoped that σ_2^2 is less than σ_1^2; that is, that $\sigma_2^2/\sigma_1^2 < 1$. In order to make a statistical inference, we find a confidence interval for the ratio σ_2^2/σ_1^2.

Consider a random sample $X_1, X_2, \cdots, X_n$ of size n from the distribution of X and a random sample $Y_1, Y_2, \cdots, Y_m$ of size m from the independent distribution of Y. Here n and m may or may not be equal. Let the means of the two samples be denoted by $\bar{X}$ and $\bar{Y}$, and the variances of the two samples by $S_1^2 = \sum_{1}^{n}(X_i - \bar{X})^2/n$ and $S_2^2 = \sum_{1}^{m}(Y_i - \bar{Y})^2/m$, respectively. Perhaps it should be pointed out that the four statistics $\bar{X}$, $\bar{Y}$, S_1^2, S_2^2 are mutually stochastically independent. For, $\bar{X}$ and S_1^2 are stochastically independent by the proof on page 125; likewise are $\bar{Y}$ and S_2^2; the assumption that X and Y have independent distributions accounts for the stochastic independence of the others. The stochastically independent random variables nS_1^2/σ_1^2 and mS_2^2/σ_2^2 have chi-square distributions with $n - 1$ and $m - 1$ degrees of freedom, respectively. On page 76, a random variable called F was defined, and through the change of variable technique the p.d.f. of F was obtained. If nS_1^2/σ_1^2 is divided by $n - 1$, the number of degrees of freedom, and if mS_2^2/σ_2^2 is divided by $m - 1$, then, by definition of an F random variable, we have that

$$F = \frac{\dfrac{nS_1^2}{\sigma_1^2(n - 1)}}{\dfrac{mS_2^2}{\sigma_2^2(m - 1)}}$$

has an F distribution with parameters $n - 1$ and $m - 1$. For numerically given values of n and m and with a preassigned probability, say, 0.95, we can determine from Table IV, in accordance with our convention, numbers $0 < a < b$ such that

$$Pr\left[a < \frac{\dfrac{nS_1^2}{\sigma_1^2(n-1)}}{\dfrac{mS_2^2}{\sigma_2^2(m-1)}} < b \right] = 0.95.$$

If the probability of this event is written in the form

$$Pr\left[a\,\frac{\dfrac{mS_2^2}{(m-1)}}{\dfrac{nS_1^2}{(n-1)}} < \frac{\sigma_2^2}{\sigma_1^2} < b\,\frac{\dfrac{mS_2^2}{(m-1)}}{\dfrac{nS_1^2}{(n-1)}} \right] = 0.95,$$

it is seen that the interval

$$\left[a\,\frac{\dfrac{mS_2^2}{(m-1)}}{\dfrac{nS_1^2}{(n-1)}},\ \ b\,\frac{\dfrac{mS_2^2}{(m-1)}}{\dfrac{nS_1^2}{(n-1)}} \right]$$

is a random interval having probability 0.95 of including the fixed but unknown point σ_2^2/σ_1^2. If the experimental values of $X_1, X_2, \cdots, X_n$ and of $Y_1, Y_2, \cdots, Y_m$ are denoted by $x_1, x_2, \cdots, x_n$ and $y_1, y_2, \cdots, y_m$, respectively, and if $ns_1^2 = \sum_{1}^{n}(x_i - \bar{x})^2$, $ms_2^2 = \sum_{1}^{m}(y_i - \bar{y})^2$, then the interval with known end points, namely,

$$\left[a\,\frac{\dfrac{ms_2^2}{(m-1)}}{\dfrac{ns_1^2}{(n-1)}},\ \ b\,\frac{\dfrac{ms_2^2}{(m-1)}}{\dfrac{ns_1^2}{(n-1)}} \right]$$

is a 95 per cent confidence interval for the ratio σ_2^2/σ_1^2 of the two unknown variances.

EXAMPLE 2. If in the preceding discussion $n = 10$, $m = 5$, $s_1^2 = 20.0$, $s_2^2 = 35.6$, then the interval

$$\left[\left(\frac{1}{4.72}\right)\frac{\dfrac{5(35.6)}{4}}{\dfrac{10(20.0)}{9}},\ (8.90)\frac{\dfrac{5(35.6)}{4}}{\dfrac{10(20.0)}{9}} \right]$$

or $(0.4, 17.8)$ is a 95 per cent confidence interval for σ_2^2/σ_1^2.

Exercises

6.8. A random sample of size 15 from the normal distribution $n(x; \mu, \sigma^2)$ yields $\bar{x} = 3.2$ and $s^2 = 4.24$. Determine a 90 per cent confidence interval for σ^2.

6.9. Let two independent random samples of sizes $n = 16$ and $m = 10$, taken from two independent normal distributions $n(x; \mu_1, \sigma_1^2)$ and $n(y; \mu_2, \sigma_2^2)$, respectively, yield $\bar{x} = 3.6$, $s_1^2 = 4.14$, $\bar{y} = 13.6$, $s_2^2 = 7.26$. Find a 90 per cent confidence interval for σ_2^2/σ_1^2 when μ_1 and μ_2 are unknown.

6.10. Discuss the problem of finding a confidence interval for the ratio σ_2^2/σ_1^2 of the two unknown variances of two independent normal distributions if the means μ_1 and μ_2 are known.

6.11. Let $X_1, X_2, \cdots, X_n$ and $Y_1, Y_2, \cdots, Y_m$ denote two independent random samples from two independent normal distributions with the same variance σ^2. Find the constant c so that $c\left[\sum_1^n (X_i - \bar{X})^2 + \sum_1^m (Y_i - \bar{Y})^2\right]$ is an unbiased statistic for σ^2. Determine the variance of this statistic.

6.4. Confidence Intervals for Means. In the preceding section it was seen that the random variable F may be used to advantage in making a statistical inference about the ratio of the variances of two independent normal distributions. It is the purpose of this section to point out some uses of the random variable T defined in Section 4.3, page 74.

In Section 3.4 there was obtained a confidence interval for μ, the mean of a normal distribution, provided the variance was known. It will now be shown that this statistical inference can be made even though σ^2 is unknown.

Let $X_1, X_2, \cdots, X_n$ denote a random sample from a normal distribution $n(x; \mu, \sigma^2)$, both μ, $-\infty < \mu < \infty$, and σ^2, $0 < \sigma^2 < \infty$, unknown. Let $\bar{X}$ and S^2 denote respectively the mean and the variance of the sample. The problem is to find a confidence interval for μ. It is now well known that $\sqrt{n}(\bar{X} - \mu)/\sigma$ has a normal distribution with zero mean and unit variance; that nS^2/σ^2 has a chi-square distribution with $n - 1$ degrees of freedom; and that $\sqrt{n}(\bar{X} - \mu)/\sigma$ and nS^2/σ^2 are stochastically independent. In Section 4.3 the random variable T was defined in terms of two such random variables as these. In fact, from that section and the foregoing results, we know that

$$T = \frac{\dfrac{\sqrt{n}(\bar{X} - \mu)}{\sigma}}{\sqrt{\dfrac{nS^2}{\sigma^2(n - 1)}}} = \frac{\bar{X} - \mu}{\dfrac{S}{\sqrt{n - 1}}}$$

has a t distribution with $n - 1$ degrees of freedom, whatever the value of $\sigma^2 > 0$. For a given positive integer n and a probability of 0.95, say, we can find numbers $a < b$ from Table III, such that

$$Pr\left[a < \frac{\bar{X} - \mu}{\dfrac{S}{\sqrt{n - 1}}} < b\right] = 0.95.$$

Since the graph of the p.d.f. of the random variable T is symmetric about the vertical axis through the origin, our convention requires that $a = -b$, $b > 0$. If the probability of this event is written (with $a = -b$) in the form

$$Pr\left[\bar{X} - \frac{bS}{\sqrt{n-1}} < \mu < \bar{X} + \frac{bS}{\sqrt{n-1}} \right] = 0.95,$$

then the interval $[\bar{X} - (bS/\sqrt{n-1}), \bar{X} + (bS/\sqrt{n-1})]$ is a random interval having probability 0.95 of including the unknown fixed point (parameter) μ. If the experimental values of $X_1, X_2, \cdots, X_n$ are x_1, x_2, $\cdots, x_n$ with $s^2 = \sum_1^n (x_i - \bar{x})^2/n$, where $\bar{x} = \sum_1^n x_i/n$, then the interval $[\bar{x} - (bs/\sqrt{n-1}), \bar{x} + (bs/\sqrt{n-1})]$ is a 95 per cent confidence interval for μ for every $\sigma^2 > 0$.

EXAMPLE 1. If in the preceding discussion $n = 10$, $\bar{x} = 3.22$, and $s = 1.17$, then the interval $[3.22 - (2.262)(1.17)/\sqrt{9}, 3.22 + (2.262)(1.17)/\sqrt{9}]$ or $(2.34, 4.10)$ is a 95 per cent confidence interval for μ.

The random variable T may also be used to obtain a confidence interval for the difference $\mu_1 - \mu_2$ between the means of two independent normal distributions, say $n(x; \mu_1, \sigma^2)$ and $n(y; \mu_2, \sigma^2)$, when the distributions have the same, but unknown, variance σ^2.

Comment. Let X have a normal distribution with unknown parameters μ_1 and σ^2. A modification can be made in conducting the experiment so that the variance of the distribution will remain the same but the mean of the distribution will be changed; say, increased. After the modification has been effected, let the random variable be denoted by Y, and let Y have a normal distribution with unknown parameters μ_2 and σ^2. Naturally it is hoped that μ_2 is greater than μ_1; that is, that $\mu_1 - \mu_2 < 0$. Accordingly one seeks a confidence interval for $\mu_1 - \mu_2$ in order to make a statistical inference.

A confidence interval for $\mu_1 - \mu_2$ may be obtained as follows: Let X_1, $X_2, \cdots, X_n$ and $Y_1, Y_2, \cdots, Y_m$ denote respectively independent random samples from the two independent distributions having respectively the probability density functions $n(x; \mu_1, \sigma^2)$ and $n(y; \mu_2, \sigma^2)$. Denote the means of the samples by $\bar{X}$ and $\bar{Y}$ and the variances of the samples by S_1^2 and S_2^2, respectively. As was noted on page 130, these four statistics are mutually stochastically independent. Now $\bar{X}$ and $\bar{Y}$ are normally and stochastically independently distributed with means μ_1 and μ_2 and variances σ^2/n and σ^2/m, respectively. In accordance with page 49, their difference $\bar{X} - \bar{Y}$ is normally distributed with mean $\mu_1 - \mu_2$ and variance $\sigma^2/n + \sigma^2/m$. Then the random variable

$$\frac{(\bar{X} - \bar{Y}) - (\mu_1 - \mu_2)}{\sqrt{\dfrac{\sigma^2}{n} + \dfrac{\sigma^2}{m}}}$$

is normally distributed with zero mean and unit variance. This random variable may serve as the numerator of a T random variable. Further nS_1^2/σ^2 and mS_2^2/σ^2 have stochastically independent chi-square distributions with $n - 1$ and $m - 1$ degrees of freedom, respectively, so that their sum $(nS_1^2 + mS_2^2)/\sigma^2$ has a chi-square distribution with $n + m - 2$ degrees of freedom, provided $m + n - 2 > 0$. Because of the mutual stochastic independence of $\bar{X}$, $\bar{Y}$, S_1^2, and S_2^2, it is seen that

$$\sqrt{\frac{nS_1^2 + mS_2^2}{\sigma^2(n + m - 2)}}$$

may serve as the denominator of a T random variable. That is, the random variable

$$T = \frac{(\bar{X} - \bar{Y}) - (\mu_1 - \mu_2)}{\sqrt{\dfrac{nS_1^2 + mS_2^2}{n + m - 2}\left(\dfrac{1}{n} + \dfrac{1}{m}\right)}}$$

has a t distribution with $n + m - 2$ degrees of freedom. As in the earlier part of this section, we can (once n and m are specified positive integers with $n + m - 2 > 0$) find a positive number b such that

$$Pr(-b < T < b) = 0.95.$$

If we set

$$R = \sqrt{\frac{nS_1^2 + mS_2^2}{n + m - 2}\left(\frac{1}{n} + \frac{1}{m}\right)},$$

this probability may be written in the form

$$Pr[(\bar{X} - \bar{Y}) - bR < \mu_1 - \mu_2 < (\bar{X} - \bar{Y}) + bR] = 0.95.$$

It follows that the random interval

$$\left[(\bar{X} - \bar{Y}) - b\sqrt{\frac{nS_1^2 + mS_2^2}{n + m - 2}\left(\frac{1}{n} + \frac{1}{m}\right)}, \; (\bar{X} - \bar{Y}) + b\sqrt{\frac{nS_1^2 + mS_2^2}{n + m - 2}\left(\frac{1}{n} + \frac{1}{m}\right)}\right]$$

has probability 0.95 of including the unknown fixed point $(\mu_1 - \mu_2)$. As usual the experimental values of $\bar{X}$, $\bar{Y}$, S_1^2, and S_2^2, namely, $\bar{x}$, $\bar{y}$, s_1^2, and s_2^2, will provide a 95 per cent confidence interval for $\mu_1 - \mu_2$ when the variances of the two independent normal distributions are unknown but equal. A consideration of the difficulty encountered when the unknown variances of the two independent normal distributions are not equal is assigned to one of the exercises.

EXAMPLE 2. It may be verified that if in the preceding discussion $n = 10$, $m = 7$, $\bar{x} = 4.2$, $\bar{y} = 3.4$, $s_1^2 = 49$, $s_2^2 = 32$, then the interval $(-5.16, 6.76)$ is a 90 per cent confidence interval for $\mu_1 - \mu_2$.

Exercises

6.12. Let a random sample of size 17 from the normal distribution $n(x; \mu, \sigma^2)$ yield $\bar{x} = 4.7$ and $s^2 = 5.76$. Determine a 90 per cent confidence interval for μ.

6.13. Let two independent random samples, each of size 10, from two independent normal distributions $n(x; \mu_1, \sigma^2)$ and $n(y; \mu_2, \sigma^2)$ yield $\bar{x} = 4.8$, $s_1^2 = 8.64$, $\bar{y} = 5.6$, $s_2^2 = 7.88$. Find a 95 per cent confidence interval for $\mu_1 - \mu_2$.

6.14. Discuss the problem of finding a confidence interval for the difference $\mu_1 - \mu_2$ between the two means of two independent normal distributions if the variances σ_1^2 and σ_2^2 are known but not necessarily equal.

6.15. Discuss Exercise 6.14 when it is assumed that the variances are unknown and unequal. This is a very difficult problem, and the discussion should point out exactly where the difficulty lies.

CHAPTER SEVEN

LIMITING DISTRIBUTIONS

In some of the preceding chapters it has been demonstrated by example that the distribution of a statistic often depends upon certain parameters that are themselves functions of n, the sample size. For instance, the mean $\bar{X}$ of a random sample from a normal distribution with mean μ and variance σ^2 has a normal distribution with parameters μ and σ^2/n; that is, here the variance is a function of n. Under certain conditions it has been seen that $\sum_1^n (X_i - \bar{X})^2/\sigma^2$ has a chi-square distribution with $n-1$ degrees of freedom; here the parameter, the number of degrees of freedom, is a function of n.

It is not necessary to obtain the p.d.f. of a statistic to see that the distribution of the statistic depends upon n. For example, if $\bar{X}$ is the mean of a random sample $X_1, X_2, \cdots, X_n$ from a distribution having p.d.f.

$$f(x) = 1, \quad 0 < x < 1,$$
$$= 0 \text{ elsewhere,}$$

then, page 56, the moment-generating function of $\bar{X}$ is given by

$$M_{\bar{x}}(t) = \left[M_X\!\left(\frac{t}{n}\right) \right]^n.$$

Here

$$M_X(t) = \int_0^1 e^{tx}\, dx = \frac{(e^t - 1)}{t}, \quad t \neq 0.$$
$$= 1, \quad t = 0.$$

Hence,

$$M_{\bar{x}}(t) = \left(\frac{e^{\frac{t}{n}} - 1}{\frac{t}{n}} \right)^n, \quad t \neq 0.$$
$$= 1, \quad t = 0.$$

136

Since the moment-generating function of $\bar{X}$ depends upon n, the distribution of $\bar{X}$ depends upon n.   However, more powerful mathematical techniques than we have at our disposal are required to find the p.d.f. of $\bar{X}$. Nevertheless, to each positive integer n, there corresponds a distribution of the statistic $\bar{X}$ which can be described by a p.d.f.

These illustrations show that a statistic may have, for each value of n, a distribution that depends upon n even though it may be quite difficult to obtain the p.d.f. of the statistic.   Fortunately it often happens that these distributions can be approximated, provided the sample size n is large, by other distributions that have fairly simple probability density functions.   In this chapter we shall discuss some of these problems.   However, we first need to introduce a new point function, to be called the "distribution function," that is associated with a distribution of one random variable.

7.1.   The Distribution Function.   Let the random variable X have the probability set function $P(A)$ where A is a one-dimensional set.   As in Chapter One, we write $P(A) = Pr(X\epsilon A)$.   Let x be a real number and consider the set A which is an unbounded set from $-\infty$ to x, including the point x itself.   For all such sets A, $P(A) = Pr(X\epsilon A) = Pr(X \leq x)$.   This probability depends only upon the point x; that is, this probability is a function of the point x.   This point function is denoted by the symbol $F(x) = Pr(X \leq x)$ and is called the *distribution function* of the random variable X.

There are a number of properties of a distribution function $F(x)$ that can be listed as a consequence of the definition of the probability set function $P(A)$.   These are

(i) $0 \leq F(x) \leq 1$; for, $0 \leq Pr(X \leq x) \leq 1$.

(ii) $F(x)$ is a nondecreasing function of x; for, if $x' < x''$, then $\{x; x \leq x''\} = \{x; x \leq x'\} \cup \{x; x' < x \leq x''\}$ and $Pr(X \leq x'') = Pr(X \leq x') + Pr(x' < X \leq x'')$.   That is, $F(x'') - F(x') = Pr(x' < X \leq x'') \geq 0$, so that $F(x)$ is a nondecreasing function of x.

(iii) $F(\infty) = 1$ and $F(-\infty) = 0$; for, the set $\{x; x \leq \infty\}$ is the entire one-dimensional space and the set $\{x; x \leq -\infty\}$ is the null set.

It will also be shown that if X is a random variable of the discrete or the continuous type, then

(iv) $F(x)$ is always continuous to the right.

To prove property (iv), first let $f(x)$ be the p.d.f. of a discrete type of random variable X, and let $A = \{x; x = a_1, a_2, \cdots\}$ where $f(x) > 0$. Then $F(x) = Pr(X \leq x) = \sum_{a_i \leq x} f(a_i)$.   It will be shown that $F(x)$ is continuous to the right at each a_i, these being the only points at which any difficulty arises. For convenience, assume that $a_1 < a_2 < a_3 \cdots$. If $x = a_i$, then $F(x) = Pr(X \leq x) = f(a_1) + f(a_2) + \cdots + f(a_i)$; if $a_i \leq x < a_{i+1}$, then also $F(x) = Pr(X \leq x) = f(a_1) + f(a_2) + \cdots + f(a_i)$. Hence, $\lim\limits_{x \to a_i^+} F(x) = F(a_i)$, where $\lim\limits_{x \to a_i^+} F(x)$ represents the right-hand limit of $F(x)$ at a_i. By definition of continuity, $F(x)$ is then continuous to the right at a_i. This proves property (iv) when X is a random variable of the discrete type. Next, let $f(x)$ be the p.d.f. of a random variable X of the continuous type. Then $F(x) = Pr(X \leq x) = \int_{-\infty}^{x} f(w)dw$. If such an integral exists, it is a continuous function of x for every x; in particular, $F(x)$ is continuous to the right at every point x. This proves property (iv) when X is a random variable of the continuous type. It should be noted, when X is a random variable of the continuous type, that when the derivative of $F(x)$ exists, it is equal to the p.d.f. of X; that is, $F'(x) = f(x)$.

The preceding discussion may be summarized in the following manner: A nondecreasing step function $F(x)$, continuous to the right, having $F(-\infty) = 0$, $F(\infty) = 1$, and having steps at discrete points (points such that there is a finite number of these points in every finite interval), satisfies the conditions of being the distribution function of a discrete type of random variable; and a nondecreasing function $F(x)$, continuous everywhere, having $F(-\infty) = 0$, $F(\infty) = 1$, and a continuous derivative $F'(x) = f(x)$, except possibly at a finite number of points in every finite interval, satisfies the conditions of being the distribution function of a random variable of the continuous type.

If X is a random variable of the continuous type having p.d.f. $f(x)$, it has frequently proved convenient, for the purpose of making proofs, to change the definition of $f(x)$ at certain points where $f(x) > 0$ without in any way altering the distribution of probability. The freedom to do this with the p.d.f. $f(x)$ of a continuous type of random variable does not extend to the distribution function $F(x)$; for, if $F(x)$ is changed at so much as one point x, the probability $Pr(X \leq x) = F(x)$ is changed, and we have a different distribution of probability. That is, the distribution function $F(x)$, and not the p.d.f. $f(x)$, is really the fundamental concept.

Comment. The student may wonder why the distribution function was not introduced in Chapter One. That would have been done if this book had been written from a more advanced point of view. Then, in the development of the theory, there would have been no occasion to distinguish between random variables of the continuous type, of the discrete type, or a mixture of these types. However, without the use of a more general integral than the Riemann integral, this development of the theory is not possible and we would ultimately have been forced to consider the same two simple types of random variables that we did. That is, the concept of the distribution function would not have contributed to Chapter One.

Some illustrative examples of distribution functions now follow.

EXAMPLE 1.   Let X be a discrete type of random variable having p.d.f.

$$f(x) = 1, \quad x = c,$$
$$= 0 \text{ elsewhere.}$$

This simplest of discrete-type distributions, which has all the probability at one point $x = c$, is called a *degenerate distribution*. The distribution function of X is given by

$$F(x) = 0, \quad x < c,$$
$$= 1, \quad c \leq x.$$

That is, $F(x)$ is a step function which has one step of height 1 at $x = c$. The moment-generating function is

$$M_X(t) = E(e^{tX}) = \sum_x e^{tx} f(x) = e^{ct}.$$

This moment-generating function implies that the mean of the distribution is $\mu = c$ and that the variance is $\sigma^2 = 0$.

EXAMPLE 2.   If the discrete-type random variable X has p.d.f.

$$f(x) = \tfrac{1}{3}, \quad x = 0, 1, 2,$$
$$= 0 \text{ elsewhere,}$$

then the distribution function is

$$F(x) = 0, \quad x < 0,$$
$$= \tfrac{1}{3}, \quad 0 \leq x < 1,$$
$$= \tfrac{2}{3}, \quad 1 \leq x < 2,$$
$$= 1, \quad 2 \leq x.$$

Here $F(x)$ is a step function which is constant in every interval not containing 0, 1, or 2, but has a step of height $\tfrac{1}{3}$ at each of these points.

EXAMPLE 3.   Let the p.d.f. of X be

$$f(x) = 2x, \quad 0 < x < 1,$$
$$= 0 \text{ elsewhere.}$$

Then the distribution function is

$$F(x) = 0, \quad x < 0,$$
$$= x^2, \quad 0 \leq x < 1,$$
$$= 1, \quad 1 \leq x.$$

EXAMPLE 4.   The function

$$F(x) = \int_{-\infty}^{x} \frac{1}{\sqrt{2\pi}} e^{-\frac{w^2}{2}} \, dw$$

is the distribution function of a random variable that is normally distributed with mean zero and variance one.

Exercises

7.1. Let X have a distribution with p.d.f. $f(x) = 6x(1 - x)$, $0 < x < 1$, zero elsewhere. Find the distribution function $F(x)$ of X.

7.2. If X has the p.d.f. $f(x) = x/15$, $x = 1, 2, 3, 4, 5$, zero elsewhere, determine the distribution function $F(x)$ of X.

7.3. Given the distribution function

$$
\begin{aligned}
F(x) &= 0, \quad x < 0, \\
&= 2x^2, \quad 0 \le x < \tfrac{1}{2}, \\
&= 1 - 2(1 - x)^2, \quad \tfrac{1}{2} \le x < 1, \\
&= 1, \quad 1 \le x.
\end{aligned}
$$

Compute (a) $Pr(\tfrac{1}{8} < X < \tfrac{3}{4})$ and (b) the variance σ^2 of the distribution.

7.2. Limiting Distributions. In the introduction to this chapter there were described certain random variables whose distributions depend upon the sample size n. Clearly the distribution function F that corresponds to each of these distributions will also depend upon n. If Y is the random variable under discussion, we frequently denote this fact by writing the distribution function as $F_n(y)$. For instance, we would write

$$
F_n(\bar{x}) = \int_{-\infty}^{\bar{x}} \frac{1}{\sqrt{\frac{1}{n}}\sqrt{2\pi}} e^{-\frac{w^2}{2(1/n)}} \, dw
$$

for the distribution function of the mean $\bar{X}$ of a random sample of size n from a normal distribution with mean zero and variance one.

We now define a limiting distribution of a random variable whose distribution depends upon n.

Definition. Let the distribution function $F_n(y)$ of the random variable Y depend upon n, a positive integer. If $F(y)$ is a distribution function and if $\lim_{n \to \infty} F_n(y) = F(y)$ for every point y at which $F(y)$ is continuous, then the random variable Y is said to have a *limiting distribution* with distribution function $F(y)$.

The following examples are illustrative of random variables that have limiting distributions.

EXAMPLE 1. Let Y denote the nth order statistic of a random sample $X_1, X_2, \cdots, X_n$ from a distribution having p.d.f.

$$
f(x) = \frac{1}{\theta}, \quad 0 < x < \theta, \quad 0 < \theta < \infty,
$$

$$
= 0 \text{ elsewhere.}
$$

The p.d.f. of Y is

$$
g(y) = \frac{ny^{n-1}}{\theta^n}, \quad 0 < y < \theta,
$$

$$
= 0 \text{ elsewhere,}
$$

and the distribution function of Y is

$$
\begin{aligned}
F_n(y) &= 0, \quad y < 0, \\
&= \int_0^y \frac{nz^{n-1}}{\theta^n} \, dz = \left(\frac{y}{\theta}\right)^n, \quad 0 \le y < \theta, \\
&= 1, \quad \theta \le y < \infty.
\end{aligned}
$$

Then
$$\lim_{n\to\infty} F_n(y) = 0, \quad -\infty < y < \theta,$$
$$= 1, \quad \theta \le y < \infty.$$

Now
$$F(y) = 0, \quad -\infty < y < \theta,$$
$$= 1, \quad \theta \le y < \infty,$$

is a distribution function. Moreover, $\lim_{n\to\infty} F_n(y) = F(y)$ at each point of continuity of $F(y)$. In accordance with the definition of a limiting distribution, the random variable Y has a limiting distribution with distribution function $F(y)$. In this example the limiting distribution of Y is degenerate. Sometimes this is the case, sometimes a limiting distribution is not degenerate, and sometimes there is no limiting distribution at all.

EXAMPLE 2. Let $\bar{X}$ have the distribution function

Help! ok
$$F_n(\bar{x}) = \int_{-\infty}^{\bar{x}} \frac{1}{\sqrt{\frac{1}{n}}\sqrt{2\pi}} e^{-\frac{w^2}{2(1/n)}} \, dw.$$

If the change of variable $v = \sqrt{n}\, w$ is made, we have
$$F_n(\bar{x}) = \int_{-\infty}^{\sqrt{n}\,\bar{x}} \frac{1}{\sqrt{2\pi}} e^{-\frac{v^2}{2}} \, dv.$$

It is clear that

no it isn't! ok
$$\lim_{n\to\infty} F_n(\bar{x}) = 0, \quad \bar{x} < 0,$$
$$= \tfrac{1}{2}, \quad \bar{x} = 0,$$
$$= 1, \quad \bar{x} > 0.$$

Now the function
$$F(\bar{x}) = 0, \quad \bar{x} < 0,$$
$$= 1, \quad \bar{x} \ge 0,$$

is a distribution function and $\lim_{n\to\infty} F_n(\bar{x}) = F(\bar{x})$ at every point of continuity of $F(\bar{x})$. To be sure, $\lim_{n\to\infty} F_n(0) \ne F(0)$, but $F(\bar{x})$ is not continuous at $\bar{x} = 0$. Accordingly the random variable $\bar{X}$ has a limiting distribution with distribution function $F(\bar{x})$. Again this limiting distribution is degenerate and has all the probability at the one point $\bar{x} = 0$.

EXAMPLE 3. The fact that limiting distributions, if they exist, cannot in general be determined by taking the limit of the p.d.f. will now be illustrated. Let X have the p.d.f.
$$f_n(x) = 1, \quad x = 2 + \frac{1}{n},$$
$$= 0 \text{ elsewhere.}$$

don't see this o K

Clearly, $\lim_{n \to \infty} f_n(x) = 0$ for all values of x. This may suggest that X has no limiting distribution. However, the distribution function of X is

$$F_n(x) = 0, \quad x < 2 + \frac{1}{n},$$

$$= 1, \quad x \geq 2 + \frac{1}{n},$$

and

$$\lim_{n \to \infty} F_n(x) = 0, \quad x \leq 2,$$

$$= 1, \quad x > 2.$$

Since

$$F(x) = 0, \quad x < 2,$$

$$= 1, \quad x \geq 2,$$

is a distribution function, and since $\lim_{n \to \infty} F_n(x) = F(x)$ at all points of continuity of $F(x)$, there is a limiting distribution of X with distribution function $F(x)$.

Whenever the limiting distribution of a random variable is a degenerate distribution, the random variable is said to *converge stochastically* to the constant that has a probability of one. Thus Examples 1 to 3 illustrate not only the notion of a limiting distribution but also the concept of stochastic convergence. In Example 1, the statistic Y converges stochastically to θ; in Example 2, the statistic $\bar{X}$ converges stochastically to zero; and in Example 3, the random variable X converges stochastically to 2.

Exercises

7.4. Let the p.d.f. of Y be $f_n(y) = 1$, $y = n$, zero elsewhere. Show that Y does not have a limiting distribution.

7.5. Let the p.d.f. of X be $g_n(x) = nx^{n-1}$, $0 < x < 1$, zero elsewhere. Show that the limiting distribution of $Y = n(1 - X)$ is non-degenerate with distribution function

$$F(y) = 0, \quad y < 0,$$
$$= 1 - e^{-y}, \quad y \geq 0.$$

o K

7.6. Let $\bar{X}$ denote the mean of a random sample of size n from a distribution that is $n(x; \mu, \sigma^2)$. Prove that $\bar{X}$ converges stochastically to μ.

7.3. Limiting Moment-Generating Functions. To find the limiting distribution function of a random variable Y by use of the definition of limiting distribution function obviously requires that we know $F_n(y)$ for each positive integer n. But, as indicated in the introduction to this chapter, this is precisely the problem we should like to avoid. If it exists, the moment-generating function that corresponds to the distribution function $F_n(y)$ often provides a convenient method of determining the limiting distribution function. To emphasize that the distribution of a random variable Y depends upon the positive integer n, in this chapter we shall write the moment-generating function of Y in the form $M_Y(t; n)$.

The following theorem, which is essentially Curtiss' modification of a theorem of Lévy and Cramér, explains how the moment-generating function may be used in problems of limiting distributions. A proof of the theorem requires a knowledge of that same facet of analysis that permitted us to assert that a moment-generating function, when it exists, uniquely determines a distribution. Accordingly no proof of the theorem will be given.

THEOREM. Let the random variable Y have the distribution function $F_n(y)$ and the moment-generating function $M_Y(t; n)$ that exists for $-h < t < h$ for all n. If there exists a distribution function $F(y)$, with corresponding moment-generating function $M(t)$, defined for $|t| \leq h_1 < h$, such that $\lim_{n \to \infty} M_Y(t; n) = M(t)$, then Y has a limiting distribution with distribution function $F(y)$.

In this and the subsequent section are several illustrations of the use of the theorem. In some of these examples it is convenient to use a certain limit that is established in some courses in advanced calculus. We refer to a limit of the form

$$\lim_{n \to \infty} \left[1 + \frac{b}{n} + \frac{\psi(n)}{n} \right]^{cn}$$

where b and c do not depend upon n and where $\lim_{n \to \infty} \psi(n) = 0$. Then

$$\lim_{n \to \infty} \left[1 + \frac{b}{n} + \frac{\psi(n)}{n} \right]^{cn} = \lim_{n \to \infty} \left[1 + \frac{b}{n} \right]^{cn} = e^{bc}.$$

For example,

$$\lim_{n \to \infty} \left[1 - \frac{t^2}{n} + \frac{t^3}{n^{3/2}} \right]^{-\frac{n}{2}} = \lim_{n \to \infty} \left[1 - \frac{t^2}{n} + \frac{t^3/\sqrt{n}}{n} \right]^{-\frac{n}{2}}.$$

Here $b = -t^2$, $c = -1/2$, and $\psi(n) = t^3/\sqrt{n}$. Accordingly, for every fixed value of t, the limit is $e^{t^2/2}$.

EXAMPLE 1. Let Y have a binomial distribution with parameters n and p. Suppose that the mean $\mu = np$ is the same for every n; that is, $p = \mu/n$, where μ is a constant. We shall find the limiting distribution of the binomial distribution, when $p = \mu/n$, by finding the limit of $M_Y(t; n)$. Now

$$M_Y(t; n) = E(e^{tY}) = [(1 - p) + pe^t]^n = \left[1 + \frac{\mu(e^t - 1)}{n} \right]^n$$

for all real values of t. Hence, we have

$$\lim_{n \to \infty} M_Y(t; n) = e^{\mu(e^t - 1)}$$

for all real values of t. Since there exists a distribution, namely, the Poisson distribution with mean μ, that has this moment-generating function $e^{\mu(e^t-1)}$, then in accordance with the theorem and under the conditions stated, it is seen that Y has a limiting Poisson distribution with mean μ.

Whenever a random variable has a limiting distribution, we may, if we wish, use the limiting distribution as an approximation to the exact distribution function. The result of this example enables us to use the Poisson distribution as an approximation to the binomial distribution when n is large and p is small. This is clearly an advantage for it is easy to provide tables for the one parameter Poisson distribution. On the other hand, the binomial distribution has two parameters, and tables for this distribution are very ungainly. To illustrate the use of the approximation, let Y have a binomial distribution with $n = 50$ and $p = 1/25$. Then

$$Pr(Y \leq 1) = (24/25)^{50} + 50(1/25)(24/25)^{49}.$$

Since $\mu = np = 2$, the Poisson approximation to this probability is

$$e^{-2} + 2e^{-2} = 0.406, \quad \text{approximately.}$$

EXAMPLE 2. Let Z have a chi-square distribution with n degrees of freedom. Then

$$M_Z(t; n) = (1 - 2t)^{-\frac{n}{2}}, \quad t < \tfrac{1}{2}.$$

The mean and the variance of Z are respectively n and $2n$. The limiting distribution of the random variable $Y = (Z - n)/\sqrt{2n}$ will be investigated. Now

$$M_Y(t; n) = E\left[e^{t\left(\frac{Z-n}{\sqrt{2n}}\right)}\right] = E\left[e^{Y\bullet}\right]$$

$$= e^{-t\frac{n}{\sqrt{2n}}} E\left(e^{\frac{t}{\sqrt{2n}}Z}\right)$$

$$= e^{-\left(t\sqrt{\frac{2}{n}}\right)\left(\frac{n}{2}\right)}\left(1 - 2\frac{t}{\sqrt{2n}}\right)^{-\frac{n}{2}}, \quad t < \frac{\sqrt{2n}}{2}.$$

This may be written in the form

$$M_Y(t; n) = \left(e^{t\sqrt{\frac{2}{n}}} - t\sqrt{\frac{2}{n}}e^{t\sqrt{\frac{2}{n}}}\right)^{-\frac{n}{2}}, \quad t < \sqrt{\frac{n}{2}}.$$

In accordance with Taylor's formula, there exists a number $\xi(n)$, between 0 and $t\sqrt{2/n}$, such that

$$e^{t\sqrt{\frac{2}{n}}} = 1 + t\sqrt{\frac{2}{n}} + \frac{1}{2}\left(t\sqrt{\frac{2}{n}}\right)^2 + \frac{e^{\xi(n)}}{6}\left(t\sqrt{\frac{2}{n}}\right)^3.$$

If this sum is substituted for $e^{t\sqrt{2/n}}$ in the last expression for $M_Y(t; n)$, it is seen that

$$M_Y(t; n) = \left(1 - \frac{t^2}{n} + \frac{\psi(n)}{n}\right)^{-\frac{n}{2}}$$

where

$$\psi(n) = \frac{\sqrt{2}t^3 e^{\xi(n)}}{3\sqrt{n}} - \frac{\sqrt{2}t^3}{\sqrt{n}} - \frac{2t^4 e^{\xi(n)}}{3n}.$$

Since $\xi(n) \to 0$ as $n \to \infty$, then $\lim_{n \to \infty} \psi(n) = 0$ for every fixed value of t. In accordance with the limit proposition cited earlier in this section, we have

$$\lim_{n \to \infty} M_Y(t; n) = e^{\frac{t^2}{2}}$$

for all real values of t. That is, the random variable $Y = (Z - n)/\sqrt{2n}$ has a limiting normal distribution with mean zero and variance one.

Exercises

7.7. Let the random variable Z have a Poisson distribution with parameter $\mu = n$. Show that the limiting distribution of the random variable $Y = (Z - n)/\sqrt{n}$ is normal with mean zero and variance one.

7.8. Let $\bar{X}$ denote the mean of a random sample of size n from a distribution having p.d.f. $f(x) = 1, 0 < x < 1$, zero elsewhere. Then (see introductory remarks to this chapter) the moment-generating function of $\bar{X}$ is

$$M_{\bar{X}}(t; n) = \left(\frac{e^{\frac{t}{n}} - 1}{\frac{t}{n}} \right)^n, \quad t \neq 0,$$

$$= 1, \quad t = 0.$$

Show that the limiting distribution of $\bar{X}$ is degenerate.

7.9. Let $Y = S^2 = \sum_1^n (X_i - \bar{X})^2/n$ denote the variance of a random sample of size n from a distribution that is $n(x; \mu, \sigma^2)$. Then $Z = nY/\sigma^2$ has a chi-square distribution with $n - 1$ degrees of freedom. Find $M_Y(t; n)$, show that the $\lim_{n \to \infty} M_Y(t; n) = e^{\sigma^2 t}$, and deduce that $Y = S^2$ converges stochastically to σ^2. What, however, would be the limiting distribution of $[Z - (n - 1)]/\sqrt{2(n - 1)} = [nY - (n - 1)\sigma^2]/\sigma^2 \sqrt{2(n - 1)}$?

7.4. The Central Limit Theorem. It was seen, page 56, that if $X_1, X_2, \cdots, X_n$ is a random sample from a normal distribution with mean μ and variance σ^2, the random variable

$$\frac{\sum_1^n X_i - n\mu}{\sigma \sqrt{n}} = \frac{\bar{X} - \mu}{\frac{\sigma}{\sqrt{n}}}$$

is, for every positive integer n, normally distributed with zero mean and unit variance. In probability theory there is a very elegant theorem called the *Central Limit Theorem*. A special case of this theorem asserts the remarkable and important fact that if $X_1, X_2, \cdots, X_n$ denote the items of a random sample of size n from any distribution having finite variance σ^2 (and hence finite mean μ), then the random variable $\sqrt{n}(\bar{X} - \mu)/\sigma$ has a limiting normal distribution with zero mean and unit variance. If this fact can be established, it will imply, whenever the conditions of the theorem are satisfied, that the random variable $\sqrt{n}(\bar{X} - \mu)/\sigma$ has an approximate normal distribution with mean zero and variance one. It will then be possible to use this approximate normal distribution to compute approximate probabilities concerning $\bar{X}$, to find an approximate confidence interval for μ, and in Chapter Nine, to test certain statistical hypotheses without ever knowing what the exact p.d.f. of $\bar{X}$ is in every case.

Only a modified form of this special case of the Central Limit Theorem will be proved here. The modification consists in requiring the existence of a moment-generating function for the distribution from which the sample is to be taken. This is, of course, much more stringent than merely requiring the existence of the variance of that distribution. The modified form of the theorem follows.

THEOREM. Let $X_1, X_2, \cdots, X_n$ denote the items of a random sample from a distribution having mean μ, variance σ^2, and moment-generating function $M_X(t)$ that exists for $-h < t < h$. Then the random variable

$$Y = \left(\sum_1^n X_i - n\mu \right) \Big/ (\sqrt{n}\,\sigma) = \sqrt{n}(\bar{X} - \mu)/\sigma$$ has a limiting distribution

that is normal with mean zero and variance one.

PROOF. Since $M_X(t) = E(e^{tX})$ exists for $-h < t < h$, the function

$$m(t) = E[e^{t(X-\mu)}] = e^{-\mu t}M_X(t)$$

exists for $-h < t < h$. It will first be shown that

$$m(t) = 1 + \frac{\sigma^2 t^2}{2} + \frac{[m''(\xi) - \sigma^2]t^2}{2}$$

where ξ is between 0 and t. To see this, note that

$$m'(t) = e^{-\mu t}M'_X(t) - \mu e^{-\mu t}M_X(t)$$

and

$$m''(t) = e^{-\mu t}M''_X(t) - 2\mu e^{-\mu t}M'_X(t) + \mu^2 e^{-\mu t}M_X(t).$$

Now $M_X(0) = 1$, $M'_X(0) = \mu$, and $M''_X(0) = \sigma^2 + \mu^2$. Hence $m(0) = 1$, $m'(0) = 0$, and $m''(0) = \sigma^2$. By Taylor's formula there exists a number ξ between 0 and t such that

$$m(t) = m(0) + m'(0)t + \frac{m''(\xi)t^2}{2}$$

$$= 1 + \frac{m''(\xi)t^2}{2}.$$

If $\sigma^2 t^2/2$ is added and subtracted, then

$$m(t) = 1 + \frac{\sigma^2 t^2}{2} + \frac{[m''(\xi) - \sigma^2]t^2}{2}$$

as was to be shown.

Next consider $M_Y(t; n)$ where

$$M_Y(t; n) = E\left[e^{t\frac{\sum_{1}^{n} X_i - n\mu}{\sigma\sqrt{n}}}\right]$$

$$= E\left[e^{\frac{t(X_1 - \mu)}{\sigma\sqrt{n}}} e^{\frac{t(X_2 - \mu)}{\sigma\sqrt{n}}} \cdots e^{\frac{t(X_n - \mu)}{\sigma\sqrt{n}}}\right]$$

$$= E\left[e^{\frac{t}{\sigma\sqrt{n}}(X_1 - \mu)}\right] \cdots E\left[e^{\frac{t}{\sigma\sqrt{n}}(X_n - \mu)}\right]$$

$$= \left\{E\left[e^{\frac{t}{\sigma\sqrt{n}}(X - \mu)}\right]\right\}^n$$

$$= \left[m\left(\frac{t}{\sigma\sqrt{n}}\right)\right]^n, \quad -h < \frac{t}{\sigma\sqrt{n}} < h.$$

In $m(t)$,

$$m(t) = 1 + \frac{\sigma^2 t^2}{2} + \frac{[m''(\xi) - \sigma^2]t^2}{2},$$

replace t by $t/(\sigma\sqrt{n})$ to obtain

$$m\left(\frac{t}{\sigma\sqrt{n}}\right) = 1 + \frac{t^2}{2n} + \frac{[m''(\xi) - \sigma^2]t^2}{2n\sigma^2},$$

where now ξ is between 0 and $t/\sigma\sqrt{n}$ with $-h\sigma\sqrt{n} < t < h\sigma\sqrt{n}$. Accordingly $M_Y(t; n) = \left[m\left(\frac{t}{\sigma\sqrt{n}}\right)\right]^n$ becomes

$$M_Y(t; n) = \left[1 + \frac{t^2}{2n} + \frac{[m''(\xi) - \sigma^2]t^2}{2n\sigma^2}\right]^n.$$

Since $m''(t)$ is continuous at $t = 0$ and since $\xi \to 0$ as $n \to \infty$, we have

$$\lim_{n \to \infty} [m''(\xi) - \sigma^2] = 0.$$

The limit proposition cited on page 143 shows that

$$\lim_{n \to \infty} M_Y(t; n) = e^{\frac{t^2}{2}}$$

for all real values of t. This proves that the random variable $Y = \sqrt{n}(\bar{X} - \mu)/\sigma$ has a limiting normal distribution with mean zero and variance one.

We interpret this theorem as saying that the random variable $\sqrt{n}(\bar{X} - \mu)/\sigma$ has an approximate normal distribution with mean zero and variance one; and in applications we use the approximate normal p.d.f. as though it were the exact p.d.f. of $\sqrt{n}(\bar{X} - \mu)/\sigma$.

Some illustrative examples, here and later, will help show the importance of this version of the Central Limit Theorem.

EXAMPLE 1. Let $\bar{X}$ denote the mean of a random sample of size 75 from the distribution having p.d.f.

$$f(x) = 1, 0 < x < 1,$$
$$= 0 \text{ elsewhere.}$$

The exact p.d.f. of $\bar{X}$, say, $g(\bar{x})$, has a graph, at points of positive probability density, which is composed of arcs of 75 different polynomials of degree 74. The computation of such a probability as

$$Pr\,(0.45 < \bar{X} < 0.55) = \int_{0.45}^{0.55} g(\bar{x})\,d\bar{x}$$

would be extremely laborious. The conditions of the theorem are satisfied, since $M_X(t)$ exists for all real values of t. Moreover, $\mu = \frac{1}{2}$ and $\sigma^2 = 1/12$, so we have approximately

$$Pr(0.45 < \bar{X} < 0.55) = Pr\left[\frac{(0.45 - \mu)}{\dfrac{\sigma}{\sqrt{n}}} < \frac{(\bar{X} - \mu)}{\dfrac{\sigma}{\sqrt{n}}} < \frac{(0.55 - \mu)}{\dfrac{\sigma}{\sqrt{n}}}\right]$$

$$= Pr\left(-1.5 < \frac{\bar{X} - 0.5}{\dfrac{1}{30}} < 1.5\right)$$

$$= 0.866$$

from Table I.

EXAMPLE 2. Let $\bar{X}$ denote the mean of a random sample of size 25 from a distribution having a moment-generating function and having variance $\sigma^2 = 100$ and mean μ. Let the observed mean of the sample be $\bar{x} = 67.53$. Since $\sigma/\sqrt{n} = 2$, then approximately

$$Pr\left[-1.96 < \frac{(\bar{X} - \mu)}{2} < 1.96\right] = 0.95,$$

or

$$Pr(\bar{X} - 3.92 < \mu < \bar{X} + 3.92) = 0.95.$$

Accordingly the interval from $\bar{x} - 3.92 = 67.53 - 3.92 = 63.61$ to $\bar{x} + 3.92 = 71.45$ is an approximate 95 per cent confidence interval for the mean μ.

EXAMPLE 3. Let $X_1, X_2, \cdots, X_n$ denote a random sample from the distribution having p.d.f.

$$f(x) = p^x(1 - p)^{1-x}, \quad x = 0, 1 \quad \text{and} \quad 0 < p < 1,$$
$$= 0 \text{ elsewhere.}$$

Here, $\mu = p$, $\sigma^2 = p(1 - p)$ and $M_X(t)$ exists for all real values of t. If $Y = X_1 + \cdots + X_n$, it is known, page 50, that Y has a binomial distribution with parameters n and p. Calculation of probabilities concerning Y, when we do not use the Poisson approximation, can be greatly simplified by making use of the fact that $(Y - np)/\sqrt{np(1 - p)} = \sqrt{n}(\bar{X} - p)/\sqrt{p(1 - p)} = \sqrt{n}(\bar{X} - \mu)/\sigma$ has a limiting distribution that is normal with mean zero and variance one. Let $n = 100$ and $p = \frac{1}{2}$, and suppose we wish to compute $Pr(Y = 48, 49, 50, 51, 52)$. Since Y is a random variable of the discrete type, the events $Y = 48, 49, 50, 51, 52$ and $47.5 < Y < 52.5$ are equivalent. That is, $Pr(Y = 48, 49, 50, 51, 52) = Pr(47.5 < Y < 52.5)$. Since $np = 50$ and $np(1 - p) = 25$, the latter probability may be written

$$Pr(47.5 < Y < 52.5) = Pr\left(\frac{47.5 - 50}{5} < \frac{Y - 50}{5} < \frac{52.5 - 50}{5}\right)$$

$$= Pr\left(-0.5 < \frac{Y - 50}{5} < 0.5\right).$$

Since $(Y - 50)/5$ has an approximate normal distribution with mean zero and variance one, Table I shows this probability to be approximately 0.382.

The convention of selecting the event $47.5 < Y < 52.5$, instead of, say, $47.8 < Y < 52.3$, as the event equivalent to the event $Y = 48, 49, 50, 51, 52$ seems to have originated in the following manner: The probability, $Pr(Y = 48, 49, 50, 51, 52)$, can be interpreted as the sum of five rectangular areas where the rectangles have bases one but the heights are respectively $Pr(Y = 48)$, $\cdots$, $Pr(Y = 52)$. If these rectangles are so located that the mid-points of their bases are respectively at the points 48, 49, $\cdots$, 52 on a horizontal axis, then in approximating the sum of these areas by an area bounded by the horizontal axis, the graph of a normal p.d.f., and two ordinates, it seems reasonable to take the two ordinates at the points 47.5 and 52.5.

Exercises

7.10. Compute an approximate probability that the mean of a random sample of size 15 from a distribution having p.d.f. $f(x) = 3x^2$, $0 < x < 1$, zero elsewhere, is between 3/5 and 4/5.

7.11. Let Y denote the sum of the items of a random sample of size 12 from a distribution having p.d.f. $f(x) = 1/6$, $x = 1, 2, 3, 4, 5, 6$, zero elsewhere. Compute an approximate value of $Pr(36 \le Y \le 48)$.

7.12. Let $\bar{X}$ denote the mean of a random sample of size n from a distribution that has mean μ, variance $\sigma^2 = 10$, and a moment-generating function. Find n so that the probability is approximately 0.954 that the random interval $(\bar{X} - \frac{1}{2}, \bar{X} + \frac{1}{2})$ includes μ.

7.13. Let Y have a binomial distribution with parameters $n = 400$, $p = 1/5$. Compute an approximate value of $Pr(0.25 < Y/n)$.

7.14. If Y has a binomial distribution with parameters $n = 100$, $p = \frac{1}{2}$, approximate the value of $Pr(Y = 50)$.

7.15. Let Y have a binomial distribution with parameters n and $p = 0.55$. Find the smallest value of n so that (approximately) $Pr(Y/n > \frac{1}{2}) \geq 0.95$.

7.16. Let $f(x) = 1/x^2$, $1 < x < \infty$, zero elsewhere, be the p.d.f. of a random variable X. Consider a random sample of size 72 from the distribution having this p.d.f. Compute approximately the probability that more than 50 of the items of the random sample are less than 3. Note that $M_X(t)$ does not exist, but its existence is not involved here.

7.17. Let Y have a binomial distribution with parameters $n = 300$ and p. Find a random interval such that 0.954 is the approximate probability that the random interval includes the parameter p.

7.5. The Limiting Distribution of $\bar{X}$. There seems to be a tendency for some students to confuse the limiting distributions of $\bar{X}$ and $\sqrt{n}(\bar{X} - \mu)/\sigma$. In the preceding section, it was seen, when certain conditions are met, that the limiting distribution of $Y = \sqrt{n}(\bar{X} - \mu)/\sigma$ is a nondegenerate normal distribution with mean zero and variance one. That is, the limiting distribution of Y has the distribution function

$$F(y) = \int_{-\infty}^{y} \frac{1}{\sqrt{2\pi}} e^{-\frac{w^2}{2}} \, dw.$$

On the other hand, it was seen in Example 2, page 141, that in one case at least, the limiting distribution of $\bar{X}$ is degenerate. It can be proved that the limiting distribution of $\bar{X}$ is always degenerate, provided the mean μ of the distribution from which the random sample is taken is finite. We shall not prove this statement in complete generality, for we shall assume the existence of a moment-generating function. The proof, given in the next paragraph, follows closely the proof of the special case of the Central Limit Theorem.

Let $X_1, X_2, \cdots, X_n$ denote a random sample from a distribution having a moment-generating function that exists for $-h < t < h$. Let the mean of this distribution be μ and let $\bar{X}$ denote the mean of the random sample. Then

$$M_{\bar{X}}(t; n) = \left[M_X\!\left(\frac{t}{n}\right) \right]^n.$$

It will first be shown that

$$M_X(t) = 1 + \mu t + [M'_X(\xi) - \mu]t,$$

where ξ is between 0 and t. By Taylor's formula, there exists a number ξ between 0 and t such that

$$M_X(t) = M_X(0) + tM'_X(\xi).$$

Now $M_X(0) = 1$; so, if μt be added and subtracted, $M_X(t)$ can be written

$$M_X(t) = 1 + \mu t + [M'_X(\xi) - \mu]t.$$

Then

$$M_X\left(\frac{t}{n}\right) = 1 + \frac{\mu t}{n} + \frac{[M'_X(\xi) - \mu]t}{n}$$

where now ξ is between 0 and t/n with $-nh < t < nh$.   Accordingly,

$$M_{\bar{X}}(t; n) = \left[1 + \frac{\mu t}{n} + \frac{[M'_X(\xi) - \mu]t}{n}\right]^n.$$

Since $M'_X(t)$ is a continuous function at $t = 0$, since $M'_X(0) = \mu$ and since $\xi \to 0$ as $n \to \infty$, we have

$$\lim_{n \to \infty} [M'_X(\xi) - \mu] = 0.$$

Hence

$$\lim_{n \to \infty} M_{\bar{X}}(t; n) = e^{\mu t},$$

for all real values of t.   But $e^{\mu t}$ is the moment-generating function of a degenerate distribution with probability one at the point μ.   Thus the limiting distribution of $\bar{X}$ is degenerate (or $\bar{X}$ converges stochastically to μ), and the limiting distribution function of $\bar{X}$ is given by

$$F(\bar{x}) = 0, \quad \bar{x} < \mu,$$
$$= 1, \quad \bar{x} \geq \mu.$$

Exercise

7.18.   Let the random variable Y have a binomial distribution with parameters n and p.   Show that Y/n converges stochastically to the fixed parameter p.   This result is one form of the law of large numbers.

CHAPTER EIGHT

SOME DISTRIBUTION-FREE PROBLEMS

It was seen, page 138, that a nondecreasing point function $F(x)$, continuous everywhere and having $F(-\infty) = 0$, $F(\infty) = 1$, and a continuous derivative $F'(x) = f(x)$, except possibly at a finite number of points in every finite interval, satisfies the conditions of being a distribution function of a random variable X of the continuous type. In this chapter we shall restrict ourselves to random variables of the continuous type. By so doing, it is found that the marginal probability density functions of the order statistics can be expressed easily in terms of the distribution function $F(x)$ and the p.d.f. $f(x)$. But, more importantly, we can establish a certain distribution-free property of the order statistics that provides a basis for many *distribution-free statistical inferences;* that is, statistical inferences that require no assumption about the distribution other than that it is a distribution of the continuous type. We consider two important types of distribution-free statistical inference. One of these has to do with the problem of confidence intervals for what will presently be defined as "distribution quantiles." The other has to do with what will be defined as "distribution tolerance limits."

8.1. Distributions of Order Statistics. Let X denote a random variable of the continuous type having p.d.f. $f(x)$ that is positive and continuous, provided $a < x < b$, and is zero elsewhere. Then the distribution function $F(x)$ may be written

$$F(x) = 0, \quad x \leq a,$$

$$= \int_a^x f(w) \, dw, \quad a < x < b,$$

$$= 1, \quad b \leq x.$$

Accordingly, $F'(x) = f(x)$, $a < x < b$.   Moreover, if $a < x < b$,

$$1 - F(x) = F(b) - F(x)$$

$$= \int_a^b f(w)\ dw - \int_a^x f(w)\ dw$$

$$= \int_x^b f(w)\ dw.$$

Let $X_1, X_2, \cdots, X_n$ denote a random sample of size n from this distribution, and let $Y_1, Y_2, \cdots, Y_n$ denote the order statistics of this random sample.   Then, in accordance with page 85, the joint p.d.f. of $Y_1, Y_2, \cdots, Y_n$ is

$$g(y_1, y_2, \cdots, y_n) = n!\, f(y_1)f(y_2) \cdots f(y_n),\quad a < y_1 < y_2 < \cdots < y_n < b,$$
$$= 0\ \text{elsewhere}.$$

It will first be shown how the marginal p.d.f. of Y_n may be expressed in terms of the distribution function $F(x)$ and the p.d.f. $f(x)$ of the random variable X.   If $a < y_n < b$, the marginal p.d.f. of Y_n is given by

$$g_n(y_n) = \int_a^{y_n} \cdots \int_a^{y_4} \int_a^{y_3} \int_a^{y_2} n!\, f(y_1)f(y_2) \cdots f(y_n)\ dy_1\ dy_2\ dy_3 \cdots dy_{n-1}$$

$$= \int_a^{y_n} \cdots \int_a^{y_4} \int_a^{y_3} n!\left(\int_a^{y_2} f(y_1)\ dy_1 \right) f(y_2) \cdots f(y_n)\ dy_2 \cdots dy_{n-1}$$

$$= \int_a^{y_n} \cdots \int_a^{y_4} \int_a^{y_3} n!\, F(y_2)f(y_2) \cdots f(y_n)\ dy_2 \cdots dy_{n-1}$$

since $F(x) = \int_a^x f(w)dw$.   Now

$$\int_a^{y_3} F(y_2)f(y_2)\ dy_2 = \frac{[F(y_2)]^2}{2}\bigg|_a^{y_3}$$

$$= \frac{[F(y_3)]^2}{2},$$

since $F(a) = 0$.   Thus

$$g_n(y_n) = \int_a^{y_n} \cdots \int_a^{y_4} n!\frac{[F(y_3)]^2}{2}f(y_3) \cdots f(y_n)\ dy_3 \cdots dy_{n-1}.$$

But

$$\int_a^{y_4} \frac{[F(y_3)]^2}{2}f(y_3)\ dy_3 = \frac{[F(y_3)]^3}{2 \cdot 3}\bigg|_a^{y_4} = \frac{[F(y_4)]^3}{2 \cdot 3},$$

so

$$g_n(y_n) = \int_a^{y_n} \cdots \int_a^{y_5} n!\frac{[F(y_4)]^3}{3!}f(y_4) \cdots f(y_n)\ dy_4 \cdots dy_{n-1}.$$

If the successive integrations on $y_4, \cdots, y_{n-1}$ are carried out, it is seen that

$$
\begin{aligned}
g_n(y_n) &= n! \frac{[F(y_n)]^{n-1}}{(n-1)!} f(y_n) \\
&= n[F(y_n)]^{n-1} f(y_n), \quad a < y_n < b, \\
&= 0 \text{ elsewhere.}
\end{aligned}
$$

It will next be shown how to express the marginal p.d.f. of Y_1 in terms of $F(x)$ and $f(x)$. We have, for $a < y_1 < b$,

$$
g_1(y_1) = \int_{y_1}^b \cdots \int_{y_{n-2}}^b \int_{y_{n-2}}^b \int_{y_{n-1}}^b n! f(y_1) f(y_2) \cdots f(y_n) \, dy_n \, dy_{n-1} \cdots dy_2
$$

$$
= \int_{y_1}^b \cdots \int_{y_{n-2}}^b \int_{y_{n-2}}^b n! f(y_1) f(y_2) \cdots f(y_{n-1})[1 - F(y_{n-1})] dy_{n-1} \cdots dy_2.
$$

But

$$
\int_{y_{n-2}}^b [1 - F(y_{n-1})] f(y_{n-1}) dy_{n-1} = - \left. \frac{[1 - F(y_{n-1})]^2}{2} \right|_{y_{n-2}}^b
$$

$$
= \frac{[1 - F(y_{n-2})]^2}{2},
$$

so that

$$
g_1(y_1) = \int_{y_1}^b \cdots \int_{y_{n-2}}^b n! f(y_1) \cdots f(y_{n-2}) \frac{[1 - F(y_{n-2})]^2}{2} \, dy_{n-2} \cdots dy_2.
$$

Upon completing the integrations, it is found that

$$
\begin{aligned}
g_1(y_1) &= n[1 - F(y_1)]^{n-1} f(y_1), \quad a < y_1 < b, \\
&= 0 \text{ elsewhere.}
\end{aligned}
$$

Once it is observed that

$$
\int_a^x [F(w)]^{\alpha-1} f(w) \, dw = \frac{[F(x)]^\alpha}{\alpha}, \quad \alpha > 0,
$$

and that

$$
\int_y^b [1 - F(w)]^{\beta-1} f(w) \, dw = \frac{[1 - F(y)]^\beta}{\beta}, \quad \beta > 0,
$$

it is easy to express the marginal p.d.f. of any order statistic, say, Y_k, in terms of $F(x)$ and $f(x)$. This is done by evaluating the integral

$$
g_k(y_k) = \int_a^{y_k} \cdots \int_a^{y_2} \int_{y_k}^b \cdots \int_{y_{n-1}}^b n! f(y_1) f(y_2) \cdots f(y_n) \, dy_n \cdots dy_{k+1} \, dy_1 \cdots dy_{k-1}.
$$

The result is

$$
\begin{aligned}
g_k(y_k) &= \frac{n!}{(k-1)!(n-k)!} [F(y_k)]^{k-1} [1 - F(y_k)]^{n-k} f(y_k), \quad a < y_k < b, \\
&= 0 \text{ elsewhere.}
\end{aligned}
$$

Finally the joint p.d.f. of any two order statistics, say, $Y_i < Y_j$, is as easily expressed in terms of $F(x)$ and $f(x)$. We have

$$g_{ij}(y_i, y_j) = \int_a^{y_i} \cdots \int_a^{y_2} \int_{y_i}^{y_i} \cdots \int_{y_{i-2}}^{y_i} \int_{y_i}^b \cdots \int_{y_{n-1}}^b n! f(y_1) \cdots$$

$$f(y_n) \, dy_n \cdots dy_{j+1} \, dy_{j-1} \cdots dy_{i+1} \, dy_1 \cdots dy_{i-1}.$$

Since, for $\gamma > 0$,

$$\int_x^y [F(y) - F(w)]^{\gamma-1} f(w) \, dw = -\frac{[F(y) - F(w)]^\gamma}{\gamma}\bigg|_x^y$$

$$= \frac{[F(y) - F(x)]^\gamma}{\gamma},$$

it is found that

$$g_{ij}(y_i, y_j) = \frac{n!}{(i-1)!(j-i-1)!(n-j)!}[F(y_i)]^{i-1}[F(y_j) - F(y_i)]^{j-i-1}$$

$$[1 - F(y_j)]^{n-j} f(y_i) f(y_j)$$

for $a < y_i < y_j < b$, and zero elsewhere.

Two illustrative examples follow.

EXAMPLE 1. Let $Y_1 < Y_2 < Y_3 < Y_4$ denote the order statistics of a random sample of size 4 from a distribution having p.d.f.

$$f(x) = 2x, \quad 0 < x < 1,$$
$$= 0 \text{ elsewhere.}$$

We shall express the p.d.f. of Y_3 in terms of $f(x)$ and $F(x)$ and then compute $Pr(\frac{1}{2} < Y_3)$. Here $F(x) = x^2$, provided $0 < x < 1$, so that

$$g_3(y_3) = \frac{4!}{2!1!}(y_3^2)^2(1 - y_3^2)(2y_3), \quad 0 < y_3 < 1,$$

$$= 0 \text{ elsewhere.}$$

Thus

$$Pr\left(\frac{1}{2} < Y_3\right) = \int_{1/2}^\infty g_3(y_3) \, dy_3$$

$$= \int_{1/2}^1 24(y_3^5 - y_3^7) \, dy_3 = \frac{243}{256}.$$

EXAMPLE 2. Let $Y_1 < Y_2 < \cdots < Y_5$ denote the order statistics of a random sample of size 5 from a distribution having p.d.f.

$$f(x) = e^{-x}, \quad 0 < x < \infty,$$
$$= 0 \text{ elsewhere.}$$

It will be shown that the statistics $Z_1 = Y_2$ and $Z_2 = Y_4 - Y_2$ are stochastically independent. Since $F(x) = 1 - e^{-x}$, $0 < x < \infty$, the joint p.d.f. of Y_2 and Y_4 is

$$g_{24}(y_2, y_4) = \frac{5!}{1!1!1!}[1 - e^{-y_2}][e^{-y_2} - e^{-y_4}][e^{-y_4}]e^{-y_2-y_4}, \quad 0 < y_2 < y_4 < \infty,$$

$$= 0 \text{ elsewhere.}$$

The transformation $z_1 = y_2$, $z_2 = y_4 - y_2$ maps the set $\{(y_2, y_4); 0 < y_2 < y_4 < \infty\}$ into the set $\{(z_1, z_2); 0 < z_1 < \infty, 0 < z_2 < \infty\}$, and the Jacobian of the transformation is 1. Accordingly the joint p.d.f. of Z_1 and Z_2 is

$$h(z_1, z_2) = 120e^{-4z_1}(1 - e^{-z_1})e^{-2z_2}(1 - e^{-z_2}), \quad 0 < z_1 < \infty, 0 < z_2 < \infty,$$
$$= 0 \text{ elsewhere.}$$

Now the p.d.f. of $Z_1 = Y_2$ is

$$g_2(y_2) = g_2(z_1) = \frac{5!}{1!3!}(1 - e^{-z_1})(e^{-z_1})^3 e^{-z_1}$$
$$= 20e^{-4z_1}(1 - e^{-z_1}), \quad 0 < z_1 < \infty,$$
$$= 0 \text{ elsewhere.}$$

Thus $h(z_1, z_2)$ is the product of the marginal p.d.f. of z_1 and a function of z_2 alone. That function of z_2 is then the marginal p.d.f. of Z_2, and Z_1 and Z_2 are stochastically independent.

Exercises

8.1. Let $Y_1 < Y_2 < Y_3 < Y_4 < Y_5$ denote the order statistics of a random sample of size 5 from a distribution of the continuous type having distribution function $F(x)$ such that $F'(x) = f(x)$ is positive and continuous, provided $a < x < b$. Show by integrating the joint p.d.f. of $Y_1, \cdots, Y_5$ on y_1, y_3, y_4, y_5 that the p.d.f. of Y_2 is $g_2(y_2) = 20 F(y_2)[1 - F(y_2)]^3 f(y_2)$, $a < y_2 < b$, and zero elsewhere.

8.2. Let $Y_1 < Y_2 < Y_3 < Y_4 < Y_5$ denote the order statistics of a random sample of size 5 from a distribution having the p.d.f. $f(x) = 1$, $\theta - \frac{1}{2} < x < \theta + \frac{1}{2}$, $-\infty < \theta < \infty$, zero elsewhere. Compute $Pr(\theta - \frac{1}{4} < Y_3 < \theta + \frac{1}{4})$. Show how the result may be used to obtain a confidence interval for θ.

8.3. Let $Y_1 < Y_2 < Y_3 < Y_4 < Y_5$ denote the order statistics of a random sample of size 5 from a distribution having p.d.f. $f(x) = 3x^2$, $0 < x < 1$, zero elsewhere. Show that $Z_1 = Y_2/Y_4$ and $Z_2 = Y_4$ are stochastically independent.

8.2. A Distribution-free Property of the Order Statistics. We begin our discussion with an example.

EXAMPLE 1. Let the p.d.f. of a random variable X be given by

$$f(x) = 3x^2, \quad 0 < x < 1,$$
$$= 0 \text{ elsewhere.}$$

Define the random variable Z by $Z = X^3$. It will be shown that the p.d.f. of Z is

$$h(z) = 1, \quad 0 < z < 1,$$
$$= 0 \text{ elsewhere.}$$

The transformation $z = x^3$ or $x = z^{1/3}$ maps the set $\{x; 0 < x < 1\}$ into the set $\{z; 0 < z < 1\}$. The Jacobian of the transformation is

$$J = \frac{dx}{dz} = \frac{1}{3z^{2/3}}.$$

Thus the p.d.f. of z is

$$h(z) = f(z^{1/3})|J| = 3z^{2/3}\frac{1}{3z^{2/3}} = 1, \quad 0 < z < 1,$$
$$= 0 \text{ elsewhere.}$$

That is, $Z = X^3$ has a uniform distribution having this p.d.f. This result could have been obtained somewhat more easily by observing three things:

(1) $F(x) = x^3$ is the distribution function of X when $0 < x < 1$;

(2) $z = x^3 = F(x)$, so $\dfrac{dz}{dx} = 3x^2 = f(x)$ when $0 < x < 1$;

(3) $\dfrac{dx}{dz} = \dfrac{1}{\dfrac{dz}{dx}}$ if $\dfrac{dz}{dx} \neq 0.$

It follows that here

$$f(x)\left|\frac{dx}{dz}\right| = f(x)\frac{dx}{dz} = \left(\frac{dz}{dx}\right)\left(\frac{1}{\dfrac{dz}{dx}}\right) = 1.$$

When x is replaced in the preceding expression by $z^{1/3}$, it is seen that $h(z) = 1$ on the set $\{z; 0 < z < 1\}$.

The preceding example is a particular case of the following theorem.

THEOREM 1.   Let X be a random variable of the continuous type having p.d.f. $f(x)$ and distribution function $F(x)$. Then the random variable $Z = F(X)$ has a uniform distribution with p.d.f.

$$h(z) = 1, \quad 0 < z < 1,$$
$$= 0 \text{ elsewhere.}$$

PROOF.   We prove the theorem under the assumption that the p.d.f. $f(x)$ is positive and continuous, provided $a < x < b$, and is zero elsewhere. The distribution function of X may be written

$$F(x) = 0, \quad x \leq a,$$
$$= \int_a^x f(w)\, dw, \quad a < x < b,$$
$$= 1, \quad b \leq x.$$

The transformation $z = F(x)$ maps the set $\{x; a < x < b\}$ into the set $\{z; 0 < z < 1\}$. Since $dz/dx = f(x)$, $a < x < b$, then

$$f(x)\left|\frac{dx}{dz}\right| = f(x)\frac{dx}{dz} = f(x)\frac{1}{\dfrac{dz}{dx}} = f(x)\frac{1}{f(x)} = 1, \quad a < x < b.$$

That is, the p.d.f. of $Z = F(X)$ is

$$h(z) = 1, \quad 0 < z < 1,$$
$$= 0 \text{ elsewhere,}$$

as was to be shown.

The random variable $Z = F(X)$ is an important random variable. Theorem 1 describes the distribution of Z. It is our purpose now to make an interpretation. Since $Z = F(X)$ has the p.d.f.

$$h(z) = 1, \quad 0 < z < 1,$$
$$= 0 \text{ elsewhere,}$$

then, if $0 < p < 1$, we have

$$Pr[F(X) \le p] = \int_0^p dz = p.$$

Now $F(x) = Pr(X \le x)$. Since $Pr(X = x) = 0$, then $F(x)$ is the fractional part of the probability for the distribution of X that is between $-\infty$ and x. If $F(x) \le p$, then no more than $100p$ per cent of the probability for the distribution of X is between $-\infty$ and x. But recall $Pr[F(X) \le p] = p$. That is, the probability that the random variable $Z = F(X)$ is less than or equal to p is precisely the probability that the random interval $(-\infty, X)$ contains no more than $100p$ per cent of the probability for the distribution. For example, the probability that the random interval $(-\infty, X)$ contains no more than 70 per cent of the probability for the distribution is 0.70; and the probability that the random interval $(-\infty, X)$ contains more than 70 per cent of the probability for the distribution is $1 - 0.70 = 0.30$. Perhaps it should be emphasized that statements of this kind are valid for all distributions of the continuous type. That is, these are examples of distribution-free probabilities.

EXAMPLE 2. Let the random variable X have a chi-square distribution with four degrees of freedom. It is desired to determine a function Z of the random variable X that has a uniform distribution with p.d.f. $h(z) = 1$ on the set $\{z; 0 < z < 1\}$ and zero elsewhere. Here

$$f(x) = \frac{1}{\Gamma\left(\frac{4}{2}\right)2^{\frac{4}{2}}} x^{\frac{4}{2}-1} e^{-\frac{x}{2}}, \quad 0 < x < \infty,$$

$$= 0 \text{ elsewhere.}$$

Then, for $0 < x < \infty$,

$$F(x) = \int_0^x \frac{1}{4} w e^{-\frac{w}{2}} dw$$

$$= \left[-\frac{w e^{-\frac{w}{2}}}{2} - e^{-\frac{w}{2}} \right]_0^x$$

$$= 1 - \left(\frac{x+2}{2}\right) e^{-\frac{x}{2}}.$$

In accordance with Theorem 1, the random variable

$$Z = F(X) = 1 - \frac{(X+2)}{2} e^{-\frac{X}{2}}$$

has the desired distribution.

We now consider certain functions of the order statistics.   Let X_1, X_2, $\cdots$, X_n denote a random sample of size n from a distribution that has a positive and continuous p.d.f. $f(x)$ if, and only if, $a < x < b$.   Denote the order statistics of the random sample by $Y_1 < Y_2 < \cdots < Y_n$.   The joint p.d.f. of these order statistics is

$$n!\, f(y_1)f(y_2)\, \cdots f(y_n),   a < y_1 < y_2 < \cdots < y_n < b,$$

and is zero elsewhere.   Next define the n random variables Z_1, Z_2, $\cdots$, Z_n by $Z_1 = F(Y_1)$, $Z_2 = F(Y_2)$, $\cdots$, $Z_n = F(Y_n)$, where $F(x)$ is the distribution function of X, $a < x < b$.   The transformation $z_1 = F(y_1)$, $\cdots$, $z_n = F(y_n)$ maps the set $\{(y_1, \cdots, y_n); a < y_1 < y_2 < \cdots < y_n < b\}$ into the set $\{(z_1, z_2, \cdots, z_n); 0 < z_1 < z_2 < \cdots < z_n < 1\}$.   The Jacobian of the transformation is

$$
J = \begin{vmatrix} \dfrac{dy_1}{dz_1} & 0 & \cdots & 0 \\[2mm] 0 & \dfrac{dy_2}{dz_2} & \cdots & 0 \\[2mm] \vdots & \vdots & & \vdots \\[2mm] 0 & 0 & \cdots & \dfrac{dy_n}{dz_n} \end{vmatrix}
$$

$$
= \frac{dy_1}{dz_1}\frac{dy_2}{dz_2} \cdots \frac{dy_n}{dz_n}
$$

$$
= \frac{1}{\dfrac{dz_1}{dy_1}\dfrac{dz_2}{dy_2} \cdots \dfrac{dz_n}{dy_n}}
$$

$$
= \frac{1}{f(y_1)\, f(y_2)\, \cdots f(y_n)}
$$

since $dz_i/dy_i = F'(y_i) = f(y_i), a < y_i < b$.   Thus $f(y_1)f(y_2) \cdots f(y_n)|J| = 1, a < y_1 < y_2 < \cdots < y_n < b$, and the joint p.d.f. of $Z_1 = F(Y_1)$, $Z_2 = F(Y_2)$, $\cdots$, $Z_n = F(Y_n)$ is

$$h(z_1, z_2, \cdots, z_n) = n!,   0 < z_1 < z_2 < \cdots < z_n < 1,$$
$$= 0 \text{ elsewhere.}$$

This proves a special case of the following theorem.

THEOREM 2.   Let Y_1, Y_2, $\cdots$, Y_n denote the order statistics of a random sample of size n from a distribution of the continuous type having p.d.f. $f(x)$ and distribution function $F(x)$.   The joint p.d.f. of the random variables $Z_1 = F(Y_1)$, $Z_2 = F(Y_2)$, $\cdots$, $Z_n = F(Y_n)$, is

$$h(z_1, z_2, \cdots, z_n) = n!,   0 < z_1 < z_2 < \cdots < z_n < 1,$$
$$= 0 \text{ elsewhere.}$$

An interpretation of this theorem, similar to the interpretation of Theorem 1, will be made in Section 8.4. At present we merely observe that the marginal p.d.f. of $Z_k = F(Y_k)$ is the beta p.d.f. (Exercise 4.9, page 73)

$$h_k(z_k) = \int_0^{z_k} \cdots \int_0^{z_2} \int_{z_k}^1 \cdots \int_{z_{n-1}}^1 n! \, dz_n \cdots dz_{k+1} \, dz_1 \cdots dz_{k-1}$$

$$= \frac{n!}{(k-1)!(n-k)!} z_k^{k-1}(1 - z_k)^{n-k}, \quad 0 < z_k < 1,$$

$$= 0 \text{ elsewhere;}$$

and that the joint p.d.f. of $Z_i = F(Y_i)$ and $Z_j = F(Y_j)$ is, with $i < j$,

$$h_{ij}(z_i, z_j) = \int_0^{z_i} \cdots \int_0^{z_2} \int_{z_i}^{z_j} \cdots \int_{z_{j-2}}^{z_j} \int_{z_j}^1 \cdots \int_{z_{n-1}}^1$$

$$n! \, dz_n \cdots dz_{j+1} \, dz_{j-1} \cdots dz_{i+1} \, dz_1 \cdots dz_{i-1}$$

$$= \frac{n!}{(i-1)!(j-i-1)!(n-j)!} z_i^{i-1}(z_j - z_i)^{j-i-1}(1 - z_j)^{n-j},$$

$$0 < z_i < z_j < 1,$$

$$= 0 \text{ elsewhere.}$$

Exercises

8.4. Find the distribution of $Z = F(X)$ by computing the moment-generating function of Z, $M_Z(t) = E[e^{tF(X)}]$. Impose the same conditions of the proof of Theorem 1 of this section.

8.5. Let $Z_1 < Z_2 < \cdots < Z_n$ denote the order statistics of a random sample of size n from a uniform distribution on the interval $(0, 1)$. Find the joint p.d.f. of $Z_1, \cdots, Z_n$. Compare your result with Theorem 2 of this section.

8.6. Show that $F(Y_i)/F(Y_j)$, $i < j$, is stochastically independent of $F(Y_j)$.

8.7. Show that $F(Y_2)$ and $F(Y_{i+2}) - F(Y_i)$ have the same p.d.f.

8.8. Compute $E[F(Y_1)], \cdots, E[F(Y_n)]$ and $E[F(Y_{i+1}) - F(Y_i)]$.

8.9. Find the joint p.d.f. of $W_1 = F(Y_1)$, $W_2 = F(Y_2) - F(Y_1)$, $W_3 = F(Y_3) - F(Y_2)$, $\cdots$, $W_n = F(Y_n) - F(Y_{n-1})$. More generally $F(Y_j) - F(Y_i)$, $i < j$, is called the "coverage" of the random interval (Y_i, Y_j). These coverages are important in distribution-free statistical inference.

8.3. Confidence Intervals for Distribution Quantiles. Let X be a random variable of the continuous type having p.d.f. $f(x)$ and distribution function $F(x)$. Let p denote a positive proper fraction, and assume that the equation $F(x) = p$ has a unique solution for x. This unique root is denoted by the symbol ξ_p and is called the quantile (of the distribution) of order p. Thus, $Pr(X \le \xi_p) = F(\xi_p) = p$. For example, the quantile of order $\frac{1}{2}$ is the median of the distribution and $Pr(X \le \xi_{0.5}) = F(\xi_{0.5}) = \frac{1}{2}$.

Let $Y_1 < Y_2 < \cdots < Y_n$ denote the order statistics of a random sample of size n from this distribution. We shall compute the probability that the kth order statistic is less than the quantile of order p. Now

$$Pr(Y_k < \xi_p) = Pr[F(Y_k) < F(\xi_p)]$$
$$= Pr[Z_k < p],$$

since $F(\xi_p) = p$ and $Z_k = F(Y_k)$. By Theorem 2 of Section 8.2, page 159, it is known that this probability does not depend upon $F(x)$; that is, it is distribution-free. The p.d.f. of Z_k was found on page 160 to be

$$h_k(z_k) = \frac{n!}{(k-1)!(n-k)!} z_k^{k-1}(1-z_k)^{n-k}, \quad 0 < z_k < 1,$$

$$= 0 \text{ elsewhere.}$$

Accordingly,

$$(1) \quad Pr(Y_k < \xi_p) = Pr(Z_k < p) = \int_0^p \frac{n!}{(k-1)!(n-k)!} z_k^{k-1}(1-z_k)^{n-k} dz_k.$$

By repeated integration by parts (Exercise 8.10), the integral in the right-hand member of Equation (1) may be written as the right-hand member of

$$(2) \ Pr(Y_k < \xi_p) = \frac{n!}{k!(n-k)!} p^k(1-p)^{n-k} + \frac{n!}{(k+1)!(n-k-1)!} p^{k+1}(1-p)^{n-k-1}$$
$$+ \cdots + p^n$$
$$= \sum_{w=k}^{n} \frac{n!}{w!(n-w)!} p^w(1-p)^{n-w}.$$

Comment. It is interesting to observe that the right-hand member of equation (2) can be obtained by a more direct argument. If we are to have $Y_k < \xi_p$, at least k items of the random sample must be less than ξ_p. Now $Pr(X < \xi_p) = p$, where X is an item of the random sample. The sum in the right-hand member of equation (2) is precisely the probability of at least k "successes" throughout n independent trials, each trial with probability p of success. One purpose of our derivation of equation (2) is to point out the fact that a "partial sum" of a binomial p.d.f. can be expressed exactly as the integral of a beta p.d.f. over a subset of $\{x; 0 < x < 1\}$.

Equation (2) will be used to compute the probability that a certain random interval includes ξ_p, the quantile of order p. Take $Y_i < Y_j$. The event $Y_i < \xi_p$ is the union (exclusive of events of probability zero) of the two mutually exclusive events $Y_i < \xi_p < Y_j$ and $Y_i < Y_j < \xi_p$ (or $Y_j < \xi_p$). Consequently

$$Pr(Y_i < \xi_p) = Pr(Y_i < \xi_p < Y_j) + Pr(Y_j < \xi_p),$$

or

$$Pr(Y_i < \xi_p < Y_j) = Pr(Y_i < \xi_p) - Pr(Y_j < \xi_p).$$

When particular values of n, i, and j are specified, each term of the right-hand member of the last equation can be computed by using either Equation (1) or (2). By this procedure, suppose it has been found that $\gamma = Pr(Y_i < \xi_p < Y_j)$. Then the probability is γ that the random interval (Y_i, Y_j) includes the quantile of order p. If the experimental values of Y_i and Y_j are respectively y_i and y_j, then the interval (y_i, y_j) serves as a 100γ per cent confidence interval for ξ_p, the quantile of order p.

An illustrative example follows.

EXAMPLE 1. Let $Y_1 < Y_2 < Y_3 < Y_4$ be the order statistics of a random sample of size 4 from a distribution of the continuous type. The probability that the random interval (Y_1, Y_4) includes the median $\xi_{0.5}$ of the distribution will be computed. We have

$$Pr(Y_1 < \xi_{0.5} < Y_4) = Pr(Y_1 < \xi_{0.5}) - Pr(Y_4 < \xi_{0.5})$$

$$= \sum_{w=1}^{4} \frac{4!}{w!(4-w)!} \left(\frac{1}{2}\right)^4 - \sum_{w=4}^{4} \frac{4!}{w!(4-w)!} \left(\frac{1}{2}\right)^4$$

$$= \int_0^{0.5} \frac{4!}{0!3!}(1-z_1)^3 \, dz_1 - \int_0^{0.5} \frac{4!}{3!0!}z_4^3 \, dz_4$$

$$= \left[1 - \left(\frac{1}{2}\right)^4\right] - \left(\frac{1}{2}\right)^4 = 0.875.$$

If Y_1 and Y_4 are observed to be $y_1 = 2.8$ and $y_4 = 4.2$, respectively, the interval $(2.8, 4.2)$ is an 87.5 per cent confidence interval for the median $\xi_{0.5}$ of the distribution.

Exercises

8.10. Verify that

$$\int_0^p \frac{n!}{(k-1)!(n-k)!} z^{k-1}(1-z)^{n-k} \, dz = \sum_{w=k}^{n} \frac{n!}{w!(n-w)!} p^w (1-p)^{n-w}$$

where $0 < p < 1$, and k and n are positive integers such that $k \leq n$.

8.11. Let $Y_1 < Y_2 < Y_3 < Y_4 < Y_5$ denote the order statistics of a random sample of size 5 from a distribution of the continuous type. Compute

(a) $Pr(Y_1 < \xi_{0.5} < Y_5)$,

(b) $Pr(Y_1 < \xi_{0.25} < Y_3)$,

(c) $Pr(Y_4 < \xi_{0.80} < Y_5)$.

8.12. Compute $Pr(Y_3 < \xi_{0.5} < Y_7)$ if $Y_1 < \cdots < Y_9$ are the order statistics of a random sample of size 9 from a distribution of the continuous type.

8.13. Find the smallest value of n for which $Pr(Y_1 < \xi_{0.5} < Y_n) \geq 0.99$ where $Y_1 < \cdots < Y_n$ are the order statistics of a random sample of size n from a distribution of the continuous type.

8.4. Distribution Tolerance Limits. Following Theorem 1 of Section 8.2, page 158, it was remarked that the probability that the random variable $Z = F(X)$ is less than or equal to a positive proper fraction p is exactly the same as the probability that the random interval $(-\infty, X)$ contains no more than $100p$ per cent of the probability for the distribution of X. Referring now to Theorem 2 of that section, we consider the difference $Z_j - Z_i = F(Y_j) - F(Y_i)$, $i < j$. Now $F(y_j) = Pr(X \leq y_j)$ and $F(y_i) = Pr(X \leq y_i)$. Since $Pr(X = y_j) = Pr(X = y_i) = 0$, then the difference $F(y_j) - F(y_i)$ is that fractional part of the probability for the distribution of X that is between y_i and y_j. Let p denote a positive proper fraction. If $F(y_j) - F(y_i) \geq p$, then at least $100p$ per cent of the probability for the distribution of X is between y_i and y_j. Let it be given that $\gamma = Pr[F(Y_j) - F(Y_i) \geq p]$. Then the random interval (Y_i, Y_j) has probability γ of containing at least $100p$ per cent of the probability for the distribution of X. If now y_i and y_j denote, respectively, experimental values of Y_i and Y_j, the interval (y_i, y_j) either does or does not contain at least $100p$ per cent of the probability for the distribution of X. However, we refer to the interval (y_i, y_j) as a 100γ per cent tolerance interval for $100p$ per cent of the probability for the distribution of X. In like vein, y_i and y_j are called 100γ per cent tolerance limits for $100p$ per cent of the probability for the distribution of X.

Throughout the remainder of this discussion we shall take $i = 1$ and $j = n$. In accordance with Section 8.2, the joint p.d.f. of $Z_1 = F(Y_1)$ and $Z_n = F(Y_n)$ is given by

$$h_{1n}(z_1, z_n) = n(n-1)(z_n - z_1)^{n-2}, \quad 0 < z_1 < z_n < 1,$$
$$= 0 \text{ elsewhere.}$$

Then

$$\gamma = Pr[F(Y_n) - F(Y_1) \geq p]$$
$$= Pr[Z_n - Z_1 \geq p]$$
$$= \int_0^{1-p} \int_{p+z_1}^1 n(n-1)(z_n - z_1)^{n-2} dz_n \, dz_1$$
$$= 1 - np^{n-1} + (n-1)p^n.$$

An illustrative example follows.

EXAMPLE. A tolerance interval for 80 per cent of the probability for a distribution of a continuous-type random variable is to be obtained from a random sample of size 6 from the distribution. What is 100γ per cent? Here $100p$ per cent $= 80$ per cent, so $p = 0.8$, and

$$\gamma = 1 - 6(0.8)^5 + 5(0.8)^6$$
$$= 0.34 \text{ approximately.}$$

That is, the observed values of Y_1 and Y_6 will define a 34 per cent tolerance interval for 80 per cent of the probability for the distribution.

Exercises

8.14. Let Y_1 and Y_n be respectively the first and nth order statistic of a random sample of size n from a distribution of the continuous type having distribution function $F(x)$. Find the smallest value of n such that $Pr[F(Y_n) - F(Y_1) \geq 0.5]$ is at least 0.95.

8.15. Let Y_2 and Y_{n-1} denote the second and the $(n-1)$st order statistics of a random sample of size n from a distribution of the continuous type having distribution function $F(x)$. Compute $Pr[F(Y_{n-1}) - F(Y_2) \geq p]$ where $0 < p < 1$.

CHAPTER NINE

STATISTICAL HYPOTHESES

The two principal areas of statistical inference are the areas of estimation of parameters and of tests of statistical hypotheses. The problem of estimation of parameters, both point and interval estimation, has been treated. In this chapter some aspects of statistical hypotheses and tests of statistical hypotheses will be considered. The subject will be introduced in the next section by way of examples.

9.1. Some Examples and Definitions.

EXAMPLE 1. Let it be known that the outcome X of a random experiment has the p.d.f.

$$f(x; \theta) = \frac{1}{\theta}, \quad 0 < x < \theta,$$
$$= 0 \text{ elsewhere.}$$

Past experience with this random experiment indicated that $\theta = 1$. However, it is suspected, due possibly to some changes made in the method of performing the random experiment, that $\theta = 1$ no longer and that now $\theta = 2$. There is as yet no experimental evidence that $\theta = 2$; hence the statement $\theta = 2$ is a conjecture or a *statistical hypothesis*. In admitting that the statistical hypothesis $\theta = 2$ may be false, we allow, in effect, the possibility that $\theta = 1$. That is, there are actually two statistical hypotheses. First, that the unknown parameter $\theta = 1$; that is, there has been no change in θ. Second, that the unknown parameter $\theta = 2$. The first statistical hypothesis is called the *null* hypothesis because it asserts that there is no difference between the value of θ in former experiments and those to be undertaken. The null hypothesis is denoted by the symbols $H_0: \theta = 1$. The second statistical hypothesis is called the *alternative* hypothesis, and it is denoted by the symbols $H_1: \theta = 2$. In order to reach a decision as to which hypothesis to accept, the random experiment is to be repeated a number of independent times and the results observed. That is, we consider a random sample $X_1, X_2, \cdots, X_n$ from the distribution having p.d.f.

$$f(x; \theta) = \frac{1}{\theta}, \quad 0 < x < \theta,$$
$$= 0 \text{ elsewhere,}$$

and we devise a rule which will tell us what decision to make, once the experimental values, say, $x_1, x_2, \cdots, x_n$, have been determined. Such a rule is called a *test* of the null hypothesis $H_0: \theta = 1$ against the alternative hypothesis $H_1: \theta = 2$. There is no limit to the number of rules or tests that can be constructed. We shall compare two such tests, and to keep the exposition simple, the size of the random sample will be taken to be $n = 2$.

With a random sample of size $n = 2$, the space $\mathcal{A}$ of positive probability density consists of a part of the first quadrant of the x_1x_2 plane, where x_1 and x_2 are respectively the experimental values of X_1 and X_2. If H_0 is true, that is, $\theta = 1$, the space of positive probability density consists of those points (x_1, x_2) in the x_1x_2 plane which are interior to a square with opposite vertices at $(0, 0)$ and $(1, 1)$; if H_1 is true, that is, $\theta = 2$, the space of positive probability density consists of those points (x_1, x_2) in the x_1x_2 plane which are interior to a square with opposite vertices at $(0, 0)$ and $(2, 2)$. Since the probability density functions have been defined to be zero outside the respective spaces of positive probability density, it is convenient to refer to all of the first quadrant, for instance, as the sample space. This will enable us to say that a set of points in the first quadrant is a subset of the sample space. We now formulate the two tests that will be compared.

Test 1.   Reject the null hypothesis $H_0: \theta = 1$ (that is, accept the alternative hypothesis $H_1: \theta = 2$) if the experimentally determined point (x_1, x_2) plots in the shaded region of Figure 9–1.   Otherwise accept the null hypothesis $H_0: \theta = 1$.

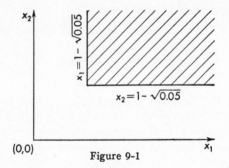

Figure 9-1

Test 2.   Reject the null hypothesis $H_0: \theta = 1$ (that is, accept the alternative hypothesis $H_1: \theta = 2$) if the experimentally determined point (x_1, x_2) plots in the shaded region of Figure 9–2.   Otherwise accept the null hypothesis $H_0: \theta = 1$.

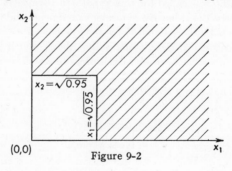

Figure 9-2

The shaded region in each figure is called the *critical region* of the test of the null hypothesis $H_0: \theta = 1$ against the alternative hypothesis $H_1: \theta = 2$. The critical region will be denoted by C. For Test 1, C is the two-dimensional set indicated by the shaded region in Figure 9–1; for Test 2, C is the two-dimensional set indicated by the shaded region in Figure 9–2. To be sure, in this example, each of the joint probability density functions is zero on much of each critical region C.

Tests 1 and 2 will be compared by obtaining answers to these questions.

(i)   What, with each test, is the probability of rejecting the null hypothesis H_0 when H_0 is true?

(ii)   What, with each test, is the probability of rejecting the null hypothesis H_0 when H_0 is false?

If H_0 is true, the joint p.d.f. of X_1 and X_2 is

$$f(x_1; 1)f(x_2; 1) = 1, \quad 0 < x_1 < 1, \quad 0 < x_2 < 1,$$
$$= 0 \text{ elsewhere.}$$

For Test 1, the probability $Pr[(X_1, X_2)\epsilon C]$ is given by

$$\int_{1-\sqrt{0.05}}^{1} \int_{1-\sqrt{0.05}}^{1} dx_1\, dx_2 = 0.05.$$

Thus, if Test 1 is used, 0.05 is the probability of rejecting the null hypothesis H_0 when H_0 is true. For Test 2, when H_0 is true, the probability $Pr[(X_1, X_2)\epsilon C]$ is given by

$$\int_{0}^{1} \int_{\sqrt{0.95}}^{1} dx_1\, dx_2 + \int_{\sqrt{0.95}}^{1} \int_{0}^{\sqrt{0.95}} dx_1\, dx_2 = 1 - \int_{0}^{\sqrt{0.95}} \int_{0}^{\sqrt{0.95}} dx_1\, dx_2 = 0.05.$$

That is, in response to question (i), the probability of rejecting H_0 when H_0 is true is 0.05, whether Test 1 or Test 2 is used. Let us turn now to question (ii).

If H_0 is false, so that $\theta = 2$, the joint p.d.f. of X_1 and X_2 is

$$f(x_1; 2)f(x_2; 2) = \frac{1}{4}, \quad 0 < x_1 < 2, \quad 0 < x_2 < 2,$$
$$= 0 \text{ elsewhere.}$$

For Test 1, the probability $Pr[(X_1, X_2)\epsilon C]$ is given by

$$\int_{1-\sqrt{0.05}}^{2} \int_{1-\sqrt{0.05}}^{2} \frac{1}{4} dx_1\, dx_2 = \frac{1.05 + 2\sqrt{0.05}}{4} = 0.37 \text{ approximately.}$$

Thus, if Test 1 is used, 0.37 is the probability of rejecting the null hypothesis H_0 when H_0 is false. For Test 2, when H_0 is false, the probability $Pr[(X_1, X_2)\epsilon C]$ is given by

$$\int_{0}^{2} \int_{\sqrt{0.95}}^{2} \frac{1}{4} dx_1\, dx_2 + \int_{\sqrt{0.95}}^{2} \int_{0}^{\sqrt{0.95}} \frac{1}{4} dx_1\, dx_2$$

$$= 1 - \int_{0}^{\sqrt{0.95}} \int_{0}^{\sqrt{0.95}} \frac{1}{4} dx_1\, dx_2 = 1 - \frac{0.95}{4} = 0.76 \text{ approximately.}$$

That is, in response to question (ii), if Test 2 is used, 0.76 is the probability of rejecting the null hypothesis H_0 when H_0 is false, whereas if Test 1 is used, that probability is only 0.37. It is seen that the two tests have the same probability, 0.05, of rejecting H_0 when H_0 is true; but that Test 2 has a greater probability of rejecting H_0 when H_0 is false. Because we want to reject H_0 when H_0 is false, Test 2 can be described as being a better test than Test 1 when testing $H_0: \theta = 1$ against $H_1: \theta = 2$.

The probability of rejecting the null hypothesis (no matter which hypothesis is true) is called the *power function*. The value of this function when the parameter has a particular value is called the power of the test for that value of the parameter. If two tests have the same power when H_0 is true, the test with the greater power when H_0 is false (H_1 is true) is called the better or the more powerful of the two tests. In Example 1, Test 2 is a more powerful test than Test 1.

It should be noted in Example 1 that the null hypothesis $H_0: \theta = 1$ specifies completely the p.d.f. $f(x; 1)$ of X, and that the alternative hypothesis $H_1: \theta = 2$ also completely specifies the p.d.f. $f(x; 2)$ of X. Any hypothesis (null or alternative) that completely specifies the p.d.f. $f(x; \theta)$ is called a *simple* hypothesis. In Example 1, then, we compared two different tests of a null simple hypothesis against an alternative simple hypothesis.

We have now given examples of the following concepts:

(i)   A statistical hypothesis, and in particular, a null simple hypothesis H_0 and an alternative simple hypothesis H_1.

(ii) A test of a null simple hypothesis against an alternative simple hypothesis and the associated concept of the critical region of the test.

(iii) The power of a test.

These concepts will now be formally defined.

Definition 1. A *statistical hypothesis* is an assertion about the distribution of one or more random variables. If the statistical hypothesis completely specifies the distribution, it is called a *simple statistical hypothesis*.

This definition indicates that a statistical hypothesis may be of a very general character. However, in this book all statistical hypotheses will concern parameters of distributions whose probability density functions are of a known functional form.

Definition 2. A *test* of a statistical hypothesis is a rule which, when the experimental sample values have been obtained, leads to a decision to accept or to reject the hypothesis under consideration.

Definition 3. Let C be that subset of the sample space which, in accordance with a prescribed test, leads to the rejection of the hypothesis under consideration. Then C is called the *critical region* of the test.

Definition 4. The *power function* of a test of a statistical hypothesis H_0 against an alternative hypothesis H_1 is that function, defined for all distributions under consideration, which yields the probability that the sample point falls in the critical region C of the test; that is, a function which yields the probability of rejecting the hypothesis under consideration. The value of the power function at a parameter point is called the *power* of the test at that point.

Definition 5. Let H_0 denote an hypothesis which is to be tested against an hypothesis H_1 in accordance with a prescribed test. The *significance level* of the test (or the *size* of the critical region C) is the value of the power function of the test when H_0 is true; that is, it is the probability of rejecting the hypothesis H_0 when H_0 is true.

An additional example may help clarify these definitions.

EXAMPLE 2. It is known that the random variable X has a p.d.f. of the form

$$f(x; \theta) = \frac{1}{\theta}e^{-x/\theta}, \ 0 < x < \infty,$$

$$= 0 \text{ elsewhere.}$$

It is desired to test the null simple hypothesis H_0: $\theta = 2$ against the alternative simple hypothesis H_1: $\theta = 4$. A random sample X_1, X_2 of size $n = 2$ will be used. Here the entire $x_1 x_2$ plane is treated as the sample space. The test to be used is defined by taking the critical region to be $C = \{(x_1, x_2); 9.5 \leq x_1 + x_2 < \infty\}$. The power function of the test and the significance level of the test will be determined.

There are but two probability density functions under consideration, namely, $f(x; 2)$ specified by H_0 and $f(x; 4)$ specified by H_1. Thus the power function is defined at but two points $\theta = 2$ and $\theta = 4$. The power function of the test is given by $Pr[(X_1, X_2) \epsilon C]$. If H_0 is true, that is, $\theta = 2$, the joint p.d.f. of X_1 and X_2 is

$$f(x_1; 2)f(x_2; 2) = \frac{1}{4}e^{-\frac{1}{2}(x_1+x_2)}, \ 0 < x_1 < \infty, \ 0 < x_2 < \infty,$$

$$= 0 \text{ elsewhere,}$$

and

$$Pr[(X_1, X_2)\epsilon C] = 1 - Pr[(X_1, X_2)\epsilon C^*]$$

$$= 1 - \int_0^{9.5} \int_0^{9.5-x_2} \frac{1}{4}e^{-\frac{1}{2}(x_1+x_2)} \, dx_1 \, dx_2$$

$$= 0.05 \text{ approximately.}$$

If H_1 is true, that is, $\theta = 4$, the joint p.d.f. of X_1 and X_2 is

$$f(x_1; 4)f(x_2; 4) = \frac{1}{16}e^{-\frac{1}{4}(x_1+x_2)}, \ 0 < x_1 < \infty, \ 0 < x_2 < \infty,$$

$$= 0 \text{ elsewhere,}$$

and

$$Pr[(X_1, X_2)\epsilon C] = 1 - \int_0^{9.5} \int_0^{9.5-x_2} \frac{1}{16}e^{-\frac{1}{4}(x_1+x_2)} \, dx_1 \, dx_2$$

$$= 0.31 \text{ approximately.}$$

Thus the power of the test is given by 0.05 for $\theta = 2$ and by 0.31 for $\theta = 4$. That is, the probability of rejecting H_0 when H_0 is true is 0.05, and the probability of rejecting H_0 when H_0 is false is 0.31. Since the significance level of a test (or the size of the critical region) is the power of the test when H_0 is true, the significance level of this test is 0.05.

The fact that the power of this test, when $\theta = 4$, is only 0.31, immediately suggests that a search be made for another test which, with the same power when $\theta = 2$, would have a power greater than 0.31 when $\theta = 4$. However, Section 9.2 will make clear that such a search would be fruitless. That is, there is no test with a significance level of 0.05 and based on a random sample of size $n = 2$ that has a greater power at $\theta = 4$. The only manner in which the situation may be improved is to have recourse to a random sample of size n greater than two.

Exercises

9.1. Let X have a p.d.f. of the form $f(x; \theta) = \theta x^{\theta-1}$, $0 < x < 1$, zero elsewhere. To test the null simple hypothesis $H_0: \theta = 1$ against the alternative simple hypothesis $H_1: \theta = 2$ use a random sample X_1, X_2 of size $n = 2$ and define the critical region to be $C = \{(x_1, x_2); 3/(4x_1) \leq x_2\}$. Find the power function of the test.

9.2. Let X have a binomial distribution with parameters $n = 10$ and p. The null simple hypothesis $H_0: p = \frac{1}{2}$ is rejected, and the alternative simple hypothesis $H_1: p = \frac{1}{4}$ is accepted if the observed value of X_1, a random sample of size one, is less than or equal to 3. Find the power function of the test.

9.3. Let X_1, X_2 be a random sample of size $n = 2$ from the distribution having p.d.f. $f(x; \theta) = (1/\theta)e^{-x/\theta}$, $0 < x < \infty$, zero elsewhere. We reject $H_0: \theta = 2$ and accept $H_1: \theta = 1$ if the observed values of X_1, X_2, say, x_1, x_2, are such that

$$\frac{f(x_1; 2)f(x_2; 2)}{f(x_1; 1)f(x_2; 1)} \leq \frac{1}{2}.$$

Find the significance level of the test and the power of the test when H_0 is false.

9.2. Certain Best Tests. In the preceding section, one test of a statistical hypothesis was described for a given sample size as being a better test than another. This mode of expression was used in the sense that if both tests have the same significance level, then the test with the greater power when H_1 is true is the better of the two tests.

Now, a test specifies a critical region; but it can also be said that a choice of a critical region defines a test. For instance, if one is given the critical region $C = \{(x_1, x_2, x_3); x_1^2 + x_2^2 + x_3^2 \geq 1\}$, the test is determined: A random sample of size $n = 3$ is to be considered; if the observed values are x_1, x_2, x_3, accept H_0 if $x_1^2 + x_2^2 + x_3^2 < 1$; otherwise, reject H_0. That is, the terms "test" and "critical region" can, in this sense, be used interchangeably so one may say that a certain critical region (for a fixed sample size) is a better critical region than another of the same size. In Example 1 of the preceding section, the critical region of size 0.05 denoted in Figure 9–2 is a better critical region than that denoted in Figure 9–1; that is, the test associated with the critical region of Figure 9–2 is a better test.

Let $f(x; \theta)$ denote the p.d.f. of a random variable X. Let $X_1, X_2, \cdots, X_n$ denote a random sample from this distribution, and consider the two simple hypotheses $H_0: \theta = \theta'$ and $H_1: \theta = \theta''$. We now define a best critical region (and hence a best test) for testing the null simple hypothesis H_0 against the alternative simple hypothesis H_1. In this definition the symbols $Pr[(X_1, X_2, \cdots, X_n) \epsilon C; H_0]$ and $Pr[(X_1, X_2, \cdots, X_n) \epsilon C; H_1]$ mean $Pr[(X_1, X_2, \cdots, X_n) \epsilon C]$ when, respectively, H_0 and H_1 are true.

Definition. Let C denote a subset of the sample space. Then C is called a *best critical region* of size α for testing the null simple hypothesis $H_0: \theta = \theta'$ against the alternative simple hypothesis $H_1: \theta = \theta''$ if

(i) $Pr[(X_1, X_2, \cdots, X_n) \epsilon C; H_0] = \alpha$ and if, for every subset A of the sample space for which $Pr[(X_1, \cdots, X_n) \epsilon A; H_0] = \alpha$

(ii) $Pr[(X_1, X_2, \cdots, X_n) \epsilon C; H_1] \geq Pr[(X_1, X_2, \cdots, X_n) \epsilon A; H_1].$

This definition states, in effect, the following: First assume H_0 to be true. There will in general be a multiplicity of subsets A of the sample space such that $Pr[(X_1, X_2, \cdots, X_n) \epsilon A] = \alpha$. Suppose there is one of these subsets, say C, such that when H_1 is true, the power of the test associated with C is at least as great as the power of the test associated with each other A. Then C is defined as a best critical region of size α for testing H_0 against H_1.

The definition of a best critical region of size α does not provide a systematic method of determining it. The following theorem, due to Neyman and Pearson, provides a solution to the problem under certain conditions.

NEYMAN–PEARSON THEOREM. Let $X_1, X_2, \cdots, X_n$ denote a random sample from a distribution having p.d.f. $f(x; \theta)$. Then the joint p.d.f. of $X_1, X_2, \cdots, X_n$ is

$$L(\theta; x_1, x_2, \cdots, x_n) = f(x_1; \theta)f(x_2, \theta) \cdots f(x_n; \theta).$$

Let θ' and θ'' be distinct fixed values of θ, and let k be a positive number. Let C be a subset of the sample space such that

(i) $\dfrac{L(\theta'; x_1, x_2, \cdots, x_n)}{L(\theta''; x_1, x_2, \cdots, x_n)} \leq k$

for each point $(x_1, x_2, \cdots, x_n) \epsilon C$ and such that

(ii) $\dfrac{L(\theta'; x_1, x_2, \cdots, x_n)}{L(\theta''; x_1, x_2, \cdots, x_n)} \geq k$

for each point $(x_1, x_2, \cdots, x_n) \epsilon C^*$. Then C is a best critical region for testing the null simple hypothesis $H_0: \theta = \theta'$ against the alternative simple hypothesis $H_1: \theta = \theta''$. The size of this best critical region is $\alpha = Pr[(X_1, X_2, \cdots, X_n) \epsilon C; H_0].$

PROOF.   If C is the only critical region of size α, the theorem is proved. If there is another critical region of size α, denote it by A.   Accordingly the test that uses the critical region C and the test that uses the critical region A have the same power α when $\theta = \theta'$.   That is,

$$\alpha = \int_C \cdots \int L(\theta'; x_1, \cdots, x_n)\, dx_1 \cdots dx_n = \int_A \cdots \int L(\theta'; x_1, \cdots, x_n)\, dx_1 \cdots dx_n,$$

or

$$\alpha = \int_C \cdots \int L(\theta') = \int_A \cdots \int L(\theta'),$$

for brevity.   Now $C \cap A$ is the set of points common to C and A, $C \cap A^*$ is the set of points in C but not in A, and $A \cap C^*$ is the set of points in A but not in C.   Thus

$$C = (C \cap A) \cup (C \cap A^*),$$

and

$$A = (C \cap A) \cup (A \cap C^*).$$

Accordingly the preceding expression may be written

$$\alpha = \int_{C \cap A} \cdots \int L(\theta') + \int_{C \cap A^*} \cdots \int L(\theta') = \int_{C \cap A} \cdots \int L(\theta') + \int_{A \cap C^*} \cdots \int L(\theta').$$

Therefore

$$(1) \qquad \int_{C \cap A^*} \cdots \int L(\theta') = \int_{A \cap C^*} \cdots \int L(\theta').$$

Consider next the powers of these tests when $\theta = \theta''$.   If H_1 is true, the power of the test which uses the critical region C is

$$(2) \quad \int_C \cdots \int L(\theta''; x_1, x_2, \cdots, x_n)\, dx_1\, dx_2 \cdots dx_n = \int_C \cdots \int L(\theta''),$$

while that of the test which uses critical region A is

$$(3) \qquad \int_A \cdots \int L(\theta''; x_1, \cdots, x_n)\, dx_1 \cdots dx_n = \int_A \cdots \int L(\theta'').$$

It is to be proved that the difference between quantities (2) and (3) is nonnegative; that is, that

$$\int_C \cdots \int L(\theta'') - \int_A \cdots \int L(\theta'') \geq 0.$$

Clearly, it is sufficient to show that

$$(4) \qquad \int_{C \cap A^*} \cdots \int L(\theta'') - \int_{A \cap C^*} \cdots \int L(\theta'') \geq 0.$$

Consider the first term of the left-hand member of inequality (4).   Each point that is an element of $C \cap A^*$ is certainly an element of C; then, by condition (i) of the hypothesis of the theorem, $L(\theta'') \geq (1/k)L(\theta')$ at each point in C.   The left-hand member of inequality (4) will not be increased if, in the first term of that member, $L(\theta'')$ is replaced by $(1/k)L(\theta')$. Consider next the second term of the left member of inequality (4).   Each point that is an element of $A \cap C^*$ is an element of C^*; by condition (ii) of the hypothesis of the theorem, $L(\theta'') \leq (1/k)L(\theta')$ at each point in C^*. Then the left-hand member of inequality (4) will not be increased if, in the second term of that member, $L(\theta'')$ is replaced by $(1/k)L(\theta')$.   If these two substitutions are made in the left-hand member of inequality (4), we have that

$$\int_{C \cap A} \cdots_* \int \frac{1}{k}L(\theta') - \int_{A \cap C} \cdots_* \int \frac{1}{k}L(\theta') = 0$$

by equality (1).   Since the left member of inequality (4) was not increased by these substitutions, then inequality (4) is valid for every other critical region A of size α.   That is, the test with critical region C has a power, when $\theta = \theta''$, that is at least as great as the power of the test that has A for the critical region.   Thus, as asserted in the theorem, C is a best critical region of size α for testing the null simple hypothesis $H_0: \theta = \theta'$ against the alternative simple hypothesis $H_1: \theta = \theta''$ when the random variables are of the continuous type. If the random variables are of the discrete type, the proof is the same, with integrations replaced by summations.

There are two important aspects of this theorem that warrant special mention.   The first has to do with the number of parameters that appear in the p.d.f. $f(x; \theta)$.   Our notation suggests that there is but one parameter.   However, a careful review of the proof will reveal that nowhere was this needed or assumed.   There may be any finite number of parameters in the p.d.f. $f(x; \theta)$.   What is essential is that the null hypothesis H_0 and the alternative hypothesis H_1 be simple; namely, that they completely specify the distributions.

The second aspect of the theorem to be emphasized is that if we take C to be the set of all points $(x_1, x_2, \cdots, x_n)$ which satisfy

$$\frac{L(\theta'; x_1, x_2, \cdots, x_n)}{L(\theta''; x_1, x_2, \cdots, x_n)} \leq k, \quad k > 0,$$

then, in accordance with the theorem, C will be a best critical region. This inequality can frequently be expressed in one of the forms (where c_1 and c_2 are constants)

$$u_1(x_1, x_2, \cdots, x_n; \theta', \theta'') \leq c_1,$$

or

$$u_2(x_1, x_2, \cdots, x_n; \theta', \theta'') \geq c_2.$$

Suppose that it is the first form, $u_1 \leq c_1$.   Since all parameters have specified values, $u_1(X_1, X_2, \cdots, X_n; \theta', \theta'')$ is a statistic; and if the p.d.f. of this statistic can be found when H_0 is true, then the significance level of the test of H_0 against H_1 can be determined from this distribution. That is,

$$\alpha = Pr[u_1(X_1, X_2, \cdots, X_n; \theta', \theta'') \leq c_1; H_0].$$

Moreover, the test may be based on this statistic; for, if the observed values of $X_1, X_2, \cdots, X_n$ are $x_1, x_2, \cdots, x_n$, we reject H_0 (accept H_1) if $u_1(x_1, x_2, \cdots, x_n) \leq c_1$.

The positive number k, which is arbitrarily selected, determines a best critical region C whose size is $\alpha = Pr[(X_1, X_2, \cdots, X_n) \epsilon C; H_0]$ for that particular k. It may be that this value of α is unsuitable for the purpose at hand; that is, it is too large or too small. However, if there is a statistic $u_1(X_1, X_2, \cdots, X_n)$, as in the preceding paragraph, whose p.d.f. can be determined when H_0 is true, we need not experiment with various values of k to obtain a desirable significance level. For if the distribution of the statistic is known, or can be found, we may determine c_1 such that $Pr[u_1(X_1, X_2, \cdots, X_n) \leq c_1; H_0]$ is a desirable significance level.

An illustrative example follows.

EXAMPLE. Let $X_1, X_2, \cdots, X_n$ denote a random sample from the distribution having the p.d.f.

$$f(x; \theta) = \frac{1}{\sqrt{2\pi}} e^{-\frac{(x-\theta)^2}{2}}, \quad -\infty < x < \infty.$$

It is desired to test the null simple hypothesis $H_0: \theta = \theta' = 0$ against the alternative simple hypothesis $H_1: \theta = \theta'' = 1$. Now

$$\frac{L(\theta'; x_1, \cdots, x_n)}{L(\theta''; x_1, \cdots, x_n)} = \frac{\left(\frac{1}{\sqrt{2\pi}}\right)^n e^{-\frac{\sum_1^n x_i^2}{2}}}{\left(\frac{1}{\sqrt{2\pi}}\right)^n e^{-\frac{\sum_1^n (x_i-1)^2}{2}}}$$

$$= e^{-\sum_1^n x_i + \frac{n}{2}}.$$

If $k > 0$, the set of all points $(x_1, x_2, \cdots, x_n)$ such that

$$e^{-\sum_1^n x_i + \frac{n}{2}} \leq k$$

is a best critical region. This inequality is valid if, and only if,

$$-\sum_1^n x_i + \frac{n}{2} \leq \ln k$$

or

$$\sum_1^n x_i \geq \frac{n}{2} - \ln k = c, \text{ say.}$$

In this case, a best critical region is the set $C = \{(x_1, x_2, \cdots, x_n); \sum_1^n x_i \geq c\}$, where c is a constant that can be determined so that the size of the critical region is a desired number α. The event $\sum_1^n X_i \geq c$ is equivalent to the event $\bar{X} \geq c/n = c_1$, say, so the test may be based upon the statistic $\bar{X}$. If H_0 is true, that is, $\theta = \theta' = 0$, then $\bar{X}$ has a distribution that is $n(\bar{x}; 0, 1/n)$. For a given positive integer n, the size of the sample, and a given significance level α, the number c_1 can be found from Table I, so that $Pr(\bar{X} \geq c_1; H_0) = \alpha$. Hence, if the experimental values of $X_1, X_2, \cdots, X_n$ were respectively $x_1, x_2, \cdots, x_n$, we would compute $\bar{x} = \sum_1^n x_i/n$. If $\bar{x} \geq c_1$, the null simple hypothesis $H_0: \theta = \theta' = 0$ would be rejected at the significance level α; if $\bar{x} < c_1$, the hypothesis H_0 would be accepted. The probability of rejecting H_0, when H_0 is true, is α; the probability of rejecting H_0, when H_0 is false, is the value of the power of the test at $\theta = \theta'' = 1$. That is,

$$Pr(\bar{X} \geq c_1; H_1) = \int_{c_1}^{\infty} \frac{1}{\sqrt{2\pi}\sqrt{\frac{1}{n}}} e^{-\frac{(\bar{x}-1)^2}{2(1/n)}} \, d\bar{x}.$$

For example, if $n = 25$ and if α is selected to be 0.05, then from Table I we find $c_1 = 1.645/\sqrt{25} = 0.329$. Thus the power of this best test of H_0 against H_1 is 0.05, when H_0 is true, and is

$$\int_{0.329}^{\infty} \frac{1}{\sqrt{2\pi}\sqrt{\frac{1}{25}}} e^{-\frac{(\bar{x}-1)^2}{2(1/25)}} \, d\bar{x} = \int_{-3.355}^{\infty} \frac{1}{\sqrt{2\pi}} e^{-\frac{w^2}{2}} \, dw = 0.999+,$$

when H_1 is true.

Exercises

9.4. In the example of this section, let the simple hypotheses read $H_0: \theta = \theta' = 0$ and $H_1: \theta = \theta'' = -1$. Show that the best test of H_0 against H_1 may be carried out by use of the statistic $\bar{X}$, and that if $n = 25$ and $\alpha = 0.05$, the power of the test is 0.999+ when H_1 is true.

9.5. Let the random variable X have the p.d.f. $f(x; \theta) = (1/\theta)e^{-x/\theta}$, $0 < x < \infty$, zero elsewhere. Consider the null simple hypothesis $H_0: \theta = \theta' = 2$ and the alternative simple hypothesis $H_1: \theta = \theta'' = 4$. Let X_1, X_2 denote a random sample of size 2 from this distribution. Show that the best test of H_0 against H_1 may be carried out by use of the statistic $X_1 + X_2$ and that the assertion in the final paragraph of Section 9.1 is correct.

9.6. Repeat Exercise 9.5 when $H_1: \theta = \theta'' = 6$. Generalize this for every $\theta'' > 2$.

9.7. Let $X_1, X_2, \cdots, X_{10}$ be a random sample of size 10 from a normal distribution $n(x; 0, \sigma^2)$. Find a best critical region of size $\alpha = 0.05$ for testing $H_0: \sigma^2 = 1$ against $H_1: \sigma^2 = 2$. Is this a best critical region of size 0.05 for testing $H_0: \sigma^2 = 1$ against $H_1: \sigma^2 = 4$? Against $H_1: \sigma^2 = \sigma_1^2 > 1$?

9.8. If $X_1, X_2, \cdots, X_n$ is a random sample from a distribution having p.d.f.

of the form $f(x; \theta) = \theta x^{\theta-1}$, $0 < x < 1$, zero elsewhere, show that a best critical region for testing $H_0: \theta = 1$ against $H_1: \theta = 2$ is $C = \{(x_1, x_2, \cdots, x_n); c \leq \prod_{i=1}^{n} x_i\}$.

9.9. Let $X_1, X_2, \cdots, X_{10}$ be a random sample from a distribution that is $n(x; \theta_1, \theta_2)$. Find a best test of the null simple hypothesis $H_0: \theta_1 = \theta'_1 = 0$, $\theta_2 = \theta'_2 = 1$ against the alternative simple hypothesis $H_1: \theta_1 = \theta''_1 = 1$, $\theta_2 = \theta''_2 = 4$.

9.10. Let $X_1, X_2, \cdots, X_n$ denote a random sample from a normal distribution $n(x; \theta, 100)$. Show that $C = \{(x_1, x_2, \cdots, x_n); c \leq \bar{x} = \sum_1^n x_i/n\}$ is a best critical region for testing $H_0: \theta = 75$ against $H_1: \theta = 78$. Find n and c so that

$$Pr[(X_1, X_2, \cdots, X_n)\epsilon C; H_0] = Pr[\bar{X} \geq c; H_0] = 0.05$$

and

$$Pr[(X_1, X_2, \cdots, X_n)\epsilon C; H_1] = Pr[\bar{X} \geq c; H_1] = 0.90 \text{ approximately.}$$

9.11. Let $X_1, X_2, \cdots, X_n$ denote a random sample from a distribution having the p.d.f. $f(x; p) = p^x(1 - p)^{1-x}$, $x = 0, 1$, zero elsewhere. Show that $C = \{(x_1, \cdots, x_n); \sum_1^n x_i \leq c\}$ is a best critical region for testing $H_0: p = \frac{1}{2}$ against $H_1: p = \frac{1}{3}$. Use the central limit theorem to find n and c so that approximately $Pr\left[\sum_1^n X_i \leq c; H_0\right] = 0.10$ and $Pr\left[\sum_1^n X_i \leq c; H_1\right] = 0.80$.

9.3. Composite Hypotheses. The basic ideas involved in tests of statistical hypotheses have now been introduced. Because these ideas seem easier to grasp when both the null and alternative hypotheses are simple hypotheses, we have, up to this point, restricted our discussion to statistical hypotheses of this class. We now define a certain kind of composite statistical hypothesis.

Definition. Let the random variable X have a p.d.f. of given functional form which involves one or more parameters $\theta_1, \theta_2, \cdots, \theta_m$. A statistical hypothesis that does not specify numerical values for each of these parameters is called a *composite statistical hypothesis.*

This section will take up the problem of a test of a null simple hypothesis H_0 against an alternative composite hypothesis H_1, and will parallel Section 9.1 in indicating how some of these tests are better than others.

EXAMPLE 1. Consider the p.d.f.

$$f(x; \theta) = \frac{1}{\theta}, \quad 0 < x < \theta,$$
$$= 0 \text{ elsewhere,}$$

that was used in Example 1 of Section 9.1. Let the null hypothesis be $H_0: \theta = \theta' = 1$, as in that example, but now take the alternative hypothesis to be $H_1: \theta > \theta' = 1$. Then H_0 is a simple hypothesis, whereas H_1 is a composite statistical hypothesis. One of the simple hypotheses of which H_1 is "composed" is $\theta = 2$, the alternative simple hypothesis of that example. Tests 1 and 2 of that example will be used to test the null simple hypothesis $H_0: \theta = \theta' = 1$ against the alternative composite hypothesis $H_1: \theta > \theta' = 1$. It was verified in Section 9.1 that if H_0 is true, the probability of rejecting H_0 is 0.05 for each test. Thus the two tests have the same significance level or the same power when $\theta = \theta' = 1$. When $\theta = 2$, it was found that Test 2 has the power 0.76, while the power of Test 1 is only 0.37. In that example, the power function of each test was defined only at two points, $\theta = 1$ and $\theta = 2$. Here, however, the power function of each test will be defined for all $\theta \geq 1$. It will be shown that the power of Test 2 is greater than the power of Test 1 for all $\theta > 1$. Let the power functions of Tests 1 and 2 be denoted respectively by $K_1(\theta)$ and $K_2(\theta)$. It is seen from Figures 9–1 and 9–2, page 166, that the power functions of these tests are respectively

$$K_1(\theta) = \int_{1-\sqrt{0.05}}^{\theta} \int_{1-\sqrt{0.05}}^{\theta} \frac{1}{\theta^2} dx_1 \, dx_2 = \left(\frac{\theta - 1 + \sqrt{0.05}}{\theta} \right)^2, \quad 1 \leq \theta,$$

and

$$K_2(\theta) = 1 - \int_0^{\sqrt{0.95}} \int_0^{\sqrt{0.95}} \frac{1}{\theta^2} dx_1 \, dx_2 = 1 - \frac{0.95}{\theta^2}, \quad 1 \leq \theta.$$

The graphs of $K_1(\theta)$ and $K_2(\theta)$ are sketched in Figure 9–3.

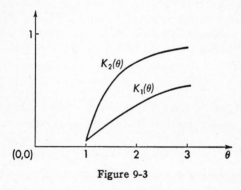

Figure 9-3

Since $K_1(1) = K_2(1) = 0.05$, the two tests have the same significance level, but $K_2(\theta) > K_1(\theta)$ for $\theta > 1$. Thus the power of Test 2 is greater than the power of Test 1 for every simple hypothesis in the composite hypothesis $H_1: \theta > 1$. In this sense, Test 2 of the simple hypothesis H_0 against the composite hypothesis H_1 is described as being a better test than Test 1.

Comment. If, in the preceding Example 1, the null hypothesis H_0 had been the composite hypothesis $H_0: 0 < \theta \leq 1$, and if Test 2 were used to test H_0 against $H_1: \theta > 1$, the power function $K(\theta)$ would be defined for all $\theta > 0$. Here H_0 is true when $0 < \theta \leq 1$, and the question would arise as to what we mean by the significance level of the test. We remark, in this connection, that whenever the null hypothesis H_0 is a composite hypothesis, the significance level of the test is the maximum (actually supremum) of $K(\theta)$ for those values of θ for which H_0 is true.

EXAMPLE 2. Consider the p.d.f.

$$f(x; \theta) = \frac{1}{\theta} e^{-\frac{x}{\theta}}, \quad 0 < x < \infty,$$

$$= 0 \text{ elsewhere,}$$

of Example 2, page 169. It is desired to test the null simple hypothesis $H_0: \theta = 2$ against the alternative composite hypothesis $H_1: \theta > 2$. A random sample X_1, X_2 of size $n = 2$ will be used, and the critical region is $C = \{(x_1, x_2); 9.5 \leq x_1 + x_2 < \infty\}$. It was shown in the example cited that the significance level of the test is approximately 0.05 and that the power of the test when $\theta = 4$ is approximately 0.31. The power function $K(\theta)$ of the test for all $\theta \geq 2$ will now be obtained. We have

$$K(\theta) = 1 - \int_0^{9.5} \int_0^{9.5-x_2} \frac{1}{\theta^2} e^{-\frac{x_1+x_2}{\theta}} \, dx_1 \, dx_2$$

$$= \left(\frac{\theta + 9.5}{\theta}\right) e^{-\frac{9.5}{\theta}}, \quad 2 \leq \theta.$$

Thus, for instance, $K(2) = 0.05$, $K(4) = 0.31$, and $K(9.5) = 2/e$. It is known, Exercise 9.6, page 175, that $C = \{(x_1, x_2); 9.5 \leq x_1 + x_2 < \infty\}$ is a best critical region of size 0.05 for testing the simple hypothesis $H_0: \theta = 2$ against each simple hypothesis in the composite hypothesis $H_1: \theta > 2$. Tests of this character will be considered in Section 9.4.

Exercises

9.12. Let X have the p.d.f. $f(x; \theta) = \theta^x(1 - \theta)^{1-x}$, $x = 0, 1$, zero elsewhere. We test the null simple hypothesis $H_0: \theta = \frac{1}{4}$ against the alternative composite hypothesis $H_1: \theta < \frac{1}{4}$ by taking a random sample of size 10 and rejecting H_0: $\theta = \frac{1}{4}$ if, and only if, the observed values $x_1, x_2, \cdots, x_{10}$ of the sample items are such that $\sum_1^{10} x_i \leq 1$. Find the power function $K(\theta)$, $0 < \theta \leq \frac{1}{4}$, of this test.

9.13. Let X have a p.d.f. of the form $f(x; \theta) = 1/\theta, 0 < x < \theta$, zero elsewhere. Let $Y_1 < Y_2 < Y_3 < Y_4$ denote the order statistics of a random sample of size 4 from this distribution. Let the observed value of Y_4 be y_4. We reject $H_0: \theta = 1$ and accept $H_1: \theta \neq 1$ if either $y_4 \leq \frac{1}{2}$ or $y_4 \geq 1$. Find the power function $K(\theta)$, $0 < \theta$, of the test.

9.14. Consider a normal distribution of the form $n(x; \theta, 4)$. The null simple hypothesis $H_0: \theta = 0$ is rejected, and the alternative composite hypothesis H_1: $\theta > 0$ is accepted if, and only if, the observed mean $\bar{x}$ of a random sample of size 25 is greater than or equal to 3/5. Find the power function $K(\theta)$, $0 \leq \theta$, of this test.

9.15. Consider the two independent normal distributions $n(x; \mu_1, 400)$ and $n(y; \mu_2, 225)$. Let $\theta = \mu_1 - \mu_2$. Let $\bar{x}$ and $\bar{y}$ denote the observed means of two independent random samples, each of size n, from these two distributions. We reject $H_0: \theta = 0$ and accept $H_1: \theta > 0$ if and only if $\bar{x} - \bar{y} \geq c$. If $K(\theta)$ is the power function of this test, find n and c so that $K(0) = 0.05$ and $K(10) = 0.90$ approximately.

9.4. Uniformly Most Powerful Tests. Example 2 of the preceding section afforded an illustration of a test of a null simple hypothesis H_0 that is a best test of H_0 against every simple hypothesis in the alternative composite hypothesis H_1. In this section we define a critical region, when it exists, that is a best critical region for testing a null simple hypothesis H_0 against an alternative composite hypothesis H_1. It seems desirable that this critical region should be a best critical region for testing H_0 against each simple hypothesis in H_1. That is, the power function of the test which corresponds to this critical region should be at least as great as the power function of any other test with the same significance level for every simple hypothesis in H_1.

Definition. The critical region C is a *uniformly most powerful critical region* of size α for testing the null simple hypothesis H_0 against an alternative composite hypothesis H_1 if the set C is a best critical region of size α for testing H_0 against each simple hypothesis in H_1. A test, defined by this critical region C, is called a *uniformly most powerful test*, with significance level α, for testing the null simple hypothesis H_0 against the alternative composite hypothesis H_1.

As will be seen presently, uniformly most powerful tests do not always exist. However, when they do exist, the Neyman–Pearson theorem provides a technique for finding them. Some illustrative examples are given here.

EXAMPLE 1. Let $X_1, X_2, \cdots, X_n$ denote a random sample from a distribution that is $n(x; 0, \theta)$, where the variance θ is an unknown positive number. It will be shown that there exists a uniformly most powerful test with significance level α for testing the null simple hypothesis $H_0: \theta = \theta'$, where θ' is a fixed positive number, against the alternative composite hypothesis $H_1: \theta > \theta'$. The joint p.d.f. of $X_1, X_2, \cdots, X_n$ is

$$L(\theta; x_1, x_2, \cdots, x_n) = \left(\frac{1}{2\pi\theta}\right)^{n/2} e^{-\frac{\sum_1^n x_i^2}{2\theta}}.$$

Let θ'' represent a number greater than θ', and let k denote a positive number. Let C be the set of points where

$$\frac{L(\theta'; x_1, x_2, \cdots, x_n)}{L(\theta''; x_1, x_2, \cdots, x_n)} \le k;$$

that is, the set of points where

$$\left(\frac{\theta''}{\theta'}\right)^{n/2} e^{-\left(\frac{\theta''-\theta'}{2\theta'\theta''}\right)\sum_1^n x_i^2} \le k$$

or

$$\sum_1^n x_i^2 \ge \frac{2\theta'\theta''}{\theta'' - \theta'}\left[\frac{n}{2}\ln\left(\frac{\theta''}{\theta'}\right) - \ln k\right] = c, \text{ say.}$$

The set $C = \{(x_1, x_2, \cdots, x_n); \sum_1^n x_i^2 \geq c\}$ is then a best critical region for testing the null simple hypothesis $H_0: \theta = \theta'$ against the simple hypothesis $\theta = \theta''$. It remains to determine c so that this critical region has the desired size α. If H_0 is true, the random variable $\sum_1^n X_i^2/\theta'$ has a chi-square distribution with n degrees of freedom. Since $\alpha = Pr\left(\sum_1^n X_i^2/\theta' \geq c/\theta'; H_0\right)$, c/θ' may be read from Table II and c determined. Then $C = \{(x_1, x_2, \cdots, x_n); \sum_1^n x_i^2 \geq c\}$ is a best critical region of size α for testing $H_0: \theta = \theta'$ against the hypothesis $\theta = \theta''$. Moreover, for each number θ'' greater than θ', the foregoing argument holds. That is, if θ''' is another number greater than θ', then $C = \{(x_1, \cdots, x_n); \sum_1^n x_i^2 \geq c\}$ is a best critical region of size α for testing $H_0: \theta = \theta'$ against the hypothesis $\theta = \theta'''$. Accordingly $C = \{(x_1, \cdots, x_n); \sum_1^n x_i^2 \geq c\}$ is a uniformly most powerful critical region of size α for testing $H_0: \theta = \theta'$ against $H_1: \theta > \theta'$. If $x_1, x_2, \cdots, x_n$ denote the experimental values of $X_1, X_2, \cdots, X_n$, then $H_0: \theta = \theta'$ is rejected at the significance level α, and $H_1: \theta > \theta'$ is accepted if $\sum_1^n x_i^2 \geq c$; otherwise $H_0: \theta = \theta'$ is accepted.

If in the preceding discussion we take $n = 15$, $\alpha = 0.05$, and $\theta' = 3$, then here the two hypotheses will be $H_0: \theta = 3$ and $H_1: \theta > 3$. From Table II, $c/3 = 25$ and hence $c = 75$.

EXAMPLE 2. Let $X_1, X_2, \cdots, X_n$ denote a random sample from a distribution that is $n(x; \theta, 1)$, where the mean θ is unknown. It will be shown that there is no uniformly most powerful test of the null simple hypothesis $H_0: \theta = \theta'$, where θ' is a fixed number, against the alternative composite hypothesis $H_1: \theta \neq \theta'$. Let θ'' be a number not equal to θ'. Let k be a positive number and consider

$$\frac{\left(\dfrac{1}{2\pi}\right)^{n/2} e^{-\dfrac{\sum_1^n (x_i - \theta')^2}{2}}}{\left(\dfrac{1}{2\pi}\right)^{n/2} e^{-\dfrac{\sum_1^n (x_i - \theta'')^2}{2}}} \leq k.$$

The preceding inequality may be written as

$$e^{-(\theta'' - \theta')\sum_1^n x_i + \frac{n}{2}[(\theta'')^2 - (\theta')^2]} \leq k$$

or as

$$(\theta'' - \theta')\sum_1^n x_i \geq \frac{n}{2}[(\theta'')^2 - (\theta')^2] - \ln k.$$

This last inequality is equivalent to

$$\sum_1^n x_i \geq \frac{n}{2}(\theta'' + \theta') - \frac{\ln k}{\theta'' - \theta'},$$

provided $\theta'' > \theta'$, and it is equivalent to

$$\sum_1^n x_i \leq \frac{n}{2}(\theta'' + \theta') - \frac{\ln k}{\theta'' - \theta'}$$

if $\theta'' < \theta'$. The first of these two expressions defines a best critical region for testing $H_0: \theta = \theta'$ against the hypothesis $\theta = \theta''$, provided $\theta'' > \theta'$, while the second expression defines a best critical region for testing $H_0: \theta = \theta'$ against the hypothesis $\theta = \theta''$, provided $\theta'' < \theta'$. That is, a best critical region for testing the null simple hypothesis against an alternative simple hypothesis, say, $\theta = \theta' + 1$, will not serve as a best critical region for testing $H_0: \theta = \theta'$ against the alternative simple hypothesis $\theta = \theta' - 1$, say. By definition, there is then no uniformly most powerful test in the case under consideration.

It should be noted that had the alternative composite hypothesis been either $H_1: \theta > \theta'$ or $H_1: \theta < \theta'$, then in each instance, a uniformly most powerful test would exist.

This section will conclude with an observation which, although obvious when pointed out, is important. Let $X_1, X_2, \cdots, X_n$ denote a random sample from a distribution having p.d.f. $f(x; \theta)$. Let $Y_1 = u_1(X_1, \cdots, X_n)$ be a sufficient statistic for θ. In accordance with the Fisher–Neyman criterion, page 101, the joint p.d.f. of $X_1, X_2, \cdots, X_n$ may be written

$$L(\theta; x_1, \cdots, x_n) = f(x_1; \theta)f(x_2; \theta) \cdots f(x_n; \theta)$$
$$= g_1[u_1(x_1, x_2, \cdots, x_n); \theta]H(x_1, x_2, \cdots, x_n),$$

where $g_1(y_1; \theta)$ is the p.d.f. of the sufficient statistic Y_1 and $H(x_1, x_2, \cdots, x_n)$ does not depend upon θ. Consequently the ratio

$$\frac{L(\theta'; x_1, \cdots, x_n)}{L(\theta''; x_1, \cdots, x_n)} = \frac{g_1[u_1(x_1, x_2, \cdots, x_n); \theta']}{g_1[u_1(x_1, x_2, \cdots, x_n); \theta'']}$$

depends upon $x_1, x_2, \cdots, x_n$ only through $y_1 = u_1(x_1, x_2, \cdots, x_n)$. Accordingly, if there is a sufficient statistic Y_1 for the parameter θ, and if a best test or a uniformly most powerful test is desired, there is no need to consider tests which are based upon any statistic other than the sufficient statistic $Y_1 = u_1(X_1, X_2, \cdots, X_n)$.

Exercises

9.16. If, in Example 1 of this section, $H_0: \theta = \theta'$, where θ' is a fixed positive number, and $H_1: \theta < \theta'$, show that the set $\{(x_1, x_2, \cdots, x_n); \sum_1^n x_i{}^2 \leq c\}$ is a uniformly most powerful critical region for testing H_0 against H_1.

9.17. If, in Example 1 of this section, $H_0: \theta = \theta'$, where θ' is a fixed positive number, and $H_1: \theta \neq \theta'$, show that there is no uniformly most powerful test for testing H_0 against H_1.

9.18. Let $X_1, X_2, \cdots, X_{25}$ denote a random sample of size 25 from a normal distribution $n(x; \theta, 100)$. Find a uniformly most powerful critical region of size $\alpha = 0.10$ for testing $H_0: \theta = 75$ against $H_1: \theta > 75$.

9.19. Let $X_1, X_2, \cdots, X_n$ denote a random sample from a normal distribution $n(x; \theta, 16)$. Find the sample size n and a uniformly most powerful test of H_0: $\theta = 25$ against $H_1: \theta < 25$ with power function $K(\theta)$ so that approximately $K(25) = 0.10$ and $K(23) = 0.90$.

9.20. Consider a distribution having a p.d.f. of the form $f(x; \theta) = \theta^x (1 - \theta)^{1-x}$, $x = 0, 1$, zero elsewhere. Let $H_0: \theta = 1/20$ and $H_1: \theta > 1/20$. Use the Central Limit Theorem to determine the sample size n of a random sample so that a uniformly most powerful test of H_0 against H_1 has a power function $K(\theta)$, with approximately $K(1/20) = 0.05$ and $K(1/10) = 0.90$.

9.5. Likelihood Ratio Tests. The notion of using the magnitude of the ratio of two probability density functions as the basis of a best test or of a uniformly most powerful test can be modified, and made intuitively appealing, to provide a method of constructing a test of a null composite hypothesis against an alternative composite hypothesis or of constructing a test of a null simple hypothesis against an alternative composite hypothesis when a uniformly most powerful test does not exist. This method leads to tests that are called "likelihood ratio tests." A likelihood ratio test, as just remarked, is not necessarily a most powerful test, but it has been proved in the literature that such a test often has desirable properties.

A certain terminology and notation will be introduced by means of an example.

EXAMPLE 1. Let the random variable X have the p.d.f.

$$f(x; \theta_1, \theta_2) = \frac{1}{\sqrt{2\pi\theta_2}} e^{-\frac{(x-\theta_1)^2}{2\theta_2}}, \quad -\infty < x < \infty.$$

The mean θ_1 may be any real number, while the variance θ_2 may be any positive number. Consider a two-dimensional rectangular coordinate system with horizontal axis for θ_1 and vertical axis for θ_2. Any point above the horizontal axis has a pair of coordinates (θ_1, θ_2) with $\theta_2 > 0$. That is, $\Omega = \{(\theta_1, \theta_2); -\infty < \theta_1 < \infty, 0 < \theta_2 < \infty\}$ has as its elements all points whose coordinates may be values of θ_1 and θ_2. We call the set Ω the *parameter space*. Let the null composite hypothesis be $H_0: \theta_1 = 0, \theta_2 > 0$, and let the alternative composite hypothesis be $H_1: \theta_1 \neq 0, \theta_2 > 0$. The set $\omega = \{(\theta_1, \theta_2); \theta_1 = 0, 0 < \theta_2 < \infty\}$ is a subset of Ω and will be called the *subspace* specified by the null hypothesis H_0. Then, for instance, the hypothesis H_0 may be described as $H_0: (\theta_1, \theta_2) \epsilon \omega$. It is proposed that we test H_0 against all alternatives in H_1.

Let $X_1, X_2, \cdots, X_n$ denote a random sample of size $n > 1$ from the distribution having p.d.f. $f(x; \theta_1, \theta_2)$ of this example. The joint p.d.f. of $X_1, X_2, \cdots, X_n$ is, at each point in Ω,

$$L(\theta_1, \theta_2; x_1, \cdots, x_n) = \left(\frac{1}{2\pi\theta_2}\right)^{n/2} e^{-\frac{\sum\limits_1^n (x_i - \theta_1)^2}{2\theta_2}} = L(\Omega).$$

At each point $(\theta_1, \theta_2)\epsilon\omega$, the joint p.d.f. of $X_1, X_2, \cdots, X_n$ is

$$L(0, \theta_2; x_1, \cdots, x_n) = \left(\frac{1}{2\pi\theta_2}\right)^{n/2} e^{-\frac{\sum\limits_1^n x_i^2}{2\theta_2}} = L(\omega).$$

The joint p.d.f., now denoted by $L(\omega)$, is not completely specified, since θ_2 may be any positive number; nor is the joint p.d.f., now denoted by $L(\Omega)$, completely specified, since θ_1 may be any real number and θ_2 any positive number. Thus the ratio of $L(\omega)$ to $L(\Omega)$ could not provide a basis for a test of H_0 against H_1. Suppose, however, we modify this ratio in the following manner: We shall find the maximum of $L(\omega)$ in ω; that is, the maximum of $L(\omega)$ with respect to θ_2. And we shall find the maximum of $L(\Omega)$ in Ω; that is, the maximum of $L(\Omega)$ with respect to θ_1 and θ_2. The ratio of these maxima will be taken as the criterion for a test of H_0 against H_1. Let the maximum of $L(\omega)$ in ω be denoted by $L(\hat{\omega})$ and let the maximum of $L(\Omega)$ in Ω be denoted by $L(\hat{\Omega})$. Then the criterion for the test of H_0 against H_1 is the likelihood ratio

$$\lambda(x_1, x_2, \cdots, x_n) = \lambda = \frac{L(\hat{\omega})}{L(\hat{\Omega})}.$$

Since $L(\omega)$ and $L(\Omega)$ are probability density functions, $\lambda \geq 0$; and since ω is a subset of Ω, $\lambda \leq 1$.

In our example, the maximum, $L(\hat{\omega})$, of $L(\omega)$ is obtained by first setting

$$\frac{d \ln L(\omega)}{d\theta_2} = -\frac{n}{2\theta_2} + \frac{\sum\limits_1^n x_i^2}{2\theta_2^2}$$

equal to zero and solving for θ_2. The solution for θ_2 is $\sum\limits_1^n x_i^2/n$, and this number maximizes $L(\omega)$. Thus the maximum is

$$L(\hat{\omega}) = \left(\frac{1}{\frac{2\pi\sum\limits_1^n x_i^2}{n}}\right)^{n/2} e^{-\frac{\sum\limits_1^n x_i^2}{\frac{2\sum\limits_1^n x_i^2}{n}}}$$

$$= \left(\frac{ne^{-1}}{2\pi\sum\limits_1^n x_i^2}\right)^{n/2}.$$

On the other hand, by using Exercise 5.33, page 122, the maximum, $L(\hat{\Omega})$, of $L(\Omega)$

is obtained by replacing θ_1 and θ_2 by $\sum_1^n x_i/n = \bar{x}$ and $\sum_1^n (x_i - \bar{x})^2/n$, respectively. That is,

$$L(\hat{\Omega}) = \left[\frac{1}{\dfrac{2\pi \sum_1^n (x_i - \bar{x})^2}{n}} \right]^{n/2} e^{-\dfrac{\sum_1^n (x_i - \bar{x})^2}{2\dfrac{\sum_1^n (x_i - \bar{x})^2}{n}}}$$

$$= \left[\frac{ne^{-1}}{2\pi \sum_1^n (x_i - \bar{x})^2} \right]^{n/2}.$$

Thus here,

$$\lambda = \left[\frac{\sum_1^n (x_i - \bar{x})^2}{\sum_1^n x_i^2} \right]^{n/2}.$$

Because $\sum_1^n x_i^2 = \sum_1^n (x_i - \bar{x})^2 + n\bar{x}^2$, λ may be written

$$\lambda = \frac{1}{\left[1 + \dfrac{n\bar{x}^2}{\sum_1^n (x_i - \bar{x})^2} \right]^{n/2}}.$$

Now the null hypothesis is $H_0: \theta_1 = 0$, $\theta_2 > 0$. If the observed number $\bar{x}$ were zero, the experiment tends to confirm H_0. But if $\bar{x} = 0$ and $\sum_1^n x_i^2 > 0$, then $\lambda = 1$. On the other hand, if $\bar{x}$ and $n\bar{x}^2/\sum_1^n (x_i - \bar{x})^2$ deviate considerably from zero, the experiment tends to negate H_0. Now the greater the deviation of $n\bar{x}^2/\sum_1^n (x_i - \bar{x})^2$ from zero, the smaller λ becomes. That is, if λ is used as a test criterion, then an intuitively appealing critical region for testing H_0 is a set defined by $0 \leq \lambda \leq \lambda_0$, where λ_0 is a positive proper fraction. Thus we reject H_0 if $\lambda \leq \lambda_0$. A test that has the critical region $\lambda \leq \lambda_0$ is a *likelihood ratio test*. In this example, $\lambda \leq \lambda_0$ when, and only when,

$$\frac{\sqrt{n}\, |\bar{x}|}{\sqrt{\dfrac{\sum_1^n (x_i - \bar{x})^2}{n - 1}}} \geq \sqrt{(n - 1)(\lambda_0^{-2/n} - 1)} = c, \text{ say.}$$

If $H_0: \theta_1 = 0$ is true, the results on page 132 show that the statistic

$$t(X_1, X_2, \cdots, X_n) = \frac{\sqrt{n}(\bar{X} - 0)}{\sqrt{\dfrac{\sum_1^n (X_i - \bar{X})^2}{n - 1}}}$$

has a t distribution with $n - 1$ degrees of freedom. Accordingly, in this example the likelihood ratio test of H_0 against H_1 may be based on a T statistic. For a given positive integer n, Table III may be used (with $n - 1$ degrees of freedom) to determine the number c such that $\alpha = Pr[|t(X_1, X_2, \cdots, X_n)| \geq c; H_0]$ is the desired significance level of the test. If the experimental values of $X_1, X_2, \cdots, X_n$ are respectively $x_1, x_2, \cdots, x_n$, then we reject H_0 if, and only if, $|t(x_1, x_2, \cdots, x_n)| \geq c$. If, for instance, $n = 6$ and $\alpha = 0.05$, then from Table III, $c = 2.571$.

The preceding example should make the following generalization easier to read: Let $X_1, X_2, \cdots, X_n$ denote n mutually stochastically independent random variables having respectively the probability density functions $f_i(x_i; \theta_1, \theta_2, \cdots, \theta_m)$, $i = 1, 2, \cdots, n$. The set that consists of all parameter points $(\theta_1, \theta_2, \cdots, \theta_m)$ is denoted by Ω, and Ω is called the *parameter space*. Let ω be a subset of the parameter space Ω. We wish to test the null (simple or composite) hypothesis $H_0: (\theta_1, \theta_2, \cdots, \theta_m)\epsilon\omega$ against all alternative hypotheses. Define the likelihood functions

$$L(\omega) = \prod_{i=1}^{n} f_i(x_i; \theta_1, \theta_2, \cdots, \theta_m), \quad (\theta_1, \theta_2, \cdots, \theta_m)\epsilon\omega,$$

and

$$L(\Omega) = \prod_{i=1}^{n} f_i(x_i; \theta_1, \theta_2, \cdots, \theta_m), \quad (\theta_1, \theta_2, \cdots, \theta_m)\epsilon\Omega.$$

Let $L(\hat{\omega})$ and $L(\hat{\Omega})$ be the maxima, which we assume to exist, of these two likelihood functions. The ratio of $L(\hat{\omega})$ to $L(\hat{\Omega})$ is called the *likelihood ratio* and is denoted by

$$\lambda(x_1, x_2, \cdots, x_n) = \lambda = \frac{L(\hat{\omega})}{L(\hat{\Omega})}.$$

Let λ_0 be a positive proper fraction. The *likelihood ratio test principle* states that the hypothesis $H_0: (\theta_1, \theta_2, \cdots, \theta_m)\epsilon\omega$ is rejected if, and only if,

$$\lambda(x_1, x_2, \cdots, x_n) = \lambda \leq \lambda_0.$$

The function λ defines a random variable $\lambda(X_1, X_2, \cdots, X_n)$, and the significance level of the test is given by

$$\alpha = Pr[\lambda(X_1, X_2, \cdots, X_n) \leq \lambda_0; H_0].$$

The likelihood ratio test principle is an intuitive one. However, the principle does lead to the same test, when testing a null simple hypothesis H_0 against an alternative simple hypothesis H_1, as that given by the Neyman–Pearson theorem (Exercise 9.23). Thus it might be expected that a test based on this principle has some desirable properties.

An example of the preceding generalization will be given.

EXAMPLE 2. Let the stochastically independent random variables X and Y have distributions that are $n(x; \theta_1, \theta_3)$ and $n(y; \theta_2, \theta_3)$, where the means θ_1 and θ_2 and common variance θ_3 are unknown. Then $\Omega = \{(\theta_1, \theta_2, \theta_3); -\infty < \theta_1 < \infty,$

$-\infty < \theta_2 < \infty$, $0 < \theta_3 < \infty$}. Let $X_1, X_2, \cdots, X_n$ and $Y_1, Y_2, \cdots, Y_m$ denote independent random samples from these distributions. The null hypothesis $H_0: \theta_1 = \theta_2$, unspecified, and θ_3 unspecified, is to be tested against all alternatives. Then $\omega = \{(\theta_1, \theta_2, \theta_3); -\infty < \theta_1 = \theta_2 < \infty, 0 < \theta_3 < \infty\}$. Here $X_1, X_2, \cdots, X_n$, $Y_1, Y_2, \cdots, Y_m$ are $n + m > 2$ mutually stochastically independent random variables having the likelihood functions

$$L(\omega) = \left(\frac{1}{2\pi\theta_3}\right)^{\frac{n+m}{2}} e^{-\frac{\sum_1^n (x_i - \theta_1)^2 + \sum_1^m (y_i - \theta_1)^2}{2\theta_3}}$$

and

$$L(\Omega) = \left(\frac{1}{2\pi\theta_3}\right)^{\frac{n+m}{2}} e^{-\frac{\sum_1^n (x_i - \theta_1)^2 + \sum_1^m (y_i - \theta_2)^2}{2\theta_3}}.$$

If

$$\frac{\partial \ln L(\omega)}{\partial \theta_1} \qquad \text{and} \qquad \frac{\partial \ln L(\omega)}{\partial \theta_3}$$

are equated to zero, then (Exercise 9.24)

(1)
$$\sum_1^n (x_i - \theta_1) + \sum_1^m (y_i - \theta_1) = 0,$$

$$-(n + m) + \frac{1}{\theta_3}\left[\sum_1^n (x_i - \theta_1)^2 + \sum_1^m (y_i - \theta_1)^2\right] = 0.$$

The solutions for θ_1 and θ_3 are respectively

$$u = \frac{\sum_1^n x_i + \sum_1^m y_i}{n + m}$$

and

$$w = \frac{\sum_1^n (x_i - u)^2 + \sum_1^m (y_i - u)^2}{n + m}$$

and u and w maximize $L(\omega)$. The maximum is

$$L(\hat{\omega}) = \left(\frac{e^{-1}}{2\pi w}\right)^{\frac{n+m}{2}}.$$

In like manner, if

$$\frac{\partial \ln L(\Omega)}{\partial \theta_1}, \qquad \frac{\partial \ln L(\Omega)}{\partial \theta_2}, \qquad \frac{\partial \ln L(\Omega)}{\partial \theta_3}$$

are equated to zero, then (Exercise 9.25)

(2)
$$\sum_1^n (x_i - \theta_1) = 0,$$

$$\sum_1^m (y_i - \theta_2) = 0,$$

$$-(n + m) + \frac{1}{\theta_3}\left[\sum_1^n (x_i - \theta_1)^2 + \sum_1^m (y_i - \theta_2)^2\right] = 0.$$

The solutions for θ_1, θ_2, and θ_3 are respectively

$$u_1 = \frac{\sum\limits_{1}^{n} x_i}{n},$$

$$u_2 = \frac{\sum\limits_{1}^{m} y_i}{m},$$

$$w' = \frac{\sum\limits_{1}^{n}(x_i - u_1)^2 + \sum\limits_{1}^{m}(y_i - u_2)^2}{n + m},$$

and u_1, u_2, and w' maximize $L(\Omega)$. The maximum is

$$L(\hat{\Omega}) = \left(\frac{e^{-1}}{2\pi w'}\right)^{\frac{n+m}{2}}$$

so that

$$\lambda(x_1, \cdots, x_n, y_1, \cdots, y_m) = \lambda = \frac{L(\hat{\omega})}{L(\hat{\Omega})} = \left(\frac{w'}{w}\right)^{\frac{n+m}{2}}.$$

The random variable defined by $\lambda^{2/(n+m)}$ is

$$\frac{\sum\limits_{1}^{n}(X_i - \bar{X})^2 + \sum\limits_{1}^{m}(Y_i - \bar{Y})^2}{\sum\limits_{1}^{n}\left(X_i - \frac{n\bar{X} + m\bar{Y}}{n + m}\right)^2 + \sum\limits_{1}^{m}\left(Y_i - \frac{n\bar{X} + m\bar{Y}}{n + m}\right)^2}.$$

Now

$$\sum\limits_{1}^{n}\left(X_i - \frac{n\bar{X} + m\bar{Y}}{n + m}\right)^2 = \sum\limits_{1}^{n}\left[(X_i - \bar{X}) + \left(\bar{X} - \frac{n\bar{X} + m\bar{Y}}{n + m}\right)\right]^2$$

$$= \sum\limits_{1}^{n}(X_i - \bar{X})^2 + n\left(\bar{X} - \frac{n\bar{X} + m\bar{Y}}{n + m}\right)^2$$

and

$$\sum\limits_{1}^{m}\left(Y_i - \frac{n\bar{X} + m\bar{Y}}{n + m}\right)^2 = \sum\limits_{1}^{m}\left[(Y_i - \bar{Y}) + \left(\bar{Y} - \frac{n\bar{X} + m\bar{Y}}{n + m}\right)\right]^2$$

$$= \sum\limits_{1}^{m}(Y_i - \bar{Y})^2 + m\left(\bar{Y} - \frac{n\bar{X} + m\bar{Y}}{n + m}\right)^2.$$

But

$$n\left(\bar{X} - \frac{n\bar{X} + m\bar{Y}}{n + m}\right)^2 = \frac{m^2 n}{(n + m)^2}(\bar{X} - \bar{Y})^2$$

and

$$m\left(\bar{Y} - \frac{n\bar{X} + m\bar{Y}}{n + m}\right)^2 = \frac{n^2 m}{(n + m)^2}(\bar{X} - \bar{Y})^2.$$

Hence the random variable defined by $\lambda^{2/(n+m)}$ may be written

$$\frac{\sum_1^n (X_i - \bar{X})^2 + \sum_1^m (Y_i - \bar{Y})^2}{\sum_1^n (X_i - \bar{X})^2 + \sum_1^m (Y_i - \bar{Y})^2 + \dfrac{nm}{n+m}(\bar{X} - \bar{Y})^2}$$

$$= \frac{1}{1 + \dfrac{[nm/(n+m)](\bar{X} - \bar{Y})^2}{\sum_1^n (X_i - \bar{X})^2 + \sum_1^m (Y_i - \bar{Y})^2}}.$$

If the null hypothesis $H_0: \theta_1 = \theta_2$ is true, the random variable

$$T = \frac{\sqrt{\dfrac{nm}{n+m}}(\bar{X} - \bar{Y})}{\sqrt{\dfrac{\sum_1^n (X_i - \bar{X})^2 + \sum_1^m (Y_i - \bar{Y})^2}{n+m-2}}}$$

has, in accordance with page 134, a t distribution with $n + m - 2$ degrees of freedom. Thus the random variable defined by $\lambda^{2/(n+m)}$ is

$$\frac{n+m-2}{(n+m-2) + T^2}.$$

The test of H_0 against all alternatives may then be based on a t distribution with $n + m - 2$ degrees of freedom.

The likelihood ratio principle calls for the rejection of H_0 if, and only if, $\lambda \leq \lambda_0 < 1$. Thus the significance level of the test is

$$\alpha = Pr[\lambda(X_1, \cdots, X_n, Y_1, \cdots, Y_m) \leq \lambda_0; H_0].$$

However $\lambda(X_1, \cdots, X_n, Y_1, \cdots, Y_m) \leq \lambda_0$ is equivalent to $|T| \geq c$, and so

$$\alpha = Pr[|T| \geq c; H_0].$$

For given values of n and m, the number c is determined from Table III (with $n + m - 2$ degrees of freedom) in such a manner as to yield a desired α. Then H_0 is rejected at a significance level α if, and only if, $|t| \geq c$, where t is the experimental value of T. If, for instance, $n = 10$ and $m = 6$ and $\alpha = 0.05$, then $c = 2.145$.

The student may wonder why the power of each likelihood ratio test in this section has been computed only when the null hypothesis is true. The reason is as follows: It was found that each of these tests could be based on some statistic which, when the null hypothesis is true, has a distribution whose p.d.f. is known. When the null hypothesis is false, these statistics have distributions whose probability density functions are far more complicated and difficult to obtain. Limitations of space, to mention one consideration, forbids their study in this book. This remark applies to the tests in Chapters Ten and Eleven.

Exercises

9.21. In Example 1, let $n = 10$, and let the experimental values of the random variables yield $\bar{x} = 0.6$ and $\sum_{1}^{10}(x_i - \bar{x})^2 = 3.6$. If the test derived in that example is used, do we accept or reject $H_0: \theta_1 = 0$ at the 5 per cent significance level?

9.22. In Example 2, let $n = m = 8$, $\bar{x} = 75.2$, $\bar{y} = 78.6$, $\sum_{1}^{8}(x_i - \bar{x})^2 = 71.2$, $\sum_{1}^{8}(y_i - \bar{y})^2 = 54.8$. If we use the test derived in that example, do we accept or reject $H_0: \theta_1 = \theta_2$ at the 5 per cent significance level?

9.23. Show that the likelihood ratio principle leads to the same test, when testing a null simple hypothesis H_0 against an alternative simple hypothesis H_1, as that given by the Neyman–Pearson theorem. Note that there are only two points in Ω.

9.24. Verify equations (1) of Example 2 of this section.

9.25. Verify equations (2) of Example 2 of this section.

9.26. Let $X_1, X_2, \cdots, X_n$ be a random sample from the normal distribution $n(x; \theta, 1)$. Show that the likelihood ratio principle for testing $H_0: \theta = \theta'$, where θ' is specified, against $H_1: \theta \neq \theta'$ leads to the inequality $|\bar{x} - \theta'| \geq c$. Is this a uniformly most powerful test of H_0 against H_1?

9.27. Let $X_1, X_2, \cdots, X_n$ be a random sample from the normal distribution $n(x; \theta_1, \theta_2)$. Show that the likelihood ratio principle for testing $H_0: \theta_2 = \theta'_2$ specified, and θ_1 unspecified, against $H_1: \theta_2 > \theta'_2$, θ_1 unspecified, leads to the inequality $\sum_{1}^{n}(x_i - \bar{x})^2 \geq c$.

9.28. Let $X_1, X_2, \cdots, X_n$ and $Y_1, Y_2, \cdots, Y_m$ be independent random samples from the distributions $n(x; \theta_1, \theta_3)$ and $n(y; \theta_2, \theta_4)$. Show that the likelihood ratio test for testing $H_0: \theta_3 = \theta_4$ unspecified, and θ_1 and θ_2 unspecified, against $H_1: \theta_3 \neq \theta_4$, θ_1 and θ_2 unspecified, can be based on the random variable

$$F = \frac{\dfrac{\sum_{1}^{n}(X_i - \bar{X})^2}{n-1}}{\dfrac{\sum_{1}^{m}(Y_i - \bar{Y})^2}{m-1}}$$

which has, provided H_0 is true, an F distribution with $n - 1$ and $m - 1$ degrees of freedom.

CHAPTER TEN

CERTAIN QUADRATIC FORMS

A homogeneous polynomial of degree two in n variables is called a *quadratic* form in those variables. If both the variables and the coefficients are real, the form is called a *real quadratic* form. Only real quadratic forms will be considered in this book. To illustrate, the form $X_1^2 + X_1 X_2 + X_2^2$ is a quadratic form in the two variables X_1 and X_2; the form $X_1^2 + X_2^2 + X_3^2 - 2X_1 X_2$ is a quadratic form in the three variables X_1, X_2, and X_3; but the form $(X_1 - 1)^2 + (X_2 - 2)^2 = X_1^2 + X_2^2 - 2X_1 - 4X_2 + 5$ is not a quadratic form in X_1 and X_2, although it is a quadratic form in the variables $X_1 - 1$ and $X_2 - 2$.

If $X_1, X_2, \cdots, X_n$ denote a random sample of size n from a distribution that is $n(x; \mu, \sigma^2)$, and if $\bar{X}$ and S^2 denote respectively the mean and the variance of the sample, then

$$nS^2 = \sum_1^n (X_i - \bar{X})^2 = \sum_1^n \left[X_i - \frac{(X_1 + X_2 + \cdots + X_n)}{n} \right]^2$$
$$= \frac{n-1}{n}(X_1^2 + X_2^2 + \cdots + X_n^2)$$
$$- \frac{2}{n}(X_1 X_2 + \cdots + X_1 X_n + \cdots + X_{n-1} X_n)$$

is a quadratic form in the n variables $X_1, X_2, \cdots, X_n$. It was proved on page 128 that the random variable nS^2/σ^2 has a chi-square distribution with $n - 1$ degrees of freedom, regardless of the value of μ. This fact proved useful in the search for a confidence interval for σ^2 when μ was unknown.

It has been seen that tests of certain statistical hypotheses require a statistic that is a quadratic form. For instance, Example 1, page 179, made use of the statistic $\sum_1^n X_i^2$, which is a quadratic form in the variables $X_1, X_2, \cdots, X_n$. Later in this chapter, tests of other statistical hypotheses

190

will be investigated, and it will be seen that functions of statistics that are quadratic forms will be needed to carry out the test in an expeditious manner. In Section 10.1 we shall make a study of the distributions of certain quadratic forms in normal and stochastically independent random variables.

10.1. A Distribution Problem. If S^2 is the variance of a random sample of size n from a distribution that is $n(x; \mu, \sigma^2)$, then

$$\sum_1^n \frac{(X_i - \mu)^2}{\sigma^2} = \frac{n(\bar{X} - \mu)^2}{\sigma^2} + \frac{nS^2}{\sigma^2}.$$

Each of the three random variables $\sum_1^n (X_i - \mu)^2$, $n(\bar{X} - \mu)^2$, and nS^2 is a quadratic form in the variables $X_1 - \mu$, $X_2 - \mu$, $\cdots$, $X_n - \mu$. Indeed, as pointed out in the introductory remarks to this chapter, nS^2 is also a quadratic form in the variables $X_1, X_2, \cdots, X_n$. The quadratic forms $\sum_1^n (X_i - \mu)^2$ and $n(\bar{X} - \mu)^2$, when divided by σ^2, have chi-square distributions with degrees of freedom n and 1, respectively. In Section 6.1 we were able to show that $n(\bar{X} - \mu)^2$ and nS^2 are stochastically independent. This stochastic independence immediately implies that nS^2/σ^2 has a chi-square distribution with $n - 1$ degrees of freedom. In that section the stochastic independence of these two quadratic forms was established by making use of a property of a certain sufficient statistic for a parameter. But in more complicated situations, soon to be encountered, we shall not always be able to use that kind of argument to establish stochastic independence.

Throughout this book the student has been encouraged to accept without proof (at this time) theorems in analysis which enable him to prove for himself theorems in probability and statistics. At this point a theorem in matrix algebra is helpful. When translated from the language of matrices into the language of probability and statistics, and when a special case is taken, adequate for the purposes of this book, the theorem may be stated as follows:

THEOREM. Let $Q = Q_1 + Q_2 + \cdots + Q_{k-1} + Q_k$ where $Q, Q_1, \cdots, Q_k$ are $k + 1$ random variables that are real quadratic forms in mutually stochastically independent random variables which are normally distributed with the same mean and the same variance σ^2. Let Q/σ^2, Q_1/σ^2, $\cdots$, Q_{k-1}/σ^2 have chi-square distributions with degrees of freedom $r, r_1, \cdots, r_{k-1}$, respectively. Let Q_k be non-negative. Then

(a) $Q_1, \cdots, Q_k$ are mutually stochastically independent, and hence

(b) Q_k/σ^2 has a chi-square distribution with $r_k = r - (r_1 + \cdots + r_{k-1})$ degrees of freedom.

Three examples illustrative of the theorem will follow. Each of these examples will deal with a distribution problem which is based on the remarks made in the subsequent paragraph.

Let the random variable X have a distribution that is $n(x; \mu, \sigma^2)$. Let a and b denote positive integers greater than one and let $n = ab$. Consider a random sample of size $n = ab$ from this normal distribution. The items of the random sample will be denoted by the symbols:

$$X_{11}, \quad X_{12}, \quad \cdots, \quad X_{1j}, \quad \cdots, \quad X_{1b}$$

$$X_{21}, \quad X_{22}, \quad \cdots, \quad X_{2j}, \quad \cdots, \quad X_{2b}$$

$$\vdots \qquad \vdots \qquad \qquad \vdots$$

$$X_{i1}, \quad X_{i2}, \quad \cdots, \quad X_{ij}, \quad \cdots, \quad X_{ib}$$

$$\vdots \qquad \vdots \qquad \qquad \vdots$$

$$X_{a1}, \quad X_{a2}, \quad \cdots, \quad X_{aj}, \quad \cdots, \quad X_{ab}$$

In this notation, the first subscript indicates the row, and the second subscript indicates the column in which the item appears. Thus, X_{ij} is in row i and column j, $i = 1, 2, \cdots, a$ and $j = 1, 2, \cdots, b$. By assumption these $n = ab$ random variables are mutually stochastically independent, and each has the same normal distribution with mean μ and variance σ^2. Thus, if we wish, we may consider each row as being a random sample of size b from the given distribution; and we may consider each column as being a random sample of size a from the given distribution. We now define $a + b + 1$ statistics. They are

$$\bar{X} = \frac{X_{11} + \cdots + X_{1b} + \cdots + X_{a1} + \cdots + X_{ab}}{ab} = \frac{\sum\limits_{i=1}^{a} \sum\limits_{j=1}^{b} X_{ij}}{ab},$$

$$\bar{X}_{i\cdot} = \frac{X_{i1} + X_{i2} + \cdots + X_{ib}}{b} = \frac{\sum\limits_{j=1}^{b} X_{ij}}{b}, \quad i = 1, 2, \cdots, a,$$

and

$$\bar{X}_{\cdot j} = \frac{X_{1j} + X_{2j} + \cdots + X_{aj}}{a} = \frac{\sum\limits_{i=1}^{a} X_{ij}}{a}, \quad j = 1, 2, \cdots, b.$$

Thus the statistic $\bar{X}$ is the mean of the random sample of size $n = ab$; the statistics $\bar{X}_{1\cdot}, \bar{X}_{2\cdot}, \cdots, \bar{X}_{a\cdot}$ are respectively the means of the rows; and the statistics $\bar{X}_{\cdot 1}, \bar{X}_{\cdot 2}, \cdots, \bar{X}_{\cdot b}$ are respectively the means of the columns. The examples illustrative of the theorem follow.

EXAMPLE 1. Consider the variance S^2 of the random sample of size $n = ab$. We have the algebraic identity

$$ab S^2 = \sum_{i=1}^{a} \sum_{j=1}^{b} (X_{ij} - \bar{X})^2$$

$$= \sum_{i=1}^{a} \sum_{j=1}^{b} [(X_{ij} - \bar{X}_{i\cdot}) + (\bar{X}_{i\cdot} - \bar{X})]^2$$

$$= \sum_{i=1}^{a} \sum_{j=1}^{b} (X_{ij} - \bar{X}_{i\cdot})^2 + \sum_{i=1}^{a} \sum_{j=1}^{b} (\bar{X}_{i\cdot} - \bar{X})^2 + 2 \sum_{i=1}^{a} \sum_{j=1}^{b} (X_{ij} - \bar{X}_{i\cdot})(\bar{X}_{i\cdot} - \bar{X}).$$

The last term of the right-hand member of this identity may be written

$$2 \sum_{i=1}^{a} \{ (\bar{X}_{i\cdot} - \bar{X}) \sum_{j=1}^{b} (X_{ij} - \bar{X}_{i\cdot}) \} = 2 \sum_{i=1}^{a} \{ (\bar{X}_{i\cdot} - \bar{X})(b\bar{X}_{i\cdot} - b\bar{X}_{i\cdot}) \} = 0$$

and the term

$$\sum_{i=1}^{a} \sum_{j=1}^{b} (\bar{X}_{i\cdot} - \bar{X})^2$$

may be written

$$b \sum_{i=1}^{a} (\bar{X}_{i\cdot} - \bar{X})^2.$$

Thus

$$abS^2 = \sum_{i=1}^{a} \sum_{j=1}^{b} (X_{ij} - \bar{X}_{i\cdot})^2 + b \sum_{i=1}^{a} (\bar{X}_{i\cdot} - \bar{X})^2$$

or, for brevity,

$$Q = Q_1 + Q_2.$$

Clearly, Q, Q_1, and Q_2 are quadratic forms in the $n = ab$ variables X_{ij}. We shall use the theorem with $k = 2$ to show that Q_1 and Q_2 are stochastically independent. Since S^2 is the variance of a random sample of size $n = ab$ from the given normal distribution, then abS^2/σ^2 has a chi-square distribution with $ab - 1$ degrees of freedom. Now

$$\frac{Q_1}{\sigma^2} = \sum_{i=1}^{a} \left\{ \frac{\sum_{j=1}^{b} (X_{ij} - \bar{X}_{i\cdot})^2}{\sigma^2} \right\}.$$

For each fixed value of i, $\sum_{j=1}^{b} (X_{ij} - \bar{X}_{i\cdot})^2 / b$ is the variance of a random sample of size b from the given normal distribution, and accordingly $\sum_{j=1}^{b} (X_{ij} - \bar{X}_{i\cdot})^2/\sigma^2$ has a chi-square distribution with $b - 1$ degrees of freedom. Because the X_{ij} are mutually stochastically independent, Q_1/σ^2 is the sum of a mutually stochastically independent random variables, each having a chi-square distribution with $b - 1$ degrees of freedom. Hence Q_1/σ^2 has a chi-square distribution with $a(b - 1)$ degrees of freedom. Now $Q_2 = b \sum_{i=1}^{a} (\bar{X}_{i\cdot} - \bar{X})^2 \geq 0$. In accordance with the theorem, Q_1 and Q_2 are stochastically independent, and Q_2/σ^2 has a chi-square distribution with $ab - 1 - a(b - 1) = a - 1$ degrees of freedom.

EXAMPLE 2. In abS^2, replace $X_{ij} - \bar{X}$ by $(X_{ij} - \bar{X}_{\cdot j}) + (\bar{X}_{\cdot j} - \bar{X})$ to obtain

$$abS^2 = \sum_{j=1}^{b} \sum_{i=1}^{a} [(X_{ij} - \bar{X}_{\cdot j}) + (\bar{X}_{\cdot j} - \bar{X})]^2,$$

or

$$abS^2 = \sum_{j=1}^{b} \sum_{i=1}^{a} (X_{ij} - \bar{X}_{\cdot j})^2 + a \sum_{j=1}^{b} (\bar{X}_{\cdot j} - \bar{X})^2,$$

or, for brevity,

$$Q = Q_3 + Q_4.$$

It is easy to show (Exercise 10.1) that Q_3/σ^2 has a chi-square distribution with $b(a-1)$ degrees of freedom. Since $Q_4 = a\sum_{j=1}^{b}(\bar{X}._j - \bar{X})^2 \geq 0$, the theorem enables us to assert that Q_3 and Q_4 are stochastically independent and that Q_4/σ^2 has a chi-square distribution with $ab - 1 - b(a-1) = b-1$ degrees of freedom.

EXAMPLE 3. In abS^2, replace $X_{ij} - \bar{X}$ by $(\bar{X}_i. - \bar{X}) + (\bar{X}._j - \bar{X}) + (X_{ij} - \bar{X}_i. - \bar{X}._j + \bar{X})$ to obtain (Exercise 10.2)

$$abS^2 = b\sum_{i=1}^{a}(\bar{X}_i. - \bar{X})^2 + a\sum_{j=1}^{b}(\bar{X}._j - \bar{X})^2 + \sum_{j=1}^{b}\sum_{i=1}^{a}(X_{ij} - \bar{X}_i. - \bar{X}._j + \bar{X})^2,$$

or, for brevity,

$$Q = Q_2 + Q_4 + Q_5,$$

where Q_2 and Q_4 are as defined in Examples 1 and 2. From Examples 1 and 2, Q/σ^2, Q_2/σ^2, and Q_4/σ^2 have chi-square distributions with $ab-1$, $a-1$, and $b-1$ degrees of freedom, respectively. Since $Q_5 \geq 0$, the theorem asserts that Q_2, Q_4, and Q_5 are mutually stochastically independent and that Q_5/σ^2 has a chi-square distribution with $ab - 1 - (a-1) - (b-1) = (a-1)(b-1)$ degrees of freedom.

Once these quadratic form statistics have been shown to be stochastically independent, a multiplicity of F statistics can be defined. For instance,

$$\frac{\dfrac{Q_4}{\sigma^2(b-1)}}{\dfrac{Q_3}{\sigma^2 b(a-1)}} = \frac{\dfrac{Q_4}{b-1}}{\dfrac{Q_3}{b(a-1)}}$$

has an F distribution with $b-1$ and $b(a-1)$ degrees of freedom; and

$$\frac{\dfrac{Q_4}{\sigma^2(b-1)}}{\dfrac{Q_5}{\sigma^2(a-1)(b-1)}} = \frac{\dfrac{Q_4}{b-1}}{\dfrac{Q_5}{a-1}}$$

has an F distribution with $b-1$ and $(a-1)(b-1)$ degrees of freedom. In the subsequent sections it will be seen that some likelihood ratio tests of certain statistical hypotheses can be based on these F statistics.

Exercises

10.1. In Example 2, verify that $Q = Q_3 + Q_4$ and that Q_3/σ^2 has a chi-square distribution with $b(a-1)$ degrees of freedom.

10.2. In Example 3, verify that $Q = Q_2 + Q_4 + Q_5$.

10.3. Let $X_1, X_2, \cdots, X_n$ be a random sample from a normal distribution $n(x; \mu, \sigma^2)$. Show that

$$\sum_{i=1}^{n}(X_i - \bar{X})^2 = \sum_{i=2}^{n}(X_i - \bar{X}')^2 + \frac{n-1}{n}(X_1 - \bar{X}')^2,$$

where $\bar{X} = \sum_{i=1}^{n}X_i/n$ and $\bar{X}' = \sum_{i=2}^{n}X_i/(n-1)$. Hint: Replace $X_i - \bar{X}$ by $(X_i - \bar{X}') - (X_1 - \bar{X}')/n$. Show that $\sum_{i=2}^{n}(X_i - \bar{X}')^2/\sigma^2$ has a chi-square distribution with $n - 2$ degrees of freedom. Prove that the two terms in the right-hand member are stochastically independent. What then is the distribution of

$$\frac{\dfrac{n-1}{n}(X_1 - \bar{X}')^2}{\sigma^2}?$$

10.4. Let X_{ijk}, $i = 1, \cdots, a; j = 1, \cdots, b; k = 1, \cdots, c$, be a random sample of size $n = abc$ from a normal distribution $n(x; \mu, \sigma^2)$. Let $\bar{X} = \sum\limits_{k=1}^{c} \sum\limits_{j=1}^{b} \sum\limits_{i=1}^{a} X_{ijk}/n$ and $\bar{X}_{i..} = \sum\limits_{k=1}^{c} \sum\limits_{j=1}^{b} X_{ijk}/(bc)$. Show that

$$\sum_{i=1}^{a}\sum_{j=1}^{b}\sum_{k=1}^{c}(X_{ijk} - \bar{X})^2 = \sum_{i=1}^{a}\sum_{j=1}^{b}\sum_{k=1}^{c}(X_{ijk} - \bar{X}_{i..})^2 + bc\sum_{i=1}^{a}(\bar{X}_{i..} - \bar{X})^2.$$

Show that $\sum\limits_{i=1}^{a}\sum\limits_{j=1}^{b}\sum\limits_{k=1}^{c}(X_{ijk} - \bar{X}_{i..})^2/\sigma^2$ has a chi-square distribution with $a(bc - 1)$ degrees of freedom. Prove that the two terms in the right-hand member are stochastically independent. What then is the distribution of $bc\sum\limits_{i=1}^{a}(\bar{X}_{i..} - \bar{X})^2/\sigma^2$?

10.2. A Test of the Equality of Several Means. Consider b mutually stochastically independent random variables having normal distributions with unknown means $\mu_1, \mu_2, \cdots, \mu_b$, respectively, and unknown but common variance σ^2. Let $X_{1j}, X_{2j}, \cdots, X_{aj}$ represent a random sample of size a from the normal distribution having mean μ_j and variance σ^2, $j = 1, 2, \cdots, b$. It is desired to test the null composite hypothesis $H_0: \mu_1 = \mu_2 = \cdots = \mu_b = \mu$, μ unspecified, against all possible alternative hypotheses. A likelihood ratio test will be used. Here the total parameter space is

$$\Omega = \{(\mu_1, \mu_2, \cdots, \mu_b, \sigma^2); \quad -\infty < \mu_j < \infty, 0 < \sigma^2 < \infty\},$$

while

$$\omega = \{(\mu_1, \mu_2, \cdots, \mu_b, \sigma^2); \quad -\infty < \mu_1 = \mu_2 = \cdots = \mu_b = \mu < \infty, 0 < \sigma^2 < \infty\}.$$

The likelihood functions, denoted by $L(\omega)$ and $L(\Omega)$, are respectively

$$L(\omega) = \left(\frac{1}{2\pi\sigma^2}\right)^{\frac{ab}{2}} e^{-\frac{1}{2\sigma^2}\sum\limits_{j=1}^{b}\sum\limits_{i=1}^{a}(x_{ij}-\mu)^2}$$

and

$$L(\Omega) = \left(\frac{1}{2\pi\sigma^2}\right)^{\frac{ab}{2}} e^{-\frac{1}{2\sigma^2}\sum\limits_{j=1}^{b}\sum\limits_{i=1}^{a}(x_{ij}-\mu_j)^2}.$$

Now

$$\frac{\partial \ln L(\omega)}{\partial \mu} = \frac{\sum\limits_{j=1}^{b}\sum\limits_{i=1}^{a}(x_{ij} - \mu)}{\sigma^2},$$

and

$$\frac{\partial \ln L(\omega)}{\partial(\sigma^2)} = -\frac{ab}{2\sigma^2} + \frac{1}{2\sigma^4}\sum_{j=1}^{b}\sum_{i=1}^{a}(x_{ij} - \mu)^2.$$

If we equate these partial derivatives to zero and denote the solutions for μ and σ^2 by u and v, respectively, we have, in ω,

(1)

$$u = \frac{\sum\limits_{j=1}^{b}\sum\limits_{i=1}^{a} x_{ij}}{ab}$$

$$v = \frac{\sum\limits_{j=1}^{b}\sum\limits_{i=1}^{a} (x_{ij} - u)^2}{ab}$$

and these numbers maximize $L(\omega)$. Further

$$\frac{\partial \ln L(\Omega)}{\partial \mu_j} = \frac{\sum\limits_{i=1}^{a} (x_{ij} - \mu_j)}{\sigma^2}, \quad j = 1, 2, \cdots, b,$$

and

$$\frac{\partial \ln L(\Omega)}{\partial (\sigma^2)} = -\frac{ab}{2\sigma^2} + \frac{1}{2\sigma^4} \sum\limits_{j=1}^{b}\sum\limits_{i=1}^{a} (x_{ij} - \mu_j)^2.$$

If we equate these partial derivatives to zero and denote the solutions for $\mu_1, \mu_2, \cdots, \mu_b$, and σ^2 by $u_1, u_2, \cdots, u_b$, and w, respectively, we have, in Ω,

(2)

$$u_j = \frac{\sum\limits_{i=1}^{a} x_{ij}}{a}, \quad j = 1, 2, \cdots, b,$$

$$w = \frac{\sum\limits_{j=1}^{b}\sum\limits_{i=1}^{a} (x_{ij} - u_j)^2}{ab},$$

and these numbers maximize $L(\Omega)$. These maxima are respectively

$$L(\hat{\omega}) = \left[\frac{ab}{2\pi \sum\limits_{j=1}^{b}\sum\limits_{i=1}^{a} (x_{ij} - u)^2} \right]^{\frac{ab}{2}} e^{ -\left[\frac{ab \sum\limits_{j=1}^{b}\sum\limits_{i=1}^{a} (x_{ij}-u)^2}{2 \sum\limits_{j=1}^{b}\sum\limits_{i=1}^{a} (x_{ij}-u)^2} \right] }$$

$$= \left[\frac{ab}{2\pi \sum\limits_{j=1}^{b}\sum\limits_{i=1}^{a} (x_{ij} - u)^2} \right]^{\frac{ab}{2}} e^{-\frac{ab}{2}}$$

and

$$L(\hat{\Omega}) = \left[\frac{ab}{2\pi \sum\limits_{j=1}^{b}\sum\limits_{i=1}^{a} (x_{ij} - u_j)^2} \right]^{\frac{ab}{2}} e^{-\frac{ab}{2}}.$$

Finally,

$$\lambda = \frac{L(\hat{\omega})}{L(\hat{\Omega})} = \left[\frac{\sum\limits_{j=1}^{b} \sum\limits_{i=1}^{a} (x_{ij} - u_j)^2}{\sum\limits_{j=1}^{b} \sum\limits_{i=1}^{a} (x_{ij} - u)^2} \right]^{\frac{ab}{2}}.$$

In the notation of Section 10.1, the statistics defined by the functions u and v given by solutions (1) of this section are $\bar{X} = \sum\limits_{j=1}^{b} \sum\limits_{i=1}^{a} X_{ij}/ab$ and $S^2 = \sum\limits_{j=1}^{b} \sum\limits_{i=1}^{a} (X_{ij} - \bar{X})^2/ab = Q/ab$; while the statistics defined by the functions $u_1, u_2, \cdots, u_b$ and w given by solutions (2) in this section are respectively $\bar{X}_{\cdot j} = \sum\limits_{i=1}^{a} X_{ij}/a$, $j = 1, 2, \cdots, b$, and $Q_3/ab = \sum\limits_{j=1}^{b} \sum\limits_{i=1}^{a} (X_{ij} - \bar{X}_{\cdot j})^2/ab$. Thus, in the notation of Section 10.1, $\lambda^{2/ab}$ defines the statistic Q_3/Q.

We reject the null hypothesis H_0 if $\lambda \leq \lambda_0$. To find λ_0 so that we have a desired significance level α, we must assume that the null hypothesis H_0 is true. If the null hypothesis H_0 is true, the random variables X_{ij} constitute a random sample of size $n = ab$ from a distribution that is normal with mean μ and variance σ^2. This being the case, it was shown in Example 2, page 193, that $Q = Q_3 + Q_4$ where $Q_4 = a\sum\limits_{j=1}^{b} (\bar{X}_{\cdot j} - \bar{X})^2$; that Q_3 and Q_4 are stochastically independent; and that Q_3/σ^2 and Q_4/σ^2 have chi-square distributions with $b(a - 1)$ and $b - 1$ degrees of freedom, respectively. Thus the statistic defined by $\lambda^{2/ab}$ may be written

$$\frac{Q_3}{Q_3 + Q_4} = \frac{1}{1 + \dfrac{Q_4}{Q_3}}.$$

The significance level of the test of H_0 is

$$\alpha = Pr\left[\frac{1}{1 + \dfrac{Q_4}{Q_3}} \leq \lambda_0^{\frac{2}{ab}}; H_0 \right]$$

$$= Pr\left[\frac{\dfrac{Q_4}{b - 1}}{\dfrac{Q_3}{b(a - 1)}} \geq c; H_0 \right]$$

where

$$c = \frac{b(a - 1)}{b - 1}\left(\lambda_0^{-\frac{2}{ab}} - 1 \right).$$

But

$$F = \frac{\dfrac{Q_4}{\sigma^2(b - 1)}}{\dfrac{Q_3}{\sigma^2 b(a - 1)}} = \frac{\dfrac{Q_4}{b - 1}}{\dfrac{Q_3}{b(a - 1)}}$$

has an F distribution with $b - 1$ and $b(a - 1)$ degrees of freedom. Hence the test of the null composite hypothesis $H_0: \mu_1 = \mu_2 = \cdots = \mu_b = \mu$, μ unspecified, against all possible alternatives may be based on an F statistic. The constant c is so selected as to yield the desired value of α.

Exercises

10.5. Let μ_1, μ_2, μ_3 be respectively the means of three independent normal distributions having common but unknown variance σ^2. In order to test, at the 5 per cent significance level, the hypothesis $H_0: \mu_1 = \mu_2 = \mu_3$ against all possible alternative hypotheses, we take a random sample of size 5 from each of these distributions. Using the F statistic considered in this section, determine whether we accept or reject H_0 if the observed values from the three distributions are respectively

3	2	4
0	5	3
-1	1	6
0	3	8
2	5	5

10.6. Let X_{1j}, X_{2j}, $\cdots$, $X_{a_j j}$ represent independent random samples of sizes a_j from normal distributions having means μ_j and variances σ^2, $j = 1, 2, \cdots, b$. Show that

$$\sum_{j=1}^{b} \sum_{i=1}^{a_j} (X_{ij} - \bar{X})^2 = \sum_{j=1}^{b} \sum_{i=1}^{a_j} (X_{ij} - \bar{X}_{\cdot j})^2 + \sum_{j=1}^{b} a_j (\bar{X}_{\cdot j} - \bar{X})^2,$$

or $Q' = Q'_3 + Q'_4$. Here $\bar{X} = \sum_{j=1}^{b} \sum_{i=1}^{a_j} X_{ij} / \sum_{j=1}^{b} a_j$, and $\bar{X}_{\cdot j} = \sum_{i=1}^{a_j} X_{ij} / a_j$. If $\mu_1 = \mu_2 = \cdots = \mu_b$, show that Q'/σ^2 and Q'_3/σ^2 have chi-square distributions. Prove that Q'_3 and Q'_4 are stochastically independent, and hence Q'_4/σ^2 also has a chi-square distribution.

10.3. The Analysis of Variance. The problem considered in the preceding section is an example of a method of statistical inference called the *analysis of variance*. This method derives its name from the fact that the quadratic form abS^2, which is a total sum of squares, is resolved into several component parts. In this section another problem in the analysis of variance will be investigated.

Let X_{ij}, $i = 1, 2, \cdots, a$ and $j = 1, 2, \cdots, b$, denote $n = ab$ random variables which are mutually stochastically independent and have normal distributions with common variance σ^2. The means of these normal distributions are $\mu_{ij} = \mu + \alpha_i + \beta_j$, where $\sum_1^a \alpha_i = 0$ and $\sum_1^b \beta_j = 0$. For example, take $a = 2$, $b = 3$, $\mu = 5$, $\alpha_1 = 1$, $\alpha_2 = -1$, $\beta_1 = 1$, $\beta_2 = 0$, and $\beta_3 = -1$. Then the $ab = 6$ random variables have means

$$\begin{array}{lll} \mu_{11} = 7 & \mu_{12} = 6 & \mu_{13} = 5 \\ \mu_{21} = 5 & \mu_{22} = 4 & \mu_{23} = 3 \end{array}$$

Had we taken $\beta_1 = \beta_2 = \beta_3 = 0$, then the six random variables would have had means

$$\begin{array}{lll} \mu_{11} = 6 & \mu_{12} = 6 & \mu_{13} = 6 \\ \mu_{21} = 4 & \mu_{22} = 4 & \mu_{23} = 4 \end{array}$$

Thus, if we wish to test the null composite hypothesis that

$$\begin{array}{ccccc} \mu_{11} &=& \mu_{12} &=& \cdots &=& \mu_{1b} \\ \mu_{21} &=& \mu_{22} &=& \cdots &=& \mu_{2b} \\ \vdots && \vdots && && \vdots \\ \mu_{a1} &=& \mu_{a2} &=& \cdots &=& \mu_{ab} \end{array}$$

we could say that we are testing the null composite hypothesis that $\beta_1 = \beta_2 = \cdots = \beta_b$ (and hence each $\beta_j = 0$, since their sum is zero). On the other hand, the null composite hypothesis

$$\begin{array}{ccccc} \mu_{11} &=& \mu_{21} &=& \cdots &=& \mu_{a1} \\ \mu_{12} &=& \mu_{22} &=& \cdots &=& \mu_{a2} \\ \vdots && \vdots && && \vdots \\ \mu_{1b} &=& \mu_{2b} &=& \cdots &=& \mu_{ab} \end{array}$$

is the same as the null composite hypothesis that $\alpha_1 = \alpha_2 = \cdots = \alpha_a = 0$.

Comment. The model just described, and others similar to it, are widely used in statistical applications. Consider a situation in which it is desirable to investigate the effects of two factors which influence an outcome. Thus the variety of a grain and the type of fertilizer used influence the yield; or the teacher and the size of a class may influence the score on a standard test. Let X_{ij} denote the yield from the use of variety i of a grain and type j of fertilizer. A test of the hypothesis that $\beta_1 = \beta_2 = \cdots = \beta_b = 0$ would then be a test of the hypothesis that the mean yield of each variety of grain is the same regardless of the type of fertilizer used.

A likelihood ratio test will be used to test the null composite hypothesis $H_0: \beta_1 = \beta_2 = \cdots = \beta_b = 0$ against all possible alternative hypotheses.

Here the parameter space is

$$\Omega = \left\{(\mu, \alpha_1, \cdots, \alpha_a, \beta_1, \cdots, \beta_b, \sigma^2); \quad \begin{array}{l} -\infty < \mu < \infty \\ -\infty < \alpha_i < \infty, \ \sum_1^a \alpha_i = 0 \\ -\infty < \beta_j < \infty, \ \sum_1^b \beta_j = 0 \\ 0 < \sigma^2 < \infty \end{array} \right\}$$

while

$$\omega = \left\{(\mu, \alpha_1, \cdots, \alpha_a, \beta_1, \cdots, \beta_b, \sigma^2); \quad \begin{array}{l} -\infty < \mu < \infty \\ -\infty < \alpha_i < \infty, \ \sum_1^a \alpha_i = 0 \\ \beta_1 = \beta_2 = \cdots = \beta_b = 0 \\ 0 < \sigma^2 < \infty \end{array} \right\}.$$

The likelihood functions, denoted by $L(\omega)$ and $L(\Omega)$, are respectively

and

$$L(\omega) = \left(\frac{1}{2\pi\sigma^2}\right)^{\frac{ab}{2}} e^{-\frac{1}{2\sigma^2} \sum\limits_{j=1}^{b} \sum\limits_{i=1}^{a}(x_{ij}-\mu-\alpha_i)^2}$$

$$L(\Omega) = \left(\frac{1}{2\pi\sigma^2}\right)^{\frac{ab}{2}} e^{-\frac{1}{2\sigma^2} \sum\limits_{j=1}^{b} \sum\limits_{i=1}^{a}(x_{ij}-\mu-\alpha_i-\beta_j)^2} .$$

Consider first the problem of maximizing $L(\Omega)$. We have

(1)
$$\frac{\partial \ln L(\Omega)}{\partial \mu} = \frac{1}{\sigma^2} \sum_{j=1}^{b} \sum_{i=1}^{a}(x_{ij} - \mu - \alpha_i - \beta_j)$$

$$= \frac{1}{\sigma^2} \sum_{j=1}^{b} \sum_{i=1}^{a}(x_{ij} - \mu),$$

since $\sum_1^a \alpha_i = \sum_1^b \beta_j = 0$, and

(2)
$$\frac{\partial \ln L(\Omega)}{\partial(\sigma^2)} = -\frac{ab}{2\sigma^2} + \frac{1}{2\sigma^4} \sum_{j=1}^{b} \sum_{i=1}^{a}(x_{ij} - \mu - \alpha_i - \beta_j)^2.$$

Now any one of the α's, say, α_a, can be written $\alpha_a = -(\alpha_1 + \cdots + \alpha_{a-1})$; and any one of the β's, say, β_b, can be written $\beta_b = -(\beta_1 + \cdots + \beta_{b-1})$. Thus there are but the $a + b - 2$ partial derivatives to be computed, namely,

$$\frac{\partial \ln L(\Omega)}{\partial \alpha_i}, \quad i = 1, 2, \cdots, a - 1, \quad \text{and} \quad \frac{\partial \ln L(\Omega)}{\partial \beta_j}, \quad j = 1, 2, \cdots, b - 1.$$

We have

(3)
$$\frac{\partial \ln L(\Omega)}{\partial \alpha_i} = -\frac{1}{2\sigma^2}\left[-2\sum_{j=1}^{b}(x_{ij} - \mu - \alpha_i - \beta_j) + 2\sum_{j=1}^{b}(x_{aj} - \mu - \alpha_a - \beta_j)\right]$$

$$= \frac{1}{\sigma^2}\left[\sum_{j=1}^{b}(x_{ij} - \alpha_i - x_{aj} + \alpha_a)\right], \quad i = 1, 2, \cdots, a - 1,$$

and

(4)
$$\frac{\partial \ln L(\Omega)}{\partial \beta_j} = -\frac{1}{2\sigma^2}\left[-2\sum_{i=1}^{a}(x_{ij} - \mu - \alpha_i - \beta_j) + 2\sum_{i=1}^{a}(x_{ib} - \mu - \alpha_i - \beta_b)\right]$$

$$= \frac{1}{\sigma^2}\left[\sum_{i=1}^{a}(x_{ij} - \beta_j - x_{ib} + \beta_b)\right], \quad j = 1, 2, \cdots, b - 1.$$

If the partial derivative, expression (1), is set equal to zero, the solution for μ is

$$u = \frac{1}{ab}\sum_{j=1}^{b}\sum_{i=1}^{a}x_{ij}.$$

If the partial derivatives, expression (3), are equated to zero, we have

(5) $$\sum_{j=1}^{b}x_{ij} - b\alpha_i - \sum_{j=1}^{b}x_{aj} + b\alpha_a = 0, \quad i = 1, 2, \cdots, a - 1.$$

Equation (5) is valid also for $i = a$, since

$$\sum_{j=1}^{b}x_{aj} - b\alpha_a - \sum_{j=1}^{b}x_{aj} + b\alpha_a = 0.$$

That is, Equation (5) may be summed on i from 1 to a to yield

$$\sum_{i=1}^{a}\sum_{j=1}^{b}x_{ij} - a\sum_{j=1}^{b}x_{aj} + ab\alpha_a = 0.$$

The solution for α_a is

$$v_a = \frac{1}{b}\sum_{j=1}^{b}x_{aj} - \frac{1}{ab}\sum_{i=1}^{a}\sum_{j=1}^{b}x_{ij} = \frac{1}{b}\sum_{j=1}^{b}x_{aj} - u.$$

Since we could have written $\alpha_i = -(\alpha_1 + \cdots + \alpha_{i-1} + \alpha_{i+1} + \cdots + \alpha_a)$, it follows from symmetry that the solution for α_i is

$$v_i = \frac{1}{b}\sum_{j=1}^{b}x_{ij} - u, \quad i = 1, 2, \cdots, a.$$

If the partial derivatives, expression (4), are equated to zero, we have

(6) $$\sum_{i=1}^{a}x_{ij} - a\beta_j - \sum_{i=1}^{a}x_{ib} + a\beta_b = 0, \quad j = 1, 2, \cdots, b - 1.$$

Equation (6) is valid for $j = b$, since

$$\sum_{i=1}^{a}x_{ib} - a\beta_b - \sum_{i=1}^{a}x_{ib} + a\beta_b = 0.$$

That is, Equation (6) may be summed on j from 1 to b to yield

$$\sum_{j=1}^{b}\sum_{i=1}^{a}x_{ij} - b\sum_{i=1}^{a}x_{ib} + ab\beta_b = 0.$$

The solution for β_b is

$$z_b = \frac{1}{a}\sum_{i=1}^{a}x_{ib} - \frac{1}{ab}\sum_{j=1}^{b}\sum_{i=1}^{a}x_{ij} = \frac{1}{a}\sum_{i=1}^{a}x_{ib} - u.$$

From symmetry, it follows that the solution for β_j is

$$z_j = \frac{1}{a}\sum_{i=1}^{a}x_{ij} - u, \quad j = 1, 2, \cdots, b.$$

Finally, if the partial derivative, expression (2), is equated to zero and if μ, α_i, β_j are replaced by u, v_i, z_j, respectively, the solution for σ^2 is

$$w = \frac{1}{ab}\sum_{j=1}^{b}\sum_{i=1}^{a}(x_{ij} - u - v_i - z_j)^2.$$

The numbers u, v_i, z_j, and w maximize $L(\Omega)$, and the maximum is

$$L(\hat{\Omega}) = \left(\frac{1}{2\pi w}\right)^{\frac{ab}{2}} e^{-\frac{ab}{2}} = \left[\frac{abe^{-1}}{2\pi\sum_{j=1}^{b}\sum_{i=1}^{a}(x_{ij} - u - v_i - z_j)^2}\right]^{\frac{ab}{2}}.$$

It is left as an exercise (Exercise 10.8) to show that the values of μ, α_i, and σ^2, which make

$$\frac{\partial \ln L(\omega)}{\partial \mu}, \quad \frac{\partial \ln L(\omega)}{\partial \alpha_i}, \quad \text{and} \quad \frac{\partial \ln L(\omega)}{\partial(\sigma^2)}$$

vanish simultaneously, are respectively

$$u = \frac{1}{ab}\sum_{j=1}^{b}\sum_{i=1}^{a}x_{ij}, \quad v_i = \frac{1}{b}\sum_{j=1}^{b}x_{ij} - u, \quad i = 1, 2, \cdots, a,$$

and

$$w' = \frac{1}{ab}\sum_{j=1}^{b}\sum_{i=1}^{a}(x_{ij} - u - v_i)^2.$$

These numbers maximize $L(\omega)$ and

$$L(\hat{\omega}) = \left(\frac{1}{2\pi w'}\right)^{\frac{ab}{2}} e^{-\frac{ab}{2}} = \left[\frac{abe^{-1}}{2\pi\sum_{j=1}^{b}\sum_{i=1}^{a}(x_{ij} - u - v_i)^2}\right]^{\frac{ab}{2}}.$$

Finally, the likelihood ratio is

$$\lambda = \frac{L(\hat{\omega})}{L(\hat{\Omega})} = \left[\frac{\sum_{j=1}^{b}\sum_{i=1}^{a}(x_{ij} - u - v_i - z_j)^2}{\sum_{j=1}^{b}\sum_{i=1}^{a}(x_{ij} - u - v_i)^2}\right]^{\frac{ab}{2}}.$$

In the notation of Section 10.1, the statistic defined by $\lambda^{2/ab}$ is

$$\frac{\displaystyle\sum_{j=1}^{b}\sum_{i=1}^{a}[X_{ij} - \bar{X} - (\bar{X}_{i.} - \bar{X}) - (\bar{X}_{.j} - \bar{X})]^2}{\displaystyle\sum_{j=1}^{b}\sum_{i=1}^{a}[X_{ij} - \bar{X} - (\bar{X}_{i.} - \bar{X})]^2}$$

$$= \frac{\displaystyle\sum_{j=1}^{b}\sum_{i=1}^{a}[X_{ij} - \bar{X}_{i.} - \bar{X}_{.j} + \bar{X}]^2}{\displaystyle\sum_{j=1}^{b}\sum_{i=1}^{a}[X_{ij} - \bar{X}_{i.}]^2}.$$

The denominator in the preceding ratio may be written (Exercise 10.9) in the form

$$\sum_{j=1}^{b}\sum_{i=1}^{a}[(X_{ij} - \bar{X}_{i.} - \bar{X}_{.j} + \bar{X}) + (\bar{X}_{.j} - \bar{X})]^2$$

$$= \sum_{j=1}^{b}\sum_{i=1}^{a}(X_{ij} - \bar{X}_{i.} - \bar{X}_{.j} + \bar{X})^2 + a\sum_{j=1}^{b}(\bar{X}_{.j} - \bar{X})^2.$$

Accordingly, in the notation of Section 10.1, the statistic defined by $\lambda^{2/ab}$ is

$$\frac{1}{1 + \dfrac{a\displaystyle\sum_{j=1}^{b}(\bar{X}_{.j} - \bar{X})^2}{\displaystyle\sum_{j=1}^{b}\sum_{i=1}^{a}(X_{ij} - \bar{X}_{i.} - \bar{X}_{.j} + \bar{X})^2}} = \frac{1}{1 + \dfrac{Q_4}{Q_5}}.$$

We reject the null hypothesis H_0 if $\lambda \leq \lambda_0$. To find λ_0 so that the test of H_0 has a desired significance level α, we must assume that the null hypothesis H_0 is true. But here, unlike the situation in the preceding section, when the null hypothesis is true, the $n = ab$ mutually stochastically independent normally distributed random variables X_{ij} do not have the same means. Thus the results of Examples 1, 2, and 3 of Section 10.1 may not be valid; that is, in particular, Q_4 and Q_5 may not be stochastically independent, and Q_4/σ^2 and Q_5/σ^2 may not have their chi-square distributions. Fortunately, however, these fears are groundless, as may be seen by the following argument. Define ab random variables Y_{ij} by

$$Y_{ij} = X_{ij} - \mu - \alpha_i, \qquad i = 1, \cdots, a \quad \text{and} \quad j = 1, \cdots, b.$$

Thus the ab random variables Y_{ij} are mutually stochastically independent, each having a normal distribution with mean zero and the same variance

σ^2 of the X_{ij}. It will now be shown, if $\bar{Y}$, $\bar{Y}_{.j}$, $\bar{Y}_{i.}$ are defined in the obvious manner, that

$$a\sum_{j=1}^{b}(\bar{X}_{.j} - \bar{X})^2 = a\sum_{j=1}^{b}(\bar{Y}_{.j} - \bar{Y})^2,$$

and that

$$\sum_{j=1}^{b}\sum_{i=1}^{a}(X_{ij} - \bar{X}_{i.} - \bar{X}_{.j} + \bar{X})^2 = \sum_{j=1}^{b}\sum_{i=1}^{a}(Y_{ij} - \bar{Y}_{i.} - \bar{Y}_{.j} + \bar{Y})^2,$$

so that, when the null hypothesis H_0 is true, the results of Section 10.1 are applicable to these quadratic forms in the X_{ij}.

We have

$$\bar{Y} = \frac{1}{ab}\sum_{j=1}^{b}\sum_{i=1}^{a}Y_{ij} = \frac{1}{ab}\sum_{j=1}^{b}\sum_{i=1}^{a}(X_{ij} - \mu - \alpha_i)$$
$$= \bar{X} - \mu$$

since $\sum_{1}^{a}\alpha_i = 0$. Moreover,

$$\bar{Y}_{i.} = \frac{1}{b}\sum_{j=1}^{b}Y_{ij} = \frac{1}{b}\sum_{j=1}^{b}(X_{ij} - \mu - \alpha_i)$$
$$= \bar{X}_{i.} - \mu - \alpha_i$$

and

$$\bar{Y}_{.j} = \frac{1}{a}\sum_{i=1}^{a}Y_{ij} = \frac{1}{a}\sum_{i=1}^{a}(X_{ij} - \mu - \alpha_i)$$
$$= \bar{X}_{.j} - \mu.$$

Accordingly,

$$a\sum_{j=1}^{b}(\bar{X}_{.j} - \bar{X})^2 = a\sum_{j=1}^{b}(\bar{Y}_{.j} + \mu - \bar{Y} - \mu)^2 = a\sum_{j=1}^{b}(\bar{Y}_{.j} - \bar{Y})^2,$$

and

$$\sum_{j=1}^{b}\sum_{i=1}^{a}(X_{ij} - \bar{X}_{i.} - \bar{X}_{.j} + \bar{X})^2$$
$$= \sum_{j=1}^{b}\sum_{i=1}^{a}(Y_{ij} + \mu + \alpha_i - \bar{Y}_{i.} - \mu - \alpha_i - \bar{Y}_{.j} - \mu + \bar{Y} + \mu)^2$$
$$= \sum_{j=1}^{b}\sum_{i=1}^{a}(Y_{ij} - \bar{Y}_{i.} - \bar{Y}_{.j} + \bar{Y})^2,$$

as was to be shown.

The significance level of the test of H_0 is

$$\alpha = Pr\left[\frac{1}{1 + \dfrac{Q_4}{Q_5}} \leq \lambda_0^{\frac{2}{ab}}; H_0\right]$$
$$= Pr\left[\frac{(a-1)Q_4}{Q_5} \geq c; H_0\right]$$

where $$c = (a - 1)[\lambda_0^{-\frac{2}{ab}} - 1].$$

But

$$F = \frac{\dfrac{Q_4}{\sigma^2(b - 1)}}{\dfrac{Q_5}{\sigma^2(a - 1)(b - 1)}} = \frac{(a - 1)Q_4}{Q_5}$$

has an F distribution with $b - 1$ and $(a - 1)(b - 1)$ degrees of freedom. Hence the test of the null composite hypothesis $H_0: \beta_1 = \beta_2 = \cdots = \beta_b = 0$, or $H_0: \mu_{ij} = \mu + \alpha_i$, $\sum_1^a \alpha_i = 0$, against the alternative composite hypothesis $H_1: \mu_{ij} = \mu + \alpha_i + \beta_j$, $\sum_1^a \alpha_i = \sum_1^b \beta_j = 0$, may be based on an F statistic. The constant c is so selected as to yield the desired value of α.

Exercises

·10.7. If in the preceding discussion $a = 4$ and $b = 3$, test at the 5 per cent significance level the null hypothesis $\beta_1 = \beta_2 = \beta_3 = 0$ if the observed values of X_{ij} are

3	5	7
−1	2	2
0	2	5
6	6	10

Hint: The computed value of Q_5 can be determined by $Q_5 = Q - Q_2 - Q_4$, once the values of terms in the right-hand member are found.

10.8. Verify that the values of μ, α_i, and σ^2, which make $L(\omega)$ a maximum, are as given in this section.

10.9. Show that

$$\sum_{j=1}^b \sum_{i=1}^a (X_{ij} - \bar{X}_{i\cdot})^2 = \sum_{j=1}^b \sum_{i=1}^a (X_{ij} - \bar{X}_{i\cdot} - \bar{X}_{\cdot j} + \bar{X})^2 + a \sum_{j=1}^b (\bar{X}_{\cdot j} - \bar{X})^2.$$

10.10. Let X_{ij} denote $n = ab$ random variables, mutually stochastically independent and having normal distributions with means $\mu_{ij} = \mu + \alpha_i + \beta_j$, $\sum_1^a \alpha_i = 0$, $\sum_1^b \beta_j = 0$, and common but unknown variance σ^2. Consider the null hypothesis $H_0: \mu_{ij} = \mu + \beta_j$ (or $H_0: \alpha_1 = \alpha_2 = \cdots = \alpha_a = 0$). Show that a likelihood ratio test of H_0 against all possible alternatives may be based, in the notation of Section 10.1, on the $F = (b - 1)(Q_2/Q_5)$ statistic having $(a - 1)$ and $(a - 1)(b - 1)$ degrees of freedom.

10.11. Use the data of Exercise 10.7 to test at the 5 per cent significance level the null hypothesis in Exercise 10.10.

10.12. Let the random variables X_{ij} be defined as in Exercise 10.10. Consider a likelihood ratio test of the null composite hypothesis $H_0: \mu_{ij} = \mu$ (or $H_0: \alpha_i = \beta_j = 0$, $i = 1, \cdots, a$, $j = 1, \cdots, b$) against $H_1: \mu_{ij} = \mu + \alpha_i + \beta_j$, $\sum_{i=1}^{a} \alpha_i = \sum_{j=1}^{b} \beta_j = 0$. Show that this test can be based on an F statistic having $a + b - 2$ and $(a - 1)(b - 1)$ degrees of freedom.

10.4. A Regression Problem. Consider a laboratory experiment the outcome of which depends upon the temperature; that is, the technician first sets a temperature dial at a fixed point c and subsequently observes the outcome of the experiment for that dial setting. From past experience, the technician knows that if he repeats the experiment with the temperature dial set at the same point c, he is not likely to observe precisely the same outcome. He then assumes that the outcome of his experiment is a random variable X whose distribution depends not only upon certain unknown parameters but also upon a nonrandom variable c which he can choose more or less at pleasure. Let $c_1, c_2, \cdots, c_n$ denote n arbitrarily selected values of c (but not all equal) and let X_i denote the outcome of the experiment when $c = c_i$, $i = 1, 2, \cdots, n$. We then have the n pairs $(X_1, c_1), \cdots, (X_n, c_n)$ in which the X_i are random variables but the c_i are known numbers and $i = 1, 2, \cdots, n$. Once the n experiments have been performed (the first with $c = c_1$, the second with $c = c_2$ and so on) and the outcome of each recorded, we have the n pairs of known numbers (x_1, c_1), $\cdots, (x_n, c_n)$. These numbers are to be used to make statistical inferences about the unknown parameters in the distribution of the random variable X. Certain problems of this sort are called *regression* problems and we shall study a particular one in some detail.

Let $c_1, c_2, \cdots, c_n$ be n given numbers, not all equal, and let $\bar{c} = \sum_{1}^{n} c_i/n$. Let $X_1, X_2, \cdots, X_n$ be n mutually stochastically independent random variables with joint p.d.f.

$$L(\alpha, \beta, \sigma^2; x_1, x_2, \cdots, x_n) = \left(\frac{1}{2\pi\sigma^2}\right)^{\frac{n}{2}} e^{-\frac{1}{2\sigma^2}\sum_{1}^{n}[x_i - \alpha - \beta(c_i - \bar{c})]^2}.$$

Thus each X_i has a normal distribution with the same variance σ^2, but the means of these distributions are $\alpha + \beta(c_i - \bar{c})$. Since the c_i are not all equal, in this regression problem the means of the normal distributions depend upon the choice of $c_1, c_2, \cdots, c_n$. We shall investigate ways of making statistical inferences about the parameters α, β, and σ^2.

First, the maximum likelihood statistics for α, β, and σ^2 will be obtained. We have

$$\frac{\partial \ln L}{\partial \alpha} = \frac{1}{\sigma^2} \sum_{1}^{n} [x_i - \alpha - \beta(c_i - \bar{c})],$$

$$\frac{\partial \ln L}{\partial \beta} = \frac{1}{\sigma^2} \sum_{1}^{n} [x_i - \alpha - \beta(c_i - \bar{c})](c_i - \bar{c}),$$

and

$$\frac{\partial \ln L}{\partial(\sigma^2)} = -\frac{n}{2\sigma^2} + \frac{1}{2\sigma^4}\sum_1^n[x_i - \alpha - \beta(c_i - \bar{c})]^2.$$

If these partial derivatives are equated to zero, the solutions for α, β, and σ^2 are respectively (Exercise 10.13)

$$u = \frac{\sum_1^n x_i}{n} = \bar{x},$$

$$v = \frac{\sum_1^n(c_i - \bar{c})(x_i - u)}{\sum_1^n(c_i - \bar{c})^2},$$

and

$$w = \frac{1}{n}\sum_1^n[x_i - u - v(c_i - \bar{c})]^2.$$

That is, the maximum likelihood statistics for α, β, and σ^2 are

$$\hat{\alpha} = \frac{\sum_1^n X_i}{n} = \bar{X},$$

$$\hat{\beta} = \frac{\sum_1^n(c_i - \bar{c})(X_i - \bar{X})}{\sum_1^n(c_i - \bar{c})^2} = \frac{\sum_1^n(c_i - \bar{c})X_i}{\sum_1^n(c_i - \bar{c})^2},$$

and

$$\hat{\sigma}^2 = \frac{1}{n}\sum_1^n[X_i - \hat{\alpha} - \hat{\beta}(c_i - \bar{c})]^2.$$

The statistic $\hat{\alpha}$ is a linear function of $X_1, X_2, \cdots, X_n$. Accordingly, $\hat{\alpha}$ has a normal distribution with mean

$$E(\hat{\alpha}) = \frac{1}{n}E(X_1 + X_2 + \cdots + X_n) = \frac{1}{n}[\alpha + \beta(c_1 - \bar{c}) + \cdots + \alpha + \beta(c_n - \bar{c})] = \alpha$$

and variance

$$\sigma_{\hat{\alpha}}^2 = \sum_{i=1}^n\left(\frac{1}{n}\right)^2\sigma_{X_i}^2 = \frac{1}{n^2}n\sigma^2 = \frac{\sigma^2}{n}.$$

The statistic $\hat{\beta}$ is also a linear function of $X_1, X_2, \cdots, X_n$, and it too has a normal distribution with mean

$$E(\hat{\beta}) = \frac{\sum_{1}^{n}(c_i - \bar{c})E(X_i)}{\sum_{1}^{n}(c_i - \bar{c})^2}$$

$$= \frac{\sum_{1}^{n}(c_i - \bar{c})[\alpha + \beta(c_i - \bar{c})]}{\sum_{1}^{n}(c_i - \bar{c})^2}$$

$$= \frac{\alpha\sum_{1}^{n}(c_i - \bar{c}) + \beta\sum_{1}^{n}(c_i - \bar{c})^2}{\sum_{1}^{n}(c_i - \bar{c})^2} = \beta,$$

and variance

$$\sigma_{\hat{\beta}}^2 = \sum_{1}^{n}\left(\frac{c_i - \bar{c}}{\sum_{1}^{n}(c_i - \bar{c})^2}\right)^2 \sigma_{X_i}^2$$

$$= \frac{\sum_{1}^{n}(c_i - \bar{c})^2}{\left[\sum_{1}^{n}(c_i - \bar{c})^2\right]^2}\sigma^2 = \frac{\sigma^2}{\sum_{1}^{n}(c_i - \bar{c})^2}.$$

Consider next the algebraic identity (Exercise 10.15)

$$\sum_{1}^{n}[X_i - \alpha - \beta(c_i - \bar{c})]^2 = \sum_{1}^{n}\{(\hat{\alpha} - \alpha) + (\hat{\beta} - \beta)(c_i - \bar{c}) + [X_i - \hat{\alpha} - \hat{\beta}(c_i - \bar{c})]\}^2$$

$$= n(\hat{\alpha} - \alpha)^2 + (\hat{\beta} - \beta)^2\sum_{1}^{n}(c_i - \bar{c})^2 + \sum_{1}^{n}[X_i - \hat{\alpha} - \hat{\beta}(c_i - \bar{c})]^2,$$

or

$$\sum_{1}^{n}[X_i - \alpha - \beta(c_i - \bar{c})]^2 = n(\hat{\alpha} - \alpha)^2 + (\hat{\beta} - \beta)^2\sum_{1}^{n}(c_i - \bar{c})^2 + n\hat{\sigma}^2,$$

or, for brevity,

$$Q = Q_1 + Q_2 + Q_3.$$

Here Q, Q_1, Q_2, and Q_3 are real quadratic forms in the variables

$$X_i - \alpha - \beta(c_i - \bar{c}), \ i = 1, 2, \cdots, n.$$

In this equation, Q represents the sum of the squares of n mutually stochastically independent random variables that have normal distributions with means zero and variances σ^2. Thus Q/σ^2 has a chi-square distribution with n degrees of freedom. Each of the random variables $\sqrt{n}(\hat{\alpha} - \alpha)/\sigma$ and $\sqrt{\sum_1^n (c_i - \bar{c})^2}(\hat{\beta} - \beta)/\sigma$ has a normal distribution with zero mean and unit variance; thus each of Q_1/σ^2 and Q_2/σ^2 has a chi-square distribution with one degree of freedom. Since Q_3 is non-negative, we have, in accordance with the theorem of Section 10.1, page 191, that Q_1, Q_2, and Q_3 are mutually stochastically independent, so that Q_3/σ^2 has a chi-square distribution with $n - 1 - 1 = n - 2$ degrees of freedom. Then each of the random variables

$$T_1 = \frac{\dfrac{\sqrt{n}(\hat{\alpha} - \alpha)}{\sigma}}{\sqrt{\dfrac{Q_3}{\sigma^2(n-2)}}} = \frac{\hat{\alpha} - \alpha}{\sqrt{\dfrac{\hat{\sigma}^2}{n-2}}}$$

and

$$T_2 = \frac{\dfrac{\sqrt{\sum_1^n (c_i - \bar{c})^2}(\hat{\beta} - \beta)}{\sigma}}{\sqrt{\dfrac{Q_3}{\sigma^2(n-2)}}} = \frac{\hat{\beta} - \beta}{\sqrt{\dfrac{n\hat{\sigma}^2}{(n-2)\sum_1^n (c_i - \bar{c})^2}}}$$

has a t distribution with $n - 2$ degrees of freedom. These facts enable us to obtain confidence intervals for α and β. The fact that $n\hat{\sigma}^2/\sigma^2$ has a chi-square distribution with $n - 2$ degrees of freedom provides a means of determining a confidence interval for σ^2. These are some of the statistical inferences about the parameters to which reference was made in the introductory remarks of this section.

Exercises

10.13. Verify that the maximum likelihood statistics for α, β, and σ^2 are the $\hat{\alpha}$, $\hat{\beta}$, and $\hat{\sigma}^2$ given in this section.

10.14. What theorem was used to obtain $\sigma_{\hat{\alpha}}^2$ and $\sigma_{\hat{\beta}}^2$ in the manner in which they were obtained?

10.15. Verify that $\sum_1^n [X_i - \alpha - \beta(c_i - \bar{c})]^2 = Q_1 + Q_2 + Q_3$, as stated in the text.

10.16. Let the mutually stochastically independent random variables X_1, X_2, $\cdots$, X_n have respectively the probability density functions $n(x_i; \beta c_i, \gamma^2 c_i^2)$, $i = 1$, 2, $\cdots$, n, where the given numbers c_1, c_2, $\cdots$, c_n are not all equal and no one is zero. Find the maximum likelihood statistics for β and γ^2.

10.17. Let the mutually stochastically independent random variables $X_1, \cdots,$ X_n have the joint p.d.f.

$$L(\alpha, \beta, \sigma^2; x_1, \cdots, x_n) = \left(\frac{1}{2\pi\sigma^2}\right)^{n/2} e^{-\frac{\sum_{1}^{n}[x_i-\alpha-\beta(c_i-\bar{c})]^2}{2\sigma^2}}$$

where the given numbers $c_1, c_2, \cdots, c_n$ are not all equal. Let $H_0: \beta = 0$ (α and σ^2 unspecified). It is desired to use a likelihood ratio test to test H_0 against all possible alternatives. Find λ and see whether the test can be based on a familiar statistic. *Hint*: In the notation of this section show that

$$\sum_{1}^{n}(X_i - \hat{\alpha})^2 = Q_3 + \hat{\beta}^2\sum_{1}^{n}(c_i - \bar{c})^2.$$

CHAPTER ELEVEN

MULTIVARIATE DISTRIBUTIONS

This chapter will be concerned primarily with a few selected problems associated with distributions of more than one random variable. Some of the more interesting of these problems can become quite complicated if they are not discussed from the point of view of matrix algebra. On this account, the number of problems that can be appropriately selected for inclusion in this chapter is quite limited.

In Section 11.1, some mathematical expectations associated with distributions of more than one random variable are defined.

11.1. Certain Mathematical Expectations. Let X, Y, and Z denote random variables having joint p.d.f. $f(x, y, z)$. If $u(x, y, z)$ is a function of x, y, and z, then $E[u(X, Y, Z)]$ was defined, subject to its existence, page 18. The existence of all mathematical expectations will be assumed in this discussion. The means of X, Y, and Z, say, μ_1, μ_2, and μ_3, are obtained by taking $u(x, y, z)$ to be x, y, and z, respectively; and the variances of X, Y, and Z, say, $\sigma_1{}^2$, $\sigma_2{}^2$, and $\sigma_3{}^2$, are obtained by setting the function $u(x, y, z)$ equal to $(x - \mu_1)^2$, $(y - \mu_2)^2$, and $(z - \mu_3)^2$, respectively. Consider the mathematical expectation

$$
\begin{aligned}
E[(X - \mu_1)(Y - \mu_2)] &= E(XY - \mu_2 X - \mu_1 Y + \mu_1\mu_2) \\
&= E(XY) - \mu_2 E(X) - \mu_1 E(Y) + \mu_1\mu_2 \\
&= E(XY) - \mu_1\mu_2.
\end{aligned}
$$

This number is called the *covariance* of X and Y. The covariance of X and Z is given by $E[(X - \mu_1)(Z - \mu_3)]$, and the covariance of Y and Z is $E[(Y - \mu_2)(Z - \mu_3)]$. If each of σ_1 and σ_2 is positive, the number

$$
\rho_{12} = \frac{E[(X - \mu_1)(Y - \mu_2)]}{\sigma_1\sigma_2}
$$

is called the *correlation coefficient* of X and Y. If the standard deviations are positive, the correlation coefficient of any two random variables is defined to be the covariance of the two random variables divided by the product of the standard deviations of the two random variables.

EXAMPLE 1.   Let the random variables X and Y have the joint p.d.f.

$$f(x, y) = x + y, \quad 0 < x < 1, \quad 0 < y < 1,$$
$$= 0 \text{ elsewhere.}$$

We shall compute the correlation coefficient of X and Y. When only two variables are under consideration, we shall denote the correlation coefficient by ρ.   Now

$$\mu_1 = E(X) = \int_0^1 \int_0^1 x(x + y) \, dx \, dy = \frac{7}{12},$$

and

$$\sigma_1{}^2 = E(X^2) - \mu_1{}^2 = \int_0^1 \int_0^1 x^2(x + y) \, dx \, dy - \left(\frac{7}{12}\right)^2 = \frac{11}{144}.$$

Similarly,

$$\mu_2 = E(Y) = \frac{7}{12} \quad \text{and} \quad \sigma_2{}^2 = E(Y^2) - \mu_2{}^2 = \frac{11}{144}.$$

The covariance of X and Y is

$$E(XY) - \mu_1\mu_2 = \int_0^1 \int_0^1 xy(x + y) \, dx \, dy - \left(\frac{7}{12}\right)^2 = -\frac{1}{144}.$$

Accordingly the correlation coefficient of X and Y is

$$\rho = \frac{-\dfrac{1}{144}}{\sqrt{\left(\dfrac{11}{144}\right)\left(\dfrac{11}{144}\right)}} = -\frac{1}{11}.$$

Next, let $f(x, y)$ denote the joint p.d.f. of two random variables X and Y, and let $f_1(x)$ denote the marginal p.d.f. of X.   The conditional p.d.f. of Y, given $X = x$, is

$$h(y|x) = \frac{f(x, y)}{f_1(x)}$$

at points where $f_1(x) > 0$.   Consider now the conditional expectation of Y, given $X = x$.   We have

$$E(Y|x) = \int_{-\infty}^{\infty} yh(y|x) \, dy = \frac{\displaystyle\int_{-\infty}^{\infty} yf(x, y) \, dy}{f_1(x)}$$

when dealing with random variables of the continuous type.   It was remarked on page 92 that this conditional expectation is a function of x alone, say, $\phi(x)$.   By analogy with the regression problem, but in a different context, we call $\phi(x)$ the regression function of Y on X.   The conditional expectation $E(X|y) = \psi(y)$, say, defines the regression function of X on Y.

In case $\phi(x)$ is a linear function of x, say, $\phi(x) = a + bx$, we say the regression of Y on X is linear.   When the regression of Y on X is linear, the constants a and b have simple values, which will now be determined. It will be assumed that neither σ_1^2 nor σ_2^2, the variances of X and Y, is zero.   From

$$E(Y|x) = \frac{\int_{-\infty}^{\infty} yf(x, y)\, dy}{f_1(x)} = a + bx$$

we have

(1) $$\int_{-\infty}^{\infty} yf(x, y)\, dy = (a + bx)f_1(x).$$

If both members of Equation (1) are integrated on x, it is seen that

$$E(Y) = a + bE(X),$$

or

(2) $$\mu_2 = a + b\mu_1,$$

where $\mu_1 = E(X)$ and $\mu_2 = E(Y)$.   If both members of Equation (1) are first multiplied by x and then integrated on x, we have

$$E(XY) = aE(X) + bE(X^2),$$

or

(3) $$\rho\sigma_1\sigma_2 + \mu_1\mu_2 = a\mu_1 + b(\sigma_1^2 + \mu_1^2),$$

where $\rho\sigma_1\sigma_2$ is the covariance of X and Y.   The simultaneous solution of Equations (2) and (3) yields

$$a = \mu_2 - \rho\frac{\sigma_2}{\sigma_1}\mu_1 \quad \text{and} \quad b = \rho\frac{\sigma_2}{\sigma_1}.$$

That is,

$$\phi(x) = E(Y|x) = \mu_2 + \rho\frac{\sigma_2}{\sigma_1}(x - \mu_1)$$

is the regression function of Y on X.   If the regression function $\psi(y)$ of X on Y is linear, then that regression function is

$$\psi(y) = E(X|y) = \mu_1 + \rho\frac{\sigma_1}{\sigma_2}(y - \mu_2).$$

The mean, $E(Y|x)$, of a conditional distribution of Y, given $X = x$, when the regression function of Y on X is linear, has been investigated. Let us now turn to the variance of that conditional distribution.   The variance is

(4)
$$E\{[Y - E(Y|x)]^2|x\} = \int_{-\infty}^{\infty} \left[y - \mu_2 - \rho\frac{\sigma_2}{\sigma_1}(x - \mu_1)\right]^2 h(y|x)\, dy$$

$$= \frac{\int_{-\infty}^{\infty} \left[(y - \mu_2) - \rho\frac{\sigma_2}{\sigma_1}(x - \mu_1)\right]^2 f(x, y)\, dy}{f_1(x)}$$

when the random variables are of the continuous type. This variance is non-negative and is at most a function of x alone. If then, it is multiplied by $f_1(x)$ and integrated on x, the result obtained will be non-negative. This result is

$$\int_{-\infty}^{\infty}\int_{-\infty}^{\infty}\left[(y-\mu_2)-\rho\frac{\sigma_2}{\sigma_1}(x-\mu_1)\right]^2 f(x,y)\,dy\,dx$$

$$=\int_{-\infty}^{\infty}\int_{-\infty}^{\infty}\left[(y-\mu_2)^2-2\rho\frac{\sigma_2}{\sigma_1}(y-\mu_2)(x-\mu_1)+\rho^2\frac{\sigma_2{}^2}{\sigma_1{}^2}(x-\mu_1)^2\right]f(x,y)\,dy\,dx$$

$$=E[(Y-\mu_2)^2]-2\rho\frac{\sigma_2}{\sigma_1}E[(X-\mu_1)(Y-\mu_2)]+\rho^2\frac{\sigma_2{}^2}{\sigma_1{}^2}E[(X-\mu_1)^2]$$

$$=\sigma_2{}^2-2\rho\frac{\sigma_2}{\sigma_1}\rho\sigma_1\sigma_2+\rho^2\frac{\sigma_2{}^2}{\sigma_1{}^2}\sigma_1{}^2$$

$$=\sigma_2{}^2-2\rho^2\sigma_2{}^2+\rho^2\sigma_2{}^2=\sigma_2{}^2(1-\rho^2)\geq 0.$$

That is, if the variance (4) is denoted by $k(x)$, then $E[k(X)]=\sigma_2{}^2(1-\rho^2)\geq 0$. Accordingly $\rho^2\leq 1$, or $-1\leq\rho\leq 1$.

Suppose that the variance, expression (4), is positive but not a function of x; that is, the variance is a constant $k>0$. Now if k is multiplied by $f_1(x)$ and integrated on x, the result is k, so that $k=\sigma_2{}^2(1-\rho^2)$. Thus, in this case, the variance of each conditional distribution of Y, given $X=x$, is $\sigma_2{}^2(1-\rho^2)$. If $\rho=0$, the variance of each conditional distribution of Y, given $X=x$, is $\sigma_2{}^2$, the variance of the marginal distribution of Y. On the other hand, if ρ^2 is near one, the variance of each conditional distribution of Y, given $X=x$, is relatively small, and there is a high concentration of the probability for this conditional distribution near the mean $E(Y|x)=\mu_2+\rho(\sigma_2/\sigma_1)(x-\mu_1)$.

It should be pointed out that if the random variables X and Y in the preceding discussion are taken to be of the discrete type, the results just obtained are valid.

This section will conclude with a definition and an illustrative example.

Let $f(x,y)$ denote the joint p.d.f. of the two random variables X and Y. If $E(e^{t_1 X+t_2 Y})$ exists for $-h_1<t_1<h_1$, $-h_2<t_2<h_2$, where h_1 and h_2 are positive, it is denoted by $M_{X,Y}(t_1,t_2)$ and is called the *moment-generating function* of the joint distribution of X and Y. As in the case of one random variable, the moment-generating function $M_{X,Y}(t_1,t_2)$ completely determines the joint distribution of X and Y, and hence the marginal distributions of X and Y. In fact

$$M_{X,Y}(t_1,0)=E(e^{t_1 X})=M_X(t_1),$$

and

$$M_{X,Y}(0,t_2)=E(e^{t_2 Y})=M_Y(t_2).$$

In addition, in the case of random variables of the continuous type,

$$\frac{\partial^{k+m} M_{X,Y}(t_1, t_2)}{\partial t_1{}^k \partial t_2{}^m} = \int_{-\infty}^{\infty} \int_{-\infty}^{\infty} x^k y^m e^{t_1 x + t_2 y} f(x, y) \, dx \, dy,$$

so that

$$\frac{\partial^{k+m} M_{X,Y}(t_1, t_2)}{\partial t_1{}^k \partial t_2{}^m}\bigg|_{t_1 = t_2 = 0} = \int_{-\infty}^{\infty} \int_{-\infty}^{\infty} x^k y^m f(x, y) \, dx \, dy = E(X^k Y^m).$$

For instance, in a simplified notation which appears to be clear,

$$\mu_1 = E(X) = \frac{\partial M(0, 0)}{\partial t_1}, \quad \mu_2 = E(Y) = \frac{\partial M(0, 0)}{\partial t_2},$$

(5) $\sigma_1{}^2 = E(X^2) - \mu_1{}^2 = \dfrac{\partial^2 M(0, 0)}{\partial t_1{}^2} - \mu_1{}^2, \quad \sigma_2{}^2 = E(Y^2) - \mu_2{}^2 = \dfrac{\partial^2 M(0, 0)}{\partial t_2{}^2} - \mu_2{}^2,$

$$E[(X - \mu_1)(Y - \mu_2)] = \frac{\partial^2 M(0, 0)}{\partial t_1 \partial t_2} - \mu_1 \mu_2.$$

It is fairly obvious that these results hold if X and Y are random variables of the discrete type.   An illustrative example follows.

EXAMPLE 2.   Let the discrete-type random variables X and Y have the joint p.d.f.

$$f(x, y) = \frac{n!}{x! y! (n - x - y)!} p_1{}^x p_2{}^y p_3{}^{n-(x+y)}$$

where n is a positive integer, x and y are non-negative integers with $x + y \leq n$, and p_1, p_2, p_3 are positive proper fractions with $p_1 + p_2 + p_3 = 1$; and let $f(x, y)$ be zero elsewhere.   That the non-negative function $f(x, y)$ is a p.d.f. follows from the fact that

$$\sum_y \sum_x f(x, y) = \sum_{y=0}^{n} \sum_{x=0}^{n-y} \frac{n!}{x! y! (n - x - y)!} p_1{}^x p_2{}^y p_3{}^{n-(x+y)}$$

$$= (p_1 + p_2 + p_3)^n = 1.$$

The moment-generating function of this joint distribution is

$$M_{X,Y}(t_1, t_2) = \sum_{y=0}^{n} \sum_{x=0}^{n-y} \frac{n!}{x! y! (n - x - y)!} (p_1 e^{t_1})^x (p_2 e^{t_2})^y p_3{}^{n-(x+y)}$$

$$= (p_1 e^{t_1} + p_2 e^{t_2} + p_3)^n$$

for all real values of t_1 and t_2.   For this distribution, formulas (5) become

$$\mu_1 = np_1, \quad \mu_2 = np_2,$$

(6) $\sigma_1{}^2 = np_1(1 - p_1), \quad \sigma_2{}^2 = np_2(1 - p_2),$

$$E[(X - \mu_1)(Y - \mu_2)] = -np_1 p_2.$$

Verification of formulas (6) is assigned to Exercise 11.4.   If, momentarily, we accept these results, the correlation coefficient of X and Y is

$$\rho = \frac{-np_1 p_2}{\sqrt{np_1(1 - p_1) np_2(1 - p_2)}} = -\sqrt{\frac{p_1 p_2}{(1 - p_1)(1 - p_2)}}.$$

Furthermore the moment-generating functions of the marginal distributions of X and Y are respectively

$$M_X(t_1) = M_{X,Y}(t_1, 0) = (p_1 e^{t_1} + p_2 + p_3)^n$$
$$= (1 - p_1 + p_1 e^{t_1})^n,$$

and

$$M_Y(t_2) = M_{X,Y}(0, t_2) = (p_1 + p_2 e^{t_2} + p_3)^n$$
$$= (1 - p_2 + p_2 e^{t_2})^n.$$

Thus X has a marginal distribution with a binomial p.d.f. having parameters n and p_1; and Y has a marginal distribution with a binomial p.d.f. having parameters n and p_2. On this account, we call a joint p.d.f. of the form $f(x, y)$ in this example a joint binomial p.d.f., or more simply, a *multinomial* p.d.f. A generalization of this p.d.f. will be made in Section 11.4.

A concrete interpretation can be given to the joint p.d.f. $f(x, y)$ of this example which is quite similar to the interpretation of the binomial p.d.f. given in Example 4, page 50. A random experiment is to be repeated n independent times, and on each repetition the experiment will terminate in one of three mutually exclusive ways, say, success (A_1), indifference (A_2), or failure (A_3). Assume further that the probability p_1 of success (A_1) and the probability p_2 of indifference (A_2) are the same on each repetition of the experiment, so that the probability of failure (A_3) on each repetition is $p_3 = 1 - p_1 - p_2$. Then $f(x, y)$ is the probability of exactly x successes (A_1), y indifferences (A_2), and hence $n - x - y$ failures (A_3) in these n independent repetitions of the experiment.

Exercises

11.1. Let the random variables X and Y have the joint p.d.f.

(a) $f(x, y) = \frac{1}{3}$, $(x, y) = (0, 0), (1, 1), (2, 2)$, zero elsewhere;
(b) $f(x, y) = \frac{1}{3}$, $(x, y) = (0, 2), (1, 1), (2, 0)$, zero elsewhere;
(c) $f(x, y) = \frac{1}{3}$, $(x, y) = (0, 0), (1, 1), (2, 0)$, zero elsewhere.

In each case compute the correlation coefficient of X and Y. Are X and Y stochastically independent or dependent?

11.2. Let $f(x, y) = 2$, $0 < x < y$, $0 < y < 1$, zero elsewhere, be the joint p.d.f. of X and Y. Show that the regression functions of Y on X and X on Y are respectively $(1 + x)/2$, $0 < x < 1$, and $y/2$, $0 < y < 1$. Show that the correlation coefficient of X and Y is $\rho = \frac{1}{2}$.

11.3. Show that the variance of the conditional distribution of Y, given $X = x$, in Exercise 11.2, is $(1 - x)^2/12$, $0 < x < 1$, and that the variance of the conditional distribution of X, given $Y = y$, is $y^2/12$, $0 < y < 1$.

11.4. Verify formulas (6) of this section.

11.5. Let X and Y be random variables with $\mu_1 = 1$, $\mu_2 = 4$, $\sigma_1^2 = 4$, $\sigma_2^2 = 6$, $\rho = \frac{1}{2}$. Find the mean and variance of $Z = 3X - 2Y$.

11.6. Let $X_1, X_2, \cdots, X_n$ be random variables with means μ_i, variances σ_i^2, and correlation coefficients ρ_{ij}. If $k_1, k_2, \cdots, k_n$ are constants, show that the mean and variance of $Y = k_1X_1 + k_2X_2 + \cdots + k_nX_n$ are $\mu_Y = \sum_1^n k_i\mu_i$ and $\sigma_Y^2 = \sum_1^n k_i^2\sigma_i^2$ $+ 2\sum_{j=2}^n \sum_{i=1}^{j-1} k_ik_j\rho_{ij}\sigma_i\sigma_j$, respectively.   Compare these results with those of Example 5, page 51.

11.7. Let X and Y be stochastically independent random variables with means μ_1, μ_2 and variances σ_1^2, σ_2^2. Determine the correlation coefficient of X and $Z = X - Y$ in terms of μ_1, μ_2, σ_1^2, σ_2^2.

11.8. Let X and Y be random variables with means μ_1, μ_2; variances σ_1^2, σ_2^2; and correlation coefficient ρ. Show that the correlation coefficient of $W = aX + b$, $a > 0$, and $Z = cY + d$, $c > 0$, is ρ.

11.9. Let X and Y denote stochastically independent random variables. Prove that

$$M_{X,Y}(t_1, t_2) = M_{X,Y}(t_1, 0)M_{X,Y}(0, t_2) = M_X(t_1)M_Y(t_2).$$

We remark that if, conversely, $M_{X,Y}(t_1, t_2)$ can be factored into the product of a nontrivial function of t_1 alone and a nontrivial function of t_2 alone, then X and Y are stochastically independent. The proof of this assertion is quite difficult.

11.10. Let X and Y have the joint p.d.f. $f(x, y) = 1$, $-x < y < x$, $0 < x < 1$, zero elsewhere. Show that, on the set of positive probability density, the graph of the regression function of Y on X is a straight line, while the graph of the regression function of X on Y is not a straight line. From $E(Y|x)$ determine ρ. Are X and Y stochastically independent or dependent?

11.11. Let X_1, X_2 be a random sample from the normal distribution $n(x; 0, 1)$. Let $Y = X_1 + X_2$ and $Z = X_1^2 + X_2^2$. Show that the moment-generating function of the joint distribution of Y and Z is

$$E[e^{t_1(X_1+X_2)+t_2(X_1^2+X_2^2)}] = \frac{e^{t_1^2/(1-2t_2)}}{1 - 2t_2}$$

for $-\infty < t_1 < \infty$, $-\infty < t_2 < \frac{1}{2}$. Find the correlation coefficient of Y and Z.

11.2. The Bivariate Normal Distribution. In Exercise 3.7, page 47, there was investigated a joint p.d.f. with functional form

$$g(u, v) = \frac{1}{2\pi\sqrt{1 - \rho^2}}e^{-\frac{1}{2(1-\rho^2)}[u^2-2\rho uv+v^2]}. \qquad \begin{array}{c} -\infty < u < \infty \\ -\infty < v < \infty \\ -1 < \rho < 1 \end{array}$$

That the non-negative function $g(u, v)$ actually is a joint p.d.f. can be seen as follows: Define $g_1(u)$ by

$$g_1(u) = \int_{-\infty}^{\infty} \frac{1}{2\pi\sqrt{1 - \rho^2}}e^{-\frac{1}{2(1-\rho^2)}[u^2-2\rho uv+v^2]}\, dv.$$

Now $v^2 - 2\rho uv + u^2 = (v - \rho u)^2 + (1 - \rho^2)u^2$. Thus

$$g_1(u) = \frac{1}{\sqrt{2\pi}}e^{-\frac{u^2}{2}}\int_{-\infty}^{\infty} \frac{1}{\sqrt{2\pi}\sqrt{1 - \rho^2}}e^{-\frac{(v-\rho u)^2}{2(1-\rho^2)}}\, dv.$$

For the purpose of this integration, the integrand may be considered a normal p.d.f. with mean ρu and variance $(1 - \rho^2)$. Thus the integral is equal to one and

$$g_1(u) = \frac{1}{\sqrt{2\pi}} e^{-\frac{u^2}{2}}, \quad -\infty < u < \infty.$$

Since $\displaystyle\int_{-\infty}^{\infty} g_1(u)\, du = 1$, the non-negative function $g(u, v)$ is a joint p.d.f. of two random variables U and V. Moreover, it has just been seen that U has a marginal p.d.f. that is $n(u; 0, 1)$. In like manner, the marginal p.d.f. of V is $n(v; 0, 1)$.

Let us define the random variables X and Y by

$$U = \frac{X - a}{b}, \quad b > 0, \quad \text{and} \quad V = \frac{Y - c}{d}, \quad d > 0.$$

Since $E(U) = E(V) = 0$ and $E(U^2) = E(V^2) = 1$, then X has mean $\mu_1 = a$ and variance $\sigma_1^2 = b^2$, and Y has mean $\mu_2 = c$ and variance $\sigma_2^2 = d^2$. The Jacobian of the associated one-to-one transformation is $J = 1/bd = 1/\sigma_1\sigma_2 > 0$. The joint p.d.f. of X and Y is

$$f(x, y) = \frac{1}{2\pi\sigma_1\sigma_2\sqrt{1 - \rho^2}} e^{-\frac{1}{2(1-\rho^2)}\left[\frac{(x-\mu_1)^2}{\sigma_1^2} - 2\rho\frac{(x-\mu_1)(y-\mu_2)}{\sigma_1\sigma_2} + \frac{(y-\mu_2)^2}{\sigma_2^2}\right]},$$

where $-\infty < x < \infty$, $-\infty < y < \infty$. A joint p.d.f. of this form is called a joint *normal* p.d.f., and the random variables X and Y are said to have a *bivariate normal distribution*. The marginal distributions of U and V make it clear that X has a marginal distribution that is $n(x; \mu_1, \sigma_1^2)$, and that Y has a marginal distribution that is $n(y; \mu_2, \sigma_2^2)$. It will now be shown that the number ρ is actually the correlation coefficient of X and Y.

Now the correlation coefficient of X and Y is

$$E\left[\frac{(X - \mu_1)(Y - \mu_2)}{\sigma_1\sigma_2}\right] = \int_{-\infty}^{\infty} \int_{-\infty}^{\infty} \frac{(x - \mu_1)(y - \mu_2)}{\sigma_1\sigma_2} f(x, y)\, dx\, dy.$$

The change of variables effected by $u = (x - \mu_1)/\sigma_1$ and $v = (y - \mu_2)/\sigma_2$, with $J = \sigma_1\sigma_2 > 0$, enables us to write the right-hand member of the preceding equation in the form

$$\int_{-\infty}^{\infty} \int_{-\infty}^{\infty} uv \frac{1}{2\pi\sqrt{1 - \rho^2}} e^{-\frac{1}{2(1-\rho^2)}[u^2 - 2\rho uv + v^2]}\, du\, dv$$

$$= \int_{-\infty}^{\infty} \frac{ue^{-\frac{u^2}{2}}}{\sqrt{2\pi}} \left\{ \int_{-\infty}^{\infty} \frac{v}{\sqrt{2\pi}\sqrt{1 - \rho^2}} e^{-\frac{(v-\rho u)^2}{2(1-\rho^2)}}\, dv \right\} du.$$

For the purpose of evaluating the integral within the braces, note that the integrand may be interpreted as the product of v and a normal p.d.f. in v

with mean ρu and variance $(1 - \rho^2)$. That is, the integral within braces is equal to the mean ρu. Hence the correlation coefficient of X and Y is

$$\rho \int_{-\infty}^{\infty} \frac{u^2}{\sqrt{2\pi}} e^{-\frac{u^2}{2}} du = \rho.$$

That is, the number ρ, $-1 < \rho < 1$, that appears in the bivariate normal p.d.f. is the correlation coefficient of X and Y. Incidentally, since

$$E\left[\frac{(X - \mu_1)(Y - \mu_2)}{\sigma_1 \sigma_2}\right] = E[UV],$$

we have proved that the correlation coefficient of U and V is equal to ρ.

We now consider some conditional distributions. Specifically it will be shown that the conditional distribution of Y, given $X = x$, is itself a normal distribution having mean $E(Y|x) = \mu_2 + \rho(\sigma_2/\sigma_1)(x - \mu_1)$ and variance $\sigma_2^2(1 - \rho^2)$. Symmetry will then imply that also the conditional distribution of X, given $Y = y$, is a normal distribution with mean $E(X|y) = \mu_1 + \rho(\sigma_1/\sigma_2)(y - \mu_2)$ and variance $\sigma_1^2(1 - \rho^2)$. The conditional p.d.f. of Y, given $X = x$, is

$$h(y|x) = \frac{\sigma_1 \sqrt{2\pi}}{2\pi \sigma_1 \sigma_2 \sqrt{1 - \rho^2}} \frac{e^{-\frac{1}{2(1-\rho^2)}\left[\frac{(x-\mu_1)^2}{\sigma_1^2} - 2\rho\frac{(x-\mu_1)(y-\mu_2)}{\sigma_1 \sigma_2} + \frac{(y-\mu_2)^2}{\sigma_2^2}\right]}}{e^{-\frac{(x-\mu_1)^2}{2\sigma_1^2}}}$$

$$= \frac{1}{\sqrt{2\pi}\sigma_2 \sqrt{1 - \rho^2}} e^{-\frac{1}{2(1-\rho^2)}\left[\frac{(y-\mu_2)^2}{\sigma_2^2} - 2\rho\frac{(x-\mu_1)(y-\mu_2)}{\sigma_1 \sigma_2} + \rho^2\frac{(x-\mu_1)^2}{\sigma_1^2}\right]}$$

$$= \frac{1}{\sqrt{2\pi}\sigma_2 \sqrt{1 - \rho^2}} e^{-\frac{1}{2\sigma_2^2(1-\rho^2)}\left[y - \mu_2 - \rho\frac{\sigma_2}{\sigma_1}(x-\mu_1)\right]^2}.$$

For each given x, $-\infty < x < \infty$, $h(y|x)$ is a normal p.d.f. with mean $\mu_2 + \rho(\sigma_2/\sigma_1)(x - \mu_1)$ and variance $\sigma_2^2(1 - \rho^2)$. Thus, with a bivariate normal distribution, the regression function of Y on X is linear, and from symmetry, the regression function of X on Y is linear. Although the mean of the conditional distribution of Y, given $X = x$, depends upon x (unless $\rho = 0$), the variance of this conditional distribution is the same for all real values of x.

The reader may wonder why use was not made of the moment-generating function of a bivariate normal distribution. Our answer is that, for the problems under consideration, it was easier to avoid computing

$$M_{X,Y}(t_1, t_2) = \int_{-\infty}^{\infty} \int_{-\infty}^{\infty} e^{t_1 x + t_2 y} \frac{1}{2\pi \sigma_1 \sigma_2 \sqrt{1 - \rho^2}} e^{-\frac{1}{2}q} dx\, dy$$

where

$$q = \frac{1}{1 - \rho^2}\left[\frac{(x - \mu_1)^2}{\sigma_1^2} - 2\rho\frac{(x - \mu_1)(y - \mu_2)}{\sigma_1 \sigma_2} + \frac{(y - \mu_2)^2}{\sigma_2^2}\right].$$

Without the use of the algebra of matrices, it is indeed a tedious chore to show that

$$M_{X,Y}(t_1, t_2) = e^{t_1\mu_1 + t_2\mu_2 + \frac{\sigma_1^2 t_1^2 + 2\rho\sigma_1\sigma_2 t_1 t_2 + \sigma_2^2 t_2^2}{2}}.$$

In Section 11.3 there will be investigated a test of the hypothesis that two random variables having a bivariate normal distribution are stochastically independent. The following theorem is essential to that test.

THEOREM. Let X and Y have a bivariate normal distribution with means μ_1 and μ_2, variances σ_1^2 and σ_2^2, and correlation coefficient ρ. Then X and Y are stochastically independent if, and only if, $\rho = 0$.

PROOF. If $\rho = 0$, it is obvious that the joint p.d.f. $f(x, y) = f_1(x)f_2(y)$, where $f_1(x)$ is $n(x; \mu_1, \sigma_1^2)$ and $f_2(y)$ is $n(y; \mu_2, \sigma_2^2)$. Accordingly X and Y are stochastically independent. On the other hand, if X and Y are stochastically independent, then $f(x, y) = f_1(x)f_2(y)$ for all real values of x and y. In particular, $f(\mu_1, \mu_2) = f_1(\mu_1)f_2(\mu_2)$ or

$$\frac{1}{2\pi\sigma_1\sigma_2\sqrt{1 - \rho^2}} = \frac{1}{\sigma_1\sqrt{2\pi}}\frac{1}{\sigma_2\sqrt{2\pi}}.$$

Thus $\sqrt{1 - \rho^2} = 1$ and $\rho = 0$.

As a matter of fact, if any two random variables are stochastically independent and have positive standard deviations, the correlation coefficient of the two variables is zero; for as soon as X and Y are stochastically independent, we have

$$E[(X - \mu_1)(Y - \mu_2)] = E(X - \mu_1)E(Y - \mu_2) = 0,$$

regardless of the distributions of the random variables. However the converse is not in general true as was seen in Exercises 11.1(c) and 11.10, page 216. The importance of the theorem lies in the fact that we now know when, and only when, two random variables having a bivariate normal distribution are stochastically independent.

Exercises

11.12. Let X and Y have a bivariate normal distribution with parameters $\mu_1 = 3$, $\mu_2 = 1$, $\sigma_1^2 = 16$, $\sigma_2^2 = 25$, and $\rho = 3/5$. Determine the following probabilities:

(a) $Pr(3 < Y < 8)$,
(b) $Pr(3 < Y < 8 | x = 7)$,
(c) $Pr(-3 < X < 3)$,
(d) $Pr(-3 < X < 3 | y = -4)$.

11.13. Let U and V be stochastically independent random variables, each having a normal distribution with mean zero and variance one. Show that the moment-generating function $E[e^{t(UV)}]$ of the product UV is $(1 - t^2)^{-1/2}$, $-1 < t < 1$.

11.14. Assume that $M_{X,Y}(t_1, t_2)$, as given in this section, is the moment-generating function of the bivariate normal distribution with parameters μ_1, μ_2, σ_1^2, σ_2^2, and ρ. If X and Y are random variables with this bivariate distribution, show that $Z = aX + bY$ is $n(z; a\mu_1 + b\mu_2, a^2\sigma_1^2 + 2ab\rho\sigma_1\sigma_2 + b^2\sigma_2^2)$, where a and b are non-zero constants.

Hint: Find $M_Z(t) = E[e^{t(aX+bY)}]$.

11.15. Let X and Y have a bivariate normal distribution with parameters $\mu_1 = 25$, $\mu_2 = 35$, $\sigma_1^2 = 4$, $\sigma_2^2 = 16$, and $\rho = 17/32$. If $Z = 3X - 2Y$, find $Pr(-2 < Z < 19)$ by using the result of Exercise 11.14.

11.16. Let $f(x, y) = \dfrac{1}{2\pi}e^{-\frac{1}{2}(x^2+y^2)}[1 + xye^{-\frac{1}{2}(x^2+y^2-2)}]$, where $-\infty < x < \infty$, $-\infty < y < \infty$. If $f(x, y)$ is a joint p.d.f., it is not a normal bivariate p.d.f. Show that $f(x, y)$ actually is a joint p.d.f. and that each marginal p.d.f. is normal. Thus the fact that each marginal p.d.f. is normal does not imply that the joint p.d.f. is bivariate normal.

11.3. A Test of Stochastic Independence. Let X and Y have a bivariate normal distribution with means μ_1 and μ_2, variances σ_1^2 and σ_2^2, and correlation coefficient ρ. It is desired to test the null hypothesis that X and Y are stochastically independent, against the alternative hypothesis that X and Y are stochastically dependent; that is, to test $H_0: \rho = 0$ against $H_1: \rho \neq 0$. A likelihood ratio test will be used. Here

$$\Omega = \{(\mu_1, \mu_2, \sigma_1^2, \sigma_2^2, \rho); -\infty < \mu_i < \infty, 0 < \sigma_i^2 < \infty, -1 < \rho < 1\}$$

and

$$\omega = \{(\mu_1, \mu_2, \sigma_1^2, \sigma_2^2, \rho); -\infty < \mu_i < \infty, 0 < \sigma_i^2 < \infty, \rho = 0\}.$$

Let (X_1, Y_1), (X_2, Y_2), $\cdots$, (X_n, Y_n) denote a random sample (see page 117) of size $n > 2$ from the bivariate normal distribution. Then the joint p.d.f. of these $2n$ random variables is, for points in Ω,

$$L(\Omega) = \left(\frac{1}{2\pi\sigma_1\sigma_2\sqrt{1 - \rho^2}}\right)^n e^{-\frac{1}{2}\sum_1^n q_i}$$

where

$$q_i = \frac{1}{1 - \rho^2}\left[\left(\frac{x_i - \mu_1}{\sigma_1}\right)^2 - 2\rho\left(\frac{x_i - \mu_1}{\sigma_1}\right)\left(\frac{y_i - \mu_2}{\sigma_2}\right) + \left(\frac{y_i - \mu_2}{\sigma_2}\right)^2\right].$$

The joint p.d.f. is, for points in ω,

$$L(\omega) = \left(\frac{1}{2\pi\sigma_1\sigma_2}\right)^n e^{-\frac{1}{2}\sum_1^n q'_i}$$

where

$$q'_i = \left(\frac{x_i - \mu_1}{\sigma_1}\right)^2 + \left(\frac{y_i - \mu_2}{\sigma_2}\right)^2.$$

We define the following symbols

$$\bar{x} = \frac{1}{n}\sum_1^n x_i, \quad \bar{y} = \frac{1}{n}\sum_1^n y_i, \quad v_1 = \sum_1^n (x_i - \bar{x})^2,$$

$$v_2 = \sum_1^n (y_i - \bar{y})^2 \quad \text{and} \quad v = \sum_1^n (x_i - \bar{x})(y_i - \bar{y}).$$

The likelihood function $L(\omega)$ has essentially been maximized on page 122. This function attains its maximum when we take μ_1, μ_2, σ_1^2, and σ_2^2 to be $\bar{x}$, $\bar{y}$, v_1/n, and v_2/n, respectively. The maximum is

$$L(\hat{\omega}) = \left(\frac{ne^{-1}}{2\pi\sqrt{v_1 v_2}}\right)^n.$$

The problem of maximizing $L(\Omega)$ is a little more tedious. If the partial derivatives of $\ln L(\Omega)$ with respect to μ_1 and μ_2 are equated to zero, one obtains immediately that the solutions for μ_1 and μ_2 are respectively $\bar{x}$ and $\bar{y}$. If the partial derivatives of $\ln L(\Omega)$ with respect to σ_1^2 and σ_2^2 are equated to zero, these two equations may be used to show that

$$\frac{v_1}{\sigma_1^2} = \frac{v_2}{\sigma_2^2} = \frac{n(1 - \rho^2)}{1 - \dfrac{\rho v}{\sqrt{v_1 v_2}}}.$$

If these relations are used in the equation obtained by equating to zero the partial derivative of $\ln L(\Omega)$ with respect to ρ, then the simultaneous solution for μ_1, μ_2, σ_1^2, σ_2^2, and ρ is $\bar{x}$, $\bar{y}$, v_1/n, v_2/n, and $v/\sqrt{v_1 v_2}$. These numbers maximize $L(\Omega)$ and the maximum is

$$L(\hat{\Omega}) = \left(\frac{ne^{-1}}{2\pi\sqrt{v_1 v_2}\ \sqrt{1 - \dfrac{v^2}{v_1 v_2}}}\right)^n.$$

Accordingly

$$\lambda = \frac{L(\hat{\omega})}{L(\hat{\Omega})} = \left(1 - \frac{v^2}{v_1 v_2}\right)^{n/2}.$$

The statistic defined by $v/\sqrt{v_1 v_2}$ is

$$R = \frac{V}{\sqrt{V_1 V_2}} = \frac{\sum_1^n (X_i - \bar{X})(Y_i - \bar{Y})}{\sqrt{\sum_1^n (X_i - \bar{X})^2 \sum_1^n (Y_i - \bar{Y})^2}}.$$

This statistic R is called the *correlation coefficient* of the random sample (X_i, Y_i), $i = 1, 2, \cdots, n$. The likelihood ratio principle calls for the rejection of H_0 if $\lambda \leq \lambda_0$. The significance level of this test is

$$\begin{aligned}
\alpha &= Pr[(1 - R^2)^{n/2} \leq \lambda_0; H_0] \\
&= Pr[R^2 \geq 1 - \lambda_0^{2/n}; H_0] \\
&= Pr[|R| \geq c; H_0],
\end{aligned}$$

where $c = \sqrt{1 - \lambda_0^{2/n}}$. Thus the test of H_0 against H_1 may be based on the correlation coefficient R. To determine a value of c for a satisfactory significance level, it will be necessary to obtain the distribution of R when H_0 is true.

The distribution of R represents a very difficult problem in random sampling distribution theory. To aid the student in following the argument, the discussion will be broken into three parts. At the outset of each part, we shall endeavor to explain just what is to be accomplished in that part.

Part I. In this part, it will first be shown, when $\rho = 0$, that the statistic $R = V/\sqrt{V_1 V_2}$ is stochastically independent of the four statistics $\bar{X} = \sum_1^n X_i/n, \bar{Y} = \sum_1^n Y_i/n, V_1 = \sum_1^n (X_i - \bar{X})^2$, and $V_2 = \sum_1^n (Y_i - \bar{Y})^2$. With $R\sqrt{V_1 V_2} = V$, it will then follow, from this stochastic independence, that

$$E[(R\sqrt{V_1 V_2})^k] = E[V^k]$$

or

$$E[R^k]E[(\sqrt{V_1 V_2})^k] = E[V^k]$$

or

$$E[R^k] = \frac{E[V^k]}{E[(V_1 V_2)^{k/2}]}.$$

That is, $E(R^k)$ may be computed by taking the ratio of $E(V^k)$ to $E[(V_1 V_2)^{k/2}]$.

We shall appeal to sufficiency and completeness to establish the stochastic independence of R and the four statistics $\bar{X}$, $\bar{Y}$, V_1, and V_2. When $\rho = 0$, the joint p.d.f. of X and Y depends upon four parameters, μ_1, μ_2, σ_1^2, and σ_2^2. The statistics $\bar{X}$, $\bar{Y}$, V_1, and V_2 are joint sufficient statistics for these parameters, and the joint p.d.f. of the four statistics is complete. If the distribution of R does not depend upon the parameters μ_1, μ_2, σ_1^2, and σ_2^2, then, in accordance with page 124, R is stochastically independent of the four joint sufficient statistics. Consider the moment-generating function $M_R(t)$ of R. We have, when $\rho = 0$,

$$M_R(t) = \int_{-\infty}^{\infty} \cdots \int_{-\infty}^{\infty} \frac{e^{\,t\frac{\sum_1^n (x_i-\bar{x})(y_i-\bar{y})}{\sqrt{\sum_1^n (x_i-\bar{x})^2 \sum_1^n (y_i-\bar{y})^2}} - \frac{1}{2}\sum_1^n q'_i}}{(2\pi\sigma_1\sigma_2)^n}\, dx_1\, dy_1 \cdots dx_n\, dy_n$$

where

$$q'_i = \left(\frac{x_i - \mu_1}{\sigma_1}\right)^2 + \left(\frac{y_i - \mu_2}{\sigma_2}\right)^2.$$

Without evaluating the integral, the change of variables $w_i = (x_i - \mu_1)/\sigma_1$, $z_i = (y_i - \mu_2)/\sigma_2$, $i = 1, 2, \cdots, n$, shows that

$$M_R(t) = \int_{-\infty}^{\infty} \cdots \int_{-\infty}^{\infty} \frac{e^{\dfrac{t\frac{\sum\limits_{1}^{n}(w_i-\bar{w})(z_i-\bar{z})}{\sqrt{\sum\limits_{1}^{n}(w_i-\bar{w})^2 \sum\limits_{1}^{n}(z_i-\bar{z})^2}} - \frac{1}{2}\sum\limits_{1}^{n}(w_i{}^2+z_i{}^2)}}{(2\pi)^n} \, dw_1 \, dz_1 \cdots dw_n \, dz_n$$

where $\bar{w} = \sum\limits_{1}^{n} w_i/n$ and $\bar{z} = \sum\limits_{1}^{n} z_i/n$. Then $M_R(t)$ certainly does not depend upon μ_1, μ_2, $\sigma_1{}^2$, and $\sigma_2{}^2$. Thus R is stochastically independent of $\bar{X}$, $\bar{Y}$, V_1, and V_2.

Part II. In this part of the argument, we shall compute the values of $E(V^k)$ and $E[(V_1 V_2)^{k/2}]$. In accordance with Part I we may then evaluate $E(R^k)$.

Since the distribution of R does not depend upon $\sigma_1{}^2$ and $\sigma_2{}^2$, we shall simplify matters by taking $\sigma_1{}^2 = \sigma_2{}^2 = 1$. This means that in the joint p.d.f. of X and Y, there are now only two parameters, μ_1 and μ_2, since $\sigma_1{}^2 = \sigma_2{}^2 = 1$, and $\rho = 0$. The statistic $V = \sum\limits_{1}^{n}(X_i - \bar{X})(Y_i - \bar{Y})$ has a moment-generating function (and hence a distribution) that does not depend upon μ_1 and μ_2 (Exercise 11.22). But $\bar{X}$ and $\bar{Y}$ are joint sufficient statistics for μ_1 and μ_2 (when $\sigma_1{}^2 = \sigma_2{}^2 = 1$ and $\rho = 0$) and the joint p.d.f. of $\bar{X}$ and $\bar{Y}$ is complete. Thus V is stochastically independent of $\bar{X}$ and $\bar{Y}$, and hence of $n(\bar{X} - \mu_1)(\bar{Y} - \mu_2)$. That is, in the identity

$$\sum_{1}^{n}(X_i - \mu_1)(Y_i - \mu_2) = \sum_{1}^{n}(X_i - \bar{X})(Y_i - \bar{Y}) + n(\bar{X} - \mu_1)(\bar{Y} - \mu_2)$$

the two terms in the right-hand member are stochastically independent random variables. Consider the left-hand member. In Exercise 11.13, page 220, it was proved that the moment-generating function of the product of two stochastically independent random variables having normal distributions with means zero and variances one is $(1 - t^2)^{-1/2}$, $-1 < t < 1$. The left-hand member of the identity is the sum of n such mutually stochastically independent products, and thus the moment-generating function of $\sum\limits_{1}^{n}(X_i - \mu_1)(Y_i - \mu_2)$ is $(1 - t^2)^{-n/2}$, $-1 < t < 1$. However the second term $n(\bar{X} - \mu_1)(\bar{Y} - \mu_2)$ of the right-hand member is also such a product and thus has a moment-generating function $(1 - t^2)^{-1/2}$, $-1 < t < 1$. The stochastic independence of $V = \sum\limits_{1}^{n}(X_i - \bar{X})(Y_i - \bar{Y})$ and $n(\bar{X} - \mu_1)(\bar{Y} - \mu_2)$ then implies that the moment-generating function of V is

$$M_V(t) = (1 - t^2)^{-\frac{n-1}{2}}, \quad -1 < t < 1.$$

Now

$$M_V(t) = M_V(0) + M'_V(0)t + M''_V(0)\frac{t^2}{2!} + \cdots$$

$$= 1 + tE(V) + \frac{t^2}{2!}E(V^2) + \cdots,$$

so that $E(V^k)$ is the coefficient of $t^k/k!$ in the expansion of $M_V(t)$ in powers of t. Here $M_V(t) = M_V(-t)$, so all derivatives of $M_V(t)$ of odd order vanish when $t = 0$. Accordingly $E(V) = E(V^3) = \cdots = 0 = E(V^k)$, k odd. Take k to be even, say, $k = 2m$, where m is a positive integer. If $(1 - t^2)^{-(n-1)/2}$, $-1 < t < 1$, is expanded by the binomial rule, the coefficient of $t^{2m} = (t^2)^m$ is

$$\frac{(n-1)(n+1)(n+3)\cdots(n+2m-3)}{2^m m!}.$$

Therefore the coefficient of $t^{2m}/(2m)!$ is

$$E(V^{2m}) = \frac{(n-1)(n+1)(n+3)\cdots(n+2m-3)(2m)!}{2^m m!}.$$

We turn now to an evaluation of $E[(V_1 V_2)^{k/2}]$. Since $E(V^k) = 0$ when k is odd, we need evaluate $E[(V_1 V_2)^{k/2}]$ only when k is even, say, $k = 2m$. Under our conditions, $V_1 = \sum_1^n (X_i - \bar{X})^2$ and $V_2 = \sum_1^n (Y_i - \bar{Y})^2$ are stochastically independent, and each (since $\sigma_1^2 = \sigma_2^2 = 1$) has a chi-square distribution with $n - 1$ degrees of freedom. Thus

$$E[(V_1 V_2)^{2m/2}] = E(V_1^m)E(V_2^m) = \left[\frac{\Gamma\left(\dfrac{n-1}{2} + m\right)2^m}{\Gamma\left(\dfrac{n-1}{2}\right)}\right]^2.$$

Finally, in accordance with Part I, when k is even, $E(R^k) = E(R^{2m})$ is equal to

$$E[(R^2)^m] = \frac{(n-1)(n+1)(n+3)\cdots(n+2m-3)(2m)!}{2^m m!} \frac{\left[\Gamma\left(\dfrac{n-1}{2}\right)\right]^2}{\left[\Gamma\left(\dfrac{n+2m-1}{2}\right)2^m\right]^2}$$

$$= \left\{\frac{\Gamma\left(\dfrac{n-1}{2}\right)}{\Gamma\left(\dfrac{n+2m-1}{2}\right)}\right\} \left\{\frac{\Gamma\left(\dfrac{n-1}{2}\right)\left(\dfrac{n-1}{2}\right)\left(\dfrac{n+1}{2}\right)\cdots\left(\dfrac{n+2m-3}{2}\right)}{\Gamma\left(\dfrac{n+2m-1}{2}\right)}\right\} \left\{\frac{(2m)!}{2^m m!}\right\}$$

$$= \left\{\frac{\Gamma\left(\dfrac{n-1}{2}\right)}{\Gamma\left(\dfrac{n+2m-1}{2}\right)}\right\} \{1\} \left\{\frac{(2m-1)(2m-3)\cdots 5\cdot 3\cdot 1}{2^m}\right\}$$

$$= \left\{ \frac{\Gamma\left(\dfrac{n-1}{2}\right)}{\Gamma\left(\dfrac{n+2m-1}{2}\right)} \right\} \left\{ \left(m - \frac{1}{2}\right)\left(m - \frac{3}{2}\right) \cdots \frac{5}{2} \cdot \frac{3}{2} \cdot \frac{1}{2} \right\}$$

$$= \frac{\Gamma\left(\dfrac{n-1}{2}\right)\Gamma\left(m + \dfrac{1}{2}\right)}{\Gamma\left(\dfrac{n+2m-1}{2}\right)\Gamma\left(\dfrac{1}{2}\right)}.$$

PART III. In this part the p.d.f. of R will be determined. Since λ is real for every positive integer n, the random variable $(1 - R^2)^{n/2}$, defined by λ, is real, and accordingly $R^2 \le 1$. In Part II, the expectation $E[(R^2)^m]$ was proved to be equal to a ratio of the product of two gamma functions to the product of two other gamma functions. We have encountered only one p.d.f., positive on the interval $(0, 1)$, in which gamma functions are involved. That is, the beta p.d.f. of Exercises 4.9, 4.10, and 4.11, page 73. We shall reconsider this p.d.f.

We have, using Z as the random variable,

$$g_1(z) = \frac{\Gamma(\alpha + \beta)}{\Gamma(\alpha)\Gamma(\beta)} z^{\alpha-1}(1 - z)^{\beta-1}, \quad 0 < z < 1, \quad \alpha > 0, \beta > 0,$$

$$= 0 \text{ elsewhere,}$$

to be a p.d.f. as established in Exercise 4.9, page 73. Thus

$$E(Z^m) = \frac{\Gamma(\alpha + \beta)}{\Gamma(\alpha)\Gamma(\beta)} \int_0^1 z^{m+\alpha-1}(1 - z)^{\beta-1} dz.$$

Since $g_1(z)$ is a p.d.f.,

$$\int_0^1 z^{\alpha-1}(1 - z)^{\beta-1} dz = \frac{\Gamma(\alpha)\Gamma(\beta)}{\Gamma(\alpha + \beta)}.$$

Then, upon replacing α by $m + \alpha$, we have

$$\int_0^1 z^{m+\alpha-1}(1 - z)^{\beta-1} dz = \frac{\Gamma(m + \alpha)\Gamma(\beta)}{\Gamma(m + \alpha + \beta)}.$$

Consequently

$$E(Z^m) = \frac{\Gamma(\alpha + \beta)}{\Gamma(\alpha)\Gamma(\beta)} \frac{\Gamma(m + \alpha)\Gamma(\beta)}{\Gamma(m + \alpha + \beta)} = \frac{\Gamma(\alpha + \beta)\Gamma(m + \alpha)}{\Gamma(\alpha)\Gamma(m + \alpha + \beta)}.$$

But this is precisely $E[(R^2)^m]$ if $\alpha = \frac{1}{2}$ and $\beta = (n - 2)/2$. Accordingly $E[(R^2)^m] = E(Z^m)$, $m = 1, 2, \cdots$, when $\alpha = \frac{1}{2}$ and $\beta = (n - 2)/2$. Thus Z and R^2 have the same moment-generating function and hence the same distribution. That is not, however, the solution to our problem. We want the p.d.f. of R and not that of R^2. In general, the p.d.f. of a random variable cannot be determined from that of its square. But here we are more fortunate. For having observed that $E(R^k) = 0$ for all odd positive integral values of k, we know that the graph of the p.d.f. of R is symmetric with respect to the vertical axis through the origin. Hence, if we find the p.d.f. of $W = \sqrt{Z}$, say, $g_2(w)$, $0 < w < 1$, then $g(r) = (\frac{1}{2})g_2(r)$, $-1 < r < 1$, zero elsewhere, is the p.d.f. of R. We have, with $\alpha = \frac{1}{2}$ and $\beta = (n - 2)/2$,

$$g_1(z) = \frac{\Gamma\left(\dfrac{n - 1}{2}\right)}{\Gamma\left(\dfrac{1}{2}\right)\Gamma\left(\dfrac{n - 2}{2}\right)} z^{\frac{1}{2} - 1}(1 - z)^{\frac{n-4}{2}}, \quad 0 < z < 1,$$

$$= 0 \text{ elsewhere.}$$

The one-to-one transformation $w = \sqrt{z}$ has the Jacobian $J = 2w$, $w > 0$. Thus

$$g_2(w) = \frac{\Gamma\left(\dfrac{n - 1}{2}\right)}{\Gamma\left(\dfrac{1}{2}\right)\Gamma\left(\dfrac{n - 2}{2}\right)} (w^2)^{\frac{1}{2} - 1}(1 - w^2)^{\frac{n-4}{2}}(2w), \quad 0 < w < 1,$$

$$= 0 \text{ elsewhere.}$$

Finally,

$$g(r) = \frac{1}{2}g_2(r) = \frac{\Gamma\left(\dfrac{n - 1}{2}\right)}{\Gamma\left(\dfrac{1}{2}\right)\Gamma\left(\dfrac{n - 2}{2}\right)} (1 - r^2)^{\frac{n-4}{2}}, \quad -1 < r < 1,$$

$$= 0 \text{ elsewhere.}$$

This completes the very lengthy determination of the p.d.f. of the statistic R when $\rho = 0$ and $n > 2$. If $n = 2$, the student may be interested in showing that R is a random variable of the discrete type.

The likelihood ratio test of the null hypothesis $H_0: \rho = 0$ against the alternative hypothesis $H_1: \rho \neq 0$ may be based on the statistic R. For a given positive integer n, the significance level of the test is α where

$$\frac{\alpha}{2} = \int_c^1 g(r) \, dr, \quad 0 < c < 1.$$

For example, if $n = 4$ and $\alpha = 0.05$, then

$$0.025 = \int_c^1 \frac{1}{2} \, dr$$

and $c = 0.95$. That is, the null hypothesis $\rho = 0$ is rejected at the

5 per cent level of significance if r, the observed value of R in a sample of size 4, is such that $|r| \geq 0.95$.

Exercises

11.17. Show that

$$R = \frac{\sum_{1}^{n}(X_i - \bar{X})(Y_i - \bar{Y})}{\sqrt{\sum_{1}^{n}(X_i - \bar{X})^2 \sum_{1}^{n}(Y_i - \bar{Y})^2}} = \frac{\sum_{1}^{n}X_iY_i - n\bar{X}\bar{Y}}{\sqrt{\left(\sum_{1}^{n}X_i^2 - n\bar{X}^2\right)\left(\sum_{1}^{n}Y_i^2 - n\bar{Y}^2\right)}}.$$

11.18. A random sample of size $n = 6$ from a bivariate normal distribution yields the value of the correlation coefficient to be 0.89. Would we accept or reject, at the 5 per cent significance level, the null hypothesis that $\rho = 0$?

11.19. If $Pr[|R| \geq c] = \alpha$, where R is the correlation coefficient of a random sample of size 5 from a bivariate normal distribution with $\rho = 0$, show that c is a solution of the equation

$$c\sqrt{1 - c^2} + \sin^{-1}c + \frac{\pi(\alpha - 1)}{2} = 0.$$

11.20. Verify that the maximum likelihood statistics for the parameters μ_1, μ_2, σ_1^2, σ_2^2, and ρ are $\bar{X}$, $\bar{Y}$, V_1/n, V_2/n, and $R = V/\sqrt{V_1V_2}$, as stated in this section.

11.21. If, with $\rho = 0$, the bivariate normal p.d.f. is written in the Koopman-Pitman form, page 117, what are the four joint sufficient statistics $\sum_{1}^{n}K_1(X_i, Y_i)$, $\sum_{1}^{n}K_2(X_i, Y_i)$, $\sum_{1}^{n}K_3(X_i, Y_i)$, and $\sum_{1}^{n}K_4(X_i, Y_i)$ for μ_1, μ_2, σ_1^2, and σ_2^2? Why then are $\bar{X}$, $\bar{Y}$, V_1, and V_2 of Part I of the argument of this section also joint sufficient statistics for these parameters?

11.22. In Part II of the argument of this section, verify that the distribution of $V = \sum_{1}^{n}(X_i - \bar{X})(Y_i - \bar{Y})$ does not depend upon the two parameters μ_1 and μ_2.

11.23. In Part II of the argument of this section let $n = 3$ and prove that, with $\sigma_1^2 = \sigma_2^2 = 1$, the p.d.f. of $V = \sum_{1}^{3}(X_i - \bar{X})(Y_i - \bar{Y})$ is $g(v) = (\frac{1}{2})e^{-|v|}$, $-\infty < v < \infty$. Hint: Find the moment-generating function of the distribution having p.d.f. $g(v)$.

11.24. If the random variable R has the p.d.f. $g(r)$ of this section, show that $T = \sqrt{n - 2}\,R/\sqrt{1 - R^2}$ has a t distribution with $n - 2$ degrees of freedom.

11.4. A Chi-Square Test.

If the normal p.d.f. $n(x; \mu, \sigma^2)$ is written in the form

$$\frac{1}{\sigma\sqrt{2\pi}}e^{-\frac{1}{2}q_1},$$

then $q_1 = (x - \mu)^2/\sigma^2$ can be described as a non-negative quadratic form in $x - \mu$ that is zero when, and only when, $x - \mu = 0$. If the bivariate normal p.d.f. is written in the form

$$\frac{1}{2\pi\sigma_1\sigma_2\sqrt{1-\rho^2}}e^{-\frac{1}{2}q_2},$$

then

$$q_2 = \frac{(x-\mu_1)^2}{\sigma_1{}^2(1-\rho^2)} - 2\rho\frac{(x-\mu_1)(y-\mu_2)}{\sigma_1\sigma_2(1-\rho^2)} + \frac{(y-\mu_2)^2}{\sigma_2{}^2(1-\rho^2)}, \quad -1 < \rho < 1,$$

can be described as a non-negative quadratic form in the variables $x - \mu_1$ and $y - \mu_2$ that is zero when, and only when, $x - \mu_1 = 0$ and $y - \mu_2 = 0$.

It has been seen, in the one variable case, that $Q_1 = (X - \mu)^2/\sigma^2$ has a chi-square distribution with one degree of freedom. It will now be shown that in the bivariate case

$$Q_2 = \frac{(X-\mu_1)^2}{\sigma_1{}^2(1-\rho^2)} - 2\rho\frac{(X-\mu_1)(Y-\mu_2)}{\sigma_1\sigma_2(1-\rho^2)} + \frac{(Y-\mu_2)^2}{\sigma_2{}^2(1-\rho^2)}$$

has a chi-square distribution with two degrees of freedom. The moment-generating function of the random variable Q_2 is given by

$$M_{Q_2}(t) = E(e^{tQ_2}) = \int_{-\infty}^{\infty}\int_{-\infty}^{\infty} e^{tq_2}\frac{1}{2\pi\sigma_1\sigma_2\sqrt{1-\rho^2}}e^{-\frac{1}{2}q_2}dx\,dy$$

$$= \int_{-\infty}^{\infty}\int_{-\infty}^{\infty} \frac{e^{-\frac{1}{2}(1-2t)q_2}}{2\pi\sigma_1\sigma_2\sqrt{1-\rho^2}}\,dx\,dy.$$

Accordingly the change of variables $u = \sqrt{1-2t}(x-\mu_1)/\sigma_1$ and $v = \sqrt{1-2t}(y-\mu_2)/\sigma_2, t < \frac{1}{2}$, enables us to write

$$M_{Q_2}(t) = \frac{1}{1-2t}\int_{-\infty}^{\infty}\int_{-\infty}^{\infty} \frac{e^{-\frac{1}{2(1-\rho^2)}[u^2-2\rho uv+v^2]}}{2\pi\sqrt{1-\rho^2}}\,du\,dv$$

$$= \frac{1}{1-2t}, \quad t < \frac{1}{2}.$$

But $(1-2t)^{-1}, t < \frac{1}{2}$, is the moment-generating function of a chi-square distribution with two degrees of freedom, so that in the bivariate normal case, the random variable Q_2 has this distribution.

It would seem natural to define, as we do, a $k - 1$ variate normal distribution as a distribution that has a p.d.f. of the form

$$Ce^{-\frac{1}{2}q_{k-1}}$$

where q_{k-1} is a non-negative quadratic form in $k - 1$ variables and q_{k-1} defines a random variable Q_{k-1} that has a chi-square distribution with $k - 1$ degrees of freedom.

We shall next discuss some random variables that have approximate chi-square distributions. Let X have a binomial distribution with parameters n and p_1. The random variable $(X - np_1)/\sqrt{np_1(1 - p_1)}$ has, as $n \to \infty$, a limiting distribution that is normal with zero mean and unit variance, as was shown on page 149; and $Q_1 = (X - np_1)^2/np_1(1 - p_1)$ has, as $n \to \infty$, a limiting chi-square distribution with one degree of freedom. For brevity, write $Z = n - X$ and $p_2 = 1 - p_1$. Then

(1)
$$Q_1 = \frac{(X - np_1)^2}{np_1(1 - p_1)} = \frac{(X - np_1)^2}{np_1} + \frac{(X - np_1)^2}{n(1 - p_1)}$$
$$= \frac{(X - np_1)^2}{np_1} + \frac{(Z - np_2)^2}{np_2}$$

has a limiting chi-square distribution with one degree of freedom. Hence Q_1 has an approximate chi-square distribution with one degree of freedom when n is a positive integer.

Next let X and Y have the multinomial distribution of Example 2, page 215. As noted there, X and Y have marginal binomial distributions with parameters n and p_1 and n and p_2, respectively. Thus the random variables $(X - np_1)/\sqrt{np_1(1 - p_1)}$ and $(Y - np_2)/\sqrt{np_2(1 - p_2)}$ have, as $n \to \infty$, limiting distributions that are normal with means zero and variances one. The correlation coefficient of X and Y was found to be

$$\rho = -\sqrt{p_1 p_2/(1 - p_1)(1 - p_2)}.$$

It would not be surprising if the limiting joint distribution of the variables $(X - np_1)/\sqrt{np_1(1 - p_1)}$ and $(Y - np_2)/\sqrt{np_2(1 - p_2)}$ was found to be bivariate normal with means zero, variances one, and correlation coefficient $\rho = -\sqrt{p_1 p_2/(1 - p_1)(1 - p_2)}$. In fact, this is true; and in this bivariate case,

$$Q_2 = \frac{1}{1 - \rho^2}\left[\frac{(X - np_1)^2}{np_1(1 - p_1)} - 2\rho\frac{(X - np_1)(Y - np_2)}{\sqrt{np_1(1 - p_1)np_2(1 - p_2)}} + \frac{(Y - np_2)^2}{np_2(1 - p_2)}\right]$$

has a limiting chi-square distribution with two degrees of freedom. Hence Q_2 has an approximate chi-square distribution with two degrees of freedom when n is a positive integer.

It will next be shown, analogous to form (1), that here

(2)
$$Q_2 = \frac{(X - np_1)^2}{np_1} + \frac{(Y - np_2)^2}{np_2} + \frac{(Z - np_3)^2}{np_3}$$

where $Z = n - X - Y$ and $p_3 = 1 - p_1 - p_2$. To establish form (2) note first that

$$\frac{1}{1 - \rho^2} = \frac{(1 - p_1)(1 - p_2)}{1 - p_1 - p_2} = \frac{(1 - p_1)(1 - p_2)}{p_3}.$$

Then

$$Q_2 = \frac{(1-p_1)(1-p_2)}{p_3}\left[\frac{(X-np_1)^2}{np_1(1-p_1)} + 2\sqrt{\frac{p_1p_2}{(1-p_1)(1-p_2)}}\right.$$

$$\left.\frac{(X-np_1)(Y-np_2)}{\sqrt{np_1(1-p_1)np_2(1-p_2)}} + \frac{(Y-np_2)^2}{np_2(1-p_2)}\right]$$

$$= \frac{(1-p_2)(X-np_1)^2}{np_1p_3} + \frac{2(X-np_1)(Y-np_2)}{np_3} + \frac{(1-p_1)(Y-np_2)^2}{np_2p_3}.$$

Now

$$\frac{1-p_2}{p_1p_3} = \frac{1}{p_1} + \frac{1}{p_3} \quad \text{and} \quad \frac{1-p_1}{p_2p_3} = \frac{1}{p_2} + \frac{1}{p_3}$$

so that

$$Q_2 = \frac{(X-np_1)^2}{np_1} + \frac{(Y-np_2)^2}{np_2} + \frac{(X-np_1)^2 + 2(X-np_1)(Y-np_2) + (Y-np_2)^2}{np_3}.$$

However, the last term of the right-hand member is

$$\frac{[(X-np_1)+(Y-np_2)]^2}{np_3} = \frac{[(X+Y-n)+np_3]^2}{np_3} = \frac{(Z-np_3)^2}{np_3}$$

and form (2) is valid.

The relations, given in forms (1) and (2), may be generalized. Let $p_k = 1 - p_1 - \cdots - p_{k-1}$, where each $p_i > 0$, and let $x_k = n - x_1 - \cdots - x_{k-1}$. Denote by A the set where each x_i, $i = 1, 2, \cdots, k-1$, is a non-negative integer with $x_1 + \cdots + x_{k-1} \leq n$. Let

$$f(x_1, \cdots, x_{k-1}) = \frac{n!}{x_1! \cdots x_{k-1}! x_k!} p_1^{x_1} \cdots p_{k-1}^{x_{k-1}} p_k^{x_k}, \quad (x_1, \cdots, x_{k-1}) \epsilon A,$$

$$= 0 \text{ elsewhere.}$$

Then $f(x_1, \cdots, x_{k-1})$ is the joint p.d.f. of $k-1$ random variables $X_1, X_2, \cdots, X_{k-1}$. A distribution having a p.d.f. of this form is called a *multinomial distribution*. The p.d.f. $f(x_1, \cdots, x_{k-1})$ may be interpreted as follows: A random experiment is to be repeated n independent times, and on each repetition the experiment will terminate in one of k mutually exclusive ways, say, $A_1, A_2, \cdots, A_k$. If p_i, $\sum_1^k p_i = 1$, is the probability that the experiment terminates in A_i, $i = 1, 2, \cdots, k$, and if the p_i remain constant throughout the n independent repetitions, then $f(x_1, \cdots, x_{k-1})$ is the probability that exactly x_1 terminations are in A_1; $\cdots$; exactly x_{k-1} terminations are in A_{k-1}; and hence exactly $n - (x_1 + \cdots + x_{k-1})$ terminations are in A_k.

The generalization of forms (1) and (2) is

$$(3) \qquad\qquad Q_{k-1} = \sum_{i=1}^k \frac{(X_i - np_i)^2}{np_i},$$

where $X_k = n - X_1 - \cdots - X_{k-1}$. As $n \to \infty$, it can be shown that Q_{k-1} has a limiting chi-square distribution with $k - 1$ degrees of freedom. Hence Q_{k-1} has an approximate chi-square distribution with $k - 1$ degrees of freedom when n is a positive integer. Here $np_i = E(X_i)$, $i = 1, 2, \cdots, k$.

The random variable Q_{k-1} defined in form (3) may serve as the basis of tests of certain statistical hypotheses. The tests were first invented by Karl Pearson and are called *chi-square tests*. These tests have some limitations, among which is the fact that n must not be too small. One kind of chi-square test will be included in this book. The test is as follows.

Let the sample space of a random experiment be the union of a finite number k of mutually exclusive sets $A_1, A_2, \cdots, A_k$. Further, let $P(A_i) = p_i$, $i = 1, 2, \cdots, k$, where $p_k = 1 - p_1 - \cdots - p_{k-1}$, so that p_i is the probability that the outcome of the random experiment is an element of the set A_i. The random experiment is to be repeated n independent times and X_i will represent the number of times the outcome is an element of the set A_i. That is, $X_1, X_2, \cdots, X_{k-1}, X_k = n - X_1 - \cdots - X_{k-1}$ are the frequencies with which the outcome is respectively an element of A_1, $A_2, \cdots, A_k$. Then the joint p.d.f. of $X_1, X_2, \cdots, X_{k-1}$ is the multinomial p.d.f.

$$f(x_1, \cdots, x_{k-1}) = \frac{n!}{x_1! \cdots x_{k-1}! x_k!} p_1^{x_1} \cdots p_{k-1}^{x_{k-1}} p_k^{x_k}, \quad (x_1, \cdots, x_{k-1}) \epsilon \mathcal{A},$$

$$= 0 \text{ elsewhere,}$$

where $\mathcal{A}$ is as defined in this section. Consider the null simple hypothesis (concerning this multinomial p.d.f.) $H_0 : p_1 = p_{10}, p_2 = p_{20}, \cdots, p_{k-1} = p_{k-1,0}$, $(p_k = p_{k0} = 1 - p_{10} - \cdots - p_{k-1,0})$, where $p_{10}, \cdots, p_{k-1,0}$ are specified numbers. It is desired to test H_0 against all alternatives.

If the null hypothesis H_0 is true, the random variable

$$Q_{k-1} = \sum_1^k \left[\frac{(X_i - np_{i0})^2}{np_{i0}} \right]$$

has an approximate chi-square distribution with $k - 1$ degrees of freedom. Since, when H_0 is true, np_{i0} is the expected value of X_i, one would feel intuitively that experimental values of Q_{k-1} should not be too large if H_0 is true. With this in mind, we may use Table II, with $k - 1$ degrees of freedom, and find c so that $Pr(Q_{k-1} \geq c) = \alpha$, where α is the desired significance level of the test. If, then, the null hypothesis H_0 is rejected when the observed value of Q_{k-1} is at least as great as c, the test of H_0 will have a significance level that is approximately equal to α.

Some illustrative examples follow.

EXAMPLE 1. One of the first six positive integers is to be chosen by a random experiment (perhaps by the cast of a die). Let $A_i = \{x; x = i\}$, $i = 1, 2, \cdots, 6$.

The null hypothesis $H_0: P(A_i) = p_{i0} = 1/6$, $i = 1, 2, \cdots, 6$, will be tested, at the approximate 5 per cent significance level, against all alternatives. To make the test, the random experiment will be repeated, under the same conditions, 60 independent times. In this example $k = 6$ and $np_{i0} = 60(1/6) = 10$, $i = 1, 2, \cdots, 6$. Let X_i denote the frequency with which the random experiment terminates with the outcome in A_i, $i = 1, 2, \cdots, 6$, and let $Q_5 = \sum_1^6 (X_i - 10)^2/10$. If H_0 is true, Table II, with $k - 1 = 6 - 1 = 5$ degrees of freedom, shows that we have $Pr(Q_5 \geq 11.1) = 0.05$. Now suppose the experimental frequencies of A_1, A_2, $\cdots$, A_6 are respectively 13, 19, 11, 8, 5, and 4. The observed value of Q_5 is

$$\frac{(13 - 10)^2}{10} + \frac{(19 - 10)^2}{10} + \frac{(11 - 10)^2}{10} + \frac{(8 - 10)^2}{10} + \frac{(5 - 10)^2}{10} + \frac{(4 - 10)^2}{10} = 15.6.$$

Since $15.6 > 11.1$, the null hypothesis $P(A_i) = 1/6$, $i = 1, 2, \cdots, 6$, is rejected at the (approximate) 5 per cent significance level.

EXAMPLE 2. A point is to be selected from the unit interval $\{x; 0 < x < 1\}$ by a random process. Let $A_1 = \{x; 0 < x \leq \frac{1}{4}\}$, $A_2 = \{x; \frac{1}{4} < x \leq \frac{1}{2}\}$, $A_3 = \{x; \frac{1}{2} < x \leq \frac{3}{4}\}$, and $A_4 = \{x; \frac{3}{4} < x < 1\}$. Let the probabilities p_i, $i = 1, 2, 3, 4$, assigned to these sets under the null hypothesis be determined by the p.d.f. $2x$, $0 < x < 1$, zero elsewhere. Then these probabilities are respectively

$$p_{10} = \int_0^{1/4} 2x\, dx = \frac{1}{16}, \quad p_{20} = \frac{3}{16}, \quad p_{30} = \frac{5}{16}, \quad \text{and} \quad p_{40} = \frac{7}{16}.$$

Thus the null hypothesis to be tested is that p_1, p_2, p_3, and $p_4 = 1 - p_1 - p_2 - p_3$ have the preceding values in a multinomial distribution with $k = 4$. This null hypothesis is to be tested at an approximate 0.025 significance level by repeating the random experiment $n = 80$ independent times under the same conditions. Here the np_{i0}, $i = 1, 2, 3, 4$, are respectively 5, 15, 25, and 35. Suppose the observed frequencies of A_1, A_2, A_3, and A_4 to be 6, 18, 20, and 36, respectively. Then the observed value of $Q_3 = \sum_1^4 (X_i - np_{i0})^2/(np_{i0})$ is

$$\frac{(6 - 5)^2}{5} + \frac{(18 - 15)^2}{15} + \frac{(20 - 25)^2}{25} + \frac{(36 - 35)^2}{35} = \frac{64}{35}.$$

From Table II, with $4 - 1 = 3$ degrees of freedom, the value corresponding to a 0.025 significance level is $c = 9.35$. Since the observed value of Q_3 is less than 9.35, the null hypothesis is accepted at the (approximate) 0.025 level of significance.

Exercises

11.25. A number is to be selected from the interval $\{x; 0 < x < 2\}$ by a random process. Let $A_i = \{x; (i - 1)/2 < x \leq i/2\}$, $i = 1, 2, 3$, and let $A_4 = \{x; 3/2 < x < 2\}$. A certain null hypothesis assigns probabilities p_{i0} to these sets in accordance with $p_{i0} = \int_{A_i} (\frac{1}{2})(2 - x)dx$, $i = 1, 2, 3, 4$. This null hypothesis (concerning the multinomial p.d.f. with $k = 4$) is to be tested, at the 5 per cent level of significance, by a chi-square test. If the observed frequencies of the sets A_i, $i = 1, 2, 3, 4$, are respectively 30, 30, 10, 10, would H_0 be accepted at the (approximate) 5 per cent level of significance?

11.26. Let the following sets be defined. $A_1 = \{x; -\infty < x \leq 0\}$, $A_i = \{x; i - 2 < x \leq i - 1\}$, $i = 2, \cdots, 7$, and $A_8 = \{x; 6 < x < \infty\}$. A certain null hypothesis assigns probabilities p_{i0} to these sets A_i in accordance with

$$p_{i0} = \int_{A_i} \frac{1}{2\sqrt{2\pi}} e^{-\frac{(x-3)^2}{2(4)}} \, dx, \quad i = 1, 2, \cdots, 7, 8.$$

This null hypothesis (concerning the multinomial p.d.f. with $k = 8$) is to be tested, at the 5 per cent level of significance, by a chi-square test. If the observed frequencies of the sets A_i, $i = 1, 2, \cdots, 8$, are respectively 60, 96, 140, 210, 172, 160, 88, and 74, would H_0 be accepted at the (approximate) 5 per cent level of significance?

11.27. The joint moment-generating function of a multinomial distribution with $k = 4$ is given by

$$\sum_{x_3=0}^{n} \sum_{x_2=0}^{n-x_3} \sum_{x_1=0}^{n-x_2-x_3} \frac{n!}{x_1! x_2! x_3! x_4!} (p_1 e^{t_1})^{x_1} (p_2 e^{t_2})^{x_2} (p_3 e^{t_3})^{x_3} p_4^{x_4}$$

where $x_4 = n - x_1 - x_2 - x_3$ and $p_4 = 1 - p_1 - p_2 - p_3$. Show that this moment-generating function is $(p_4 + p_1 e^{t_1} + p_2 e^{t_2} + p_3 e^{t_3})^n$. Set $t_2 = t_3 = 0$, and show that the marginal distribution of X_1 is binomial with parameters n and p_1, and hence $E(X_1) = np_1$.

APPENDIX

REFERENCES

Basu, D., "On statistics independent of a complete sufficient statistic," *Sankhyā* 15, 377 (1955).

Blackwell, D., "Conditional expectation and unbiased sequential estimation," *Ann. Math. Stat.* 18, 105 (1947).

Cramér, H., *Mathematical Methods of Statistics*, Princeton University Press, Princeton (1946).

Curtiss, J. H., "A note on the theory of moment generating functions," *Ann. Math. Stat.* 13, 430 (1942).

Fisher, R. A., "On the mathematical foundations of theoretical statistics," *Phil. Trans. Royal Soc. London*, Series A, 222, 309 (1922).

Hogg, R. V., and Craig, A. T., "Sufficient statistics in elementary distribution theory," *Sankhyā* 17, 209 (1956).

Hogg, R. V., and Craig, A. T., "On the decomposition of certain chi-square variables," *Ann. Math. Stat.* 29, 608 (1958).

Koopman, B. O., "On distributions admitting a sufficient statistic," *Trans. Amer. Math. Soc.* 39, 399 (1936).

Lehmann, E. L., and Scheffé, H., "Completeness, similar regions, and unbiased estimation," *Sankhyā* 10, 305 (1950).

Lévy, P., *Théorie de l'addition des Variables Aléatoires*, Gauthier-Villars, Paris (1937).

Madow, W. G., "Contributions to the theory of multivariate statistical analysis," *Trans. Amer. Math. Soc.* 44, 454 (1938).

Neyman, J., "Su un teorema concernente le cosiddette statistiche sufficienti," *Giornale dell' Istituto degli Attuari* 6, 320 (1935).

Neyman, J., and Pearson, E. S., "On the problem of the most efficient tests of statistical hypotheses," *Phil. Trans. Royal Soc. London*, Series A, 231, 289 (1933).

Pearson, K., "On the criterion that a given system of deviations from the probable in the case of a correlated system of variables is such that it can be reasonably supposed to have arisen from random sampling," *Phil. Mag.*, Series 5, 50, 157 (1900).

Pitman, E. J. G., "Sufficient statistics and intrinsic accuracy," *Proc. Cam. Phil. Soc.* 32, 567 (1936).

Rao, C. R., "Information and accuracy obtainable in the estimation of statistical parameters," *Bull. Calcutta Math. Soc.* 37, 81 (1945).

TABLES

TABLE I

The Normal Distribution

$$N(x) = \int_{-\infty}^{x} \frac{1}{\sqrt{2\pi}} e^{-w^2/2}\, dw$$

$$[N(-x) = 1 - N(x)]$$

x	$N(x)$	x	$N(x)$
.0	0.500	1.645	0.950
.1	.540	1.7	.955
.2	.579	1.8	.964
.3	.618	1.9	.971
.4	.655	1.960	.975
.5	.691	2.0	.977
.6	.726	2.1	.982
.7	.758	2.2	.986
.8	.788	2.3	.989
.9	.816	2.326	.990
1.0	.841	2.4	.992
1.1	.864	2.5	.994
1.2	.885	2.576	.995
1.282	.900	2.6	.995
1.3	.903	2.7	.997
1.4	.919	2.8	.997
1.5	.933	2.9	.998
1.6	.945	3.0	.999

TABLE II

The Chi-square Distribution†

$$Pr(X \leq x) = \int_0^x \frac{1}{\Gamma\left(\frac{r}{2}\right)2^{r/2}} w^{\frac{r}{2}-1} e^{-\frac{w}{2}} dw$$

r	Pr(X ≤ x)			
	0.025	0.050	0.950	0.975
1	0.001	0.004	3.84	5.02
2	.051	.103	5.99	7.38
3	.216	.352	7.81	9.35
4	.484	.711	9.49	11.1
5	.831	1.15	11.1	12.8
6	1.24	1.64	12.6	14.4
7	1.69	2.17	14.1	16.0
8	2.18	2.73	15.5	17.5
9	2.70	3.33	16.9	19.0
10	3.25	3.94	18.3	20.5
11	3.82	4.57	19.7	21.9
12	4.40	5.23	21.0	23.3
13	5.01	5.89	22.4	24.7
14	5.63	6.57	23.7	26.1
15	6.26	7.26	25.0	27.5
16	6.91	7.96	26.3	28.8
17	7.56	8.67	27.6	30.2
18	8.23	9.39	28.9	31.5
19	8.91	10.1	30.1	32.9
20	9.59	10.9	31.4	34.2
21	10.3	11.6	32.7	35.5
22	11.0	12.3	33.9	36.8
23	11.7	13.1	35.2	38.1
24	12.4	13.8	36.4	39.4
25	13.1	14.6	37.7	40.6

†This table is abridged and adapted from "Tables of percentage points of the incomplete beta function and of the chi-square distribution," *Biometrika*, Vol. 32 (1941). It is published here with the kind permission of Professor E. S. Pearson on behalf of the author, Catherine M. Thompson, and of the Biometrika Trustees.

TABLE III

The t Distribution†

$$Pr(T \leq t) = \int_{-\infty}^{t} \frac{\Gamma\left(\frac{r+1}{2}\right)}{\sqrt{\pi r}\,\Gamma\left(\frac{r}{2}\right)\left(1 + \frac{w^2}{r}\right)^{\frac{r+1}{2}}}dw$$

$$[Pr(T \leq -t) = 1 - Pr(T \leq t)]$$

r	$Pr(T \leq t)$ 0.95	0.975	r	$Pr(T \leq t)$ 0.95	0.975
1	6.314	12.706	14	1.761	2.145
2	2.920	4.303	15	1.753	2.131
3	2.353	3.182	16	1.746	2.120
4	2.132	2.776	17	1.740	2.110
5	2.015	2.571	18	1.734	2.101
6	1.943	2.447	19	1.729	2.093
7	1.895	2.365	20	1.725	2.086
8	1.860	2.306	21	1.721	2.080
9	1.833	2.262	22	1.717	2.074
10	1.812	2.228	23	1.714	2.069
11	1.796	2.201	24	1.711	2.064
12	1.782	2.179	25	1.708	2.060
13	1.771	2.160			

†This table is abridged from Table III of Fisher and Yates: *Statistical Tables for Biological, Agricultural, and Medical Research*, published by Oliver and Boyd, Ltd., Edinburgh, by permission of the authors and publishers.

TABLE IV

The F Distribution†

$$Pr(F \leq f) = \int_0^f \frac{\Gamma\left(\frac{r_1 + r_2}{2}\right)\left(\frac{r_1}{r_2}\right)^{\frac{r_1}{2}} w^{\frac{r_1}{2} - 1}}{\Gamma\left(\frac{r_1}{2}\right)\Gamma\left(\frac{r_2}{2}\right)\left(1 + \frac{r_1 w}{r_2}\right)^{\frac{r_1 + r_2}{2}}} dw$$

$Pr(F \leq f)$	r_2	r_1 1	2	3	4	5	6	7	8	9	10	12	15
0.95	1	161	200	216	225	230	234	237	239	241	242	244	246
0.975		648	800	864	900	922	937	948	957	963	969	977	985
0.95	2	18.5	19.0	19.2	19.2	19.3	19.3	19.4	19.4	19.4	19.4	19.4	19.4
0.975		38.5	39.0	39.2	39.2	39.3	39.3	39.4	39.4	39.4	39.4	39.4	39.4
0.95	3	10.1	9.55	9.28	9.12	9.01	8.94	8.89	8.85	8.81	8.79	8.74	8.70
0.975		17.4	16.0	15.4	15.1	14.9	14.7	14.6	14.5	14.5	14.4	14.3	14.3
0.95	4	7.71	6.94	6.59	6.39	6.26	6.16	6.09	6.04	6.00	5.96	5.91	5.86
0.975		12.2	10.6	9.98	9.60	9.36	9.20	9.07	8.98	8.90	8.84	8.75	8.66
0.95	5	6.61	5.79	5.41	5.19	5.05	4.95	4.88	4.82	4.77	4.74	4.68	4.62
0.975		10.0	8.43	7.76	7.39	7.15	6.98	6.85	6.76	6.68	6.62	6.52	6.43
0.95	6	5.99	5.14	4.76	4.53	4.39	4.28	4.21	4.15	4.10	4.06	4.00	3.94
0.975		8.81	7.26	6.60	6.23	5.99	5.82	5.70	5.60	5.52	5.46	5.37	5.27
0.95	7	5.59	4.74	4.35	4.12	3.97	3.87	3.79	3.73	3.68	3.64	3.57	3.51
0.975		8.07	6.54	5.89	5.52	5.29	5.12	4.99	4.90	4.82	4.76	4.67	4.57
0.95	8	5.32	4.46	4.07	3.84	3.69	3.58	3.50	3.44	3.39	3.35	3.28	3.22
0.975		7.57	6.06	5.42	5.05	4.82	4.65	4.53	4.43	4.36	4.30	4.20	4.10
0.95	9	5.12	4.26	3.86	3.63	3.48	3.37	3.29	3.23	3.18	3.14	3.07	3.01
0.975		7.21	5.71	5.08	4.72	4.48	4.32	4.20	4.10	4.03	3.96	3.87	3.77
0.95	10	4.96	4.10	3.71	3.48	3.33	3.22	3.14	3.07	3.02	2.98	2.91	2.85
0.975		6.94	5.46	4.83	4.47	4.24	4.07	3.95	3.85	3.78	3.72	3.62	3.52
0.95	12	4.75	3.89	3.49	3.26	3.11	3.00	2.91	2.85	2.80	2.75	2.69	2.62
0.975		6.55	5.10	4.47	4.12	3.89	3.73	3.61	3.51	3.44	3.37	3.28	3.18
0.95	15	4.54	3.68	3.29	3.06	2.90	2.79	2.71	2.64	2.59	2.54	2.48	2.40
0.975		6.20	4.77	4.15	3.80	3.58	3.41	3.29	3.20	3.12	3.06	2.96	2.86

†This table is abridged and adapted from "Tables of percentage points of the inverted beta distribution," *Biometrika*, Vol. 33 (1943). It is published here with the kind permission of Professor E. S. Pearson on behalf of the authors, Maxine Merrington and Catherine M. Thompson, and of the Biometrika Trustees.

ANSWERS TO SELECTED EXERCISES

Chapter One

1.1. (a) $\{x; x = 0, 1, 2, 3, 4\}; \{x; x = 2\}$.

   (b) $\{x; 0 < x < 3\}; \{x; 1 \leq x < 2\}$.

1.2. (a) $\{x; 0 < x < \frac{5}{8}\}$.

1.6. $11/16; 0; 1$.   **1.7.** $16; 7; 21; 2$.

1.9. $8/3; 0; \pi/2$.

1.11. (a) $3/52$; (b) $1/13$.   **1.13.** $\frac{3}{4}$.   **1.15.** 0.3.

1.16. $\frac{5}{8}; \frac{7}{8}; \frac{3}{8}$.   **1.19.** $\frac{1}{4}$.   **1.20.** $0; 1$.

1.21. (a) $\frac{1}{2}$; (b) 1.   **1.24.** $15/64; 0; \frac{1}{2}; \frac{1}{2}$.

1.26. (a) 1;   (b) $\frac{2}{3}$;   (c) 2.   **1.28.** $f(a) = f(b)$.

1.30. $2; 432/5; -804/5$.   **1.31.** $3; 11; 27$.   **1.32.** $1/9$.

1.34. $(\frac{1}{3})(\frac{2}{3}) \neq \frac{1}{4}$.

1.35. (a) $3/2, \frac{3}{4}$;   (b) $\frac{1}{2}, 1/20$;   (c) $0, 0$;

   (d) 2, does not exist.

1.36. $\dfrac{e^t}{2 - e^t}, t < \ln 2; 2; 2$.   **1.44.** $(1 - t)^{-3}, t < 1$.

Chapter Two

2.1. $40/81$.   **2.2.** $(2e^{-2})/3$.   **2.8.** $65/81$.

2.11. $0.067; 0.685$.   **2.13.** $71.3, 189.7$.   **2.14.** $\dfrac{1}{\sqrt{\pi e^4}}$.

2.16. 0.774.   **2.17.** $\sqrt{2/\pi}; (\pi - 2)/\pi$.   **2.19.** 0.050.

2.21. 0.90 **2.24.** 0.90

2.25. $\theta/(\theta + 1); \theta/[(\theta + 2)(\theta + 1)^2]$.   **2.26.** $3; 1 - \sqrt[3]{1/2}$.

2.29. $95/7; 50/7$.

Chapter Three

3.5. $\frac{7}{8}$.   **3.7.** $0; 0; 1; 1; \rho$.

3.8.
y	2	3	4	5	6	7	8	9	10	11	12
$g(y)$	1/36	2/36	3/36	4/36	5/36	6/36	5/36	4/36	3/36	2/36	1/36

3.10. 0.24.   **3.14.** 147/512.   **3.16.** 5.   **3.18.** 8/3; 2/9.   **3.19.** 7.

3.24. 2.4; 0.048.   **3.26.** 0.405.   **3.28.** 5/2; $\frac{1}{4}$.   **3.30.** $\frac{1}{8}$.

3.32. 6.41.   **3.33.** $n = 16$.

3.35. (77.28, 85.12).   **3.36.** 24 or 25.   **3.37.** (0.43, 2.21).

Chapter Four

4.1. $1/3$, $y = 3, 5, 7$.   **4.3.** $(1/2)\sqrt[3]{y}$, $y = 1, 8, 27, \cdots$.

4.4.
y_1	1	2	3	4	6	9
$g_1(y_1)$	1/36	4/36	6/36	4/36	12/36	9/36

4.5. $1/27$, $0 < y < 27$.   **4.7.** $-\ln y_1$, $0 < y_1 < 1$.

4.10. $\alpha/(\alpha + \beta)$; $\alpha\beta/[(\alpha + \beta + 1)(\alpha + \beta)^2]$.

4.11. (a) 20;   (b) 1260;   (c) 495.

4.12. 0.05.   **4.15.** 1/4.74, 3.33.   **4.16.** $r_2/(r_2 - 2)$.

4.20. $(1/\sqrt{2\pi})^3 y_1{}^2(\sin y_3)e^{-\frac{y_1{}^2}{2}}$.   **4.22.** $\dfrac{y_1{}^5}{120\theta^6}e^{-\frac{y_1}{\theta}}$.

4.23. $y_2\,y_3{}^2 e^{-y_3}$; $\dfrac{y_3{}^2}{2}e^{-y_3}$; $2y_2$; 1.

4.24. $\dfrac{1}{2\sqrt{y}}$.   **4.25.** $\dfrac{e^{-\frac{y_1}{2\theta}}}{2\theta}$.

4.26. $1 - (1 - e^{-3})^4$.   **4.27.** $\frac{1}{8}$.   **4.28.** $\theta + (\frac{1}{3})\ln 20$.

4.31. 5/16.   **4.32.** $48z_1 z_2{}^3 z_3{}^5$; $2z_1$; $4z_2{}^3$; $6z_3{}^5$.

Chapter Five

5.1. $\dfrac{3x_1 + 2}{6x_1 + 3}$, $\dfrac{6x_1{}^2 + 6x_1 + 1}{2(6x_1 + 3)^2}$.   **5.3.** $3x_2/4$; $3x_2{}^2/80$.

5.5. $8y_1 y_2/y_3{}^4$; $4y_3{}^3/9$.

5.8. $3\theta^2/5$; $\theta^2/5$; $\theta^2/15$.   **5.9.** $\frac{1}{3}$; $\frac{2}{3}$.

5.17. $60y_3{}^2(y_5 - y_3)/\theta^5$; $6y_5/5$; $\theta^2/7$; $\theta^2/35$.

5.18. $\dfrac{e^{-\frac{y_1}{\theta}}}{\theta^2}$; $y_1/2$; $\theta^2/2$.

5.24. (a) Y_1/n;   (b) Y_1/n.   **5.25.** $Y_1 - 1/n$.

5.26. $Y_1 = \sum_1^n X_i$; $Y_1/4n$; yes.   **5.27.** $\ln(X_1 X_2 \cdots X_n)$.

5.32. (a) $\bar{X}$;   (b) $-n/\ln(X_1 X_2 \cdots X_n)$;   (c) $\bar{X}$;   (d) median;
(e) the smallest item.   **5.34.** the smallest item Y_1; $\sum_1^n (X_i - Y_1)/n$.

Chapter Six

6.5. $\dfrac{n-1}{n}\sigma^2;\ \dfrac{2(n-1)}{n^2}\sigma^4.$ **6.6.** 0.90.

6.8. (2.68, 9.68).   **6.9.** (0.71, 5.50).   **6.11.** $1/(n+m-2)$.

6.12. (3.7, 5.7).   **6.13.** $(-3.6, 2.0)$.

Chapter Seven

7.1. $3x^2 - 2x^3,\ 0 \leq x < 1.$ **7.3.** (a) 27/32; (b) 1/24.

7.10. 0.840.   **7.12.** 160.   **7.14.** 0.08.   **7.16.** 0.267.

Chapter Eight

8.4. $\dfrac{e^t - 1}{t},\ t \neq 0.$ **8.5.** $n!,\ 0 < z_1 < z_2 < \cdots < z_n < 1.$

8.8. $\dfrac{i}{n+1};\ \dfrac{1}{n+1}.$ **8.9.** $n!,\ 0 < w_i,\ w_1 + \cdots + w_n < 1.$

8.11. (a) 15/16; (b) 675/1024; (c) $(0.8)^4$.   **8.13.** 8.

Chapter Nine

9.1. $\tfrac{1}{4} + (\tfrac{3}{4})\ln(\tfrac{3}{4});\ 7/16 + (9/8)\ln(\tfrac{3}{4}).$ **9.2.** 11/64; $(31)3^8/4^9$.

9.7. $\sum_1^{10} x_i^2 \geq 18.3$; yes; yes.   **9.9.** $3\sum_1^n x_i^2 + 2\sum_1^n x_i \geq c.$

9.10. 95 or 96; 76.7.   **9.11.** 38 or 39; 15.

9.12. $(1 - \theta)^9\,(1 + 9\theta).$

9.13. $1, 0 < \theta \leq \tfrac{1}{2};\ 1/(16\theta^4),\ \tfrac{1}{2} < \theta < 1;\ 1 - 15/(16\theta^4),\ 1 \leq \theta.$

9.15. 53 or 54, 5.6.

9.18. reject H_0 if $\bar{x} \geq 77.564.$ **9.19.** 26 or 27; reject H_0 if $\bar{x} \leq 24.$

9.20. 220 or 221; reject H_0 if $y \geq 17.$

9.21. $t = 3 > 2.262$, reject H_0.   **9.22.** $|t| = 2.27 > 2.145$, reject H_0.

Chapter Ten

10.5. computed $F = 7.6 > 3.89$, reject H_0.

10.7. computed $F = 18.7 > 5.14$, reject H_0.

10.11. computed $F = 27.7 > 4.76$, reject H_0.

10.16. $\hat{\beta} = \sum(X_i/nc_i), \sum[(X_i - \hat{\beta}c_i)^2/nc_i^2].$

Chapter Eleven

11.1. (a) 1, dependent; (b) -1, dependent; (c) 0, dependent.

11.5. $-5; 60 - 12\sqrt{6}.$ **11.7.** $\sigma_1/\sqrt{\sigma_1^2 + \sigma_2^2}.$

11.12. (a) 0.264; (b) 0.440; (c) 0.433; (d) 0.642.   **11.15.** 0.818.

11.18. reject H_0.   **11.25.** computed $Q_3 = 176/21 > 7.81$, reject H_0.

INDEX